The Lightning Tamers

The Lightning Tamers

True Stories of the Dreamers and Schemers Who Harnessed Electricity and Transformed Our World

KATHY JOSEPH

http://www.smartsciencepress.com

ISBN: 979-8-9859813-0-8 (paperback)
ISBN: 979-8-9859813-1-5 (ebook)
ISBN: 979-8-9859813-2-2 (hardcover)

Ordering Information:
Special discounts are available on quantity purchases by corporations, associations, and others. For details, visit http://www.kathylovesphysics.com.

Table of Contents

Preface

The spark for this book was lit around eight years ago when I was at a dinner party and told a story of how I asked my students where electricity comes from and one of my students confidentially told me, "The wall." This response, while technically correct, wasn't exactly what I was hoping for. A woman at the table chuckled and then admitted that she, too, would have responded with, "The wall." She added that even if she'd thought of generators or different kinds of power stations, it wouldn't have mattered, because she felt that she understood none of it. Although she used electricity every day and was completely dependent upon it, it was an utter black box. After I gave her an impromptu physics lesson, she seemed excited to understand the world a little better. This made me realize that there was a desire for people to understand where electricity comes from, and this is ultimately what inspired the audacious thought of someday writing a book on the subject.

At around the same time, I showed my students a clip from a Public Broadcasting Station (PBS) documentary called *Einstein's Big Idea*. The video showed an actor portraying a young Michael Faraday and his dramatic rise from binding books to being an assistant to England's most famous chemist and to eventually discovering the electric motor. After watching the same clip, year after year, for five classes in a row, I became fascinated with the history of science. It started to hit me that discoveries didn't come from thin air but were developed by real people with real stories and real trials and tribulations.

As Marie Curie once elegantly wrote, "The life of a great scientist in their laboratory is not, as many may think, a peaceful idyll. More often it is a bitter battle with things, with one's surroundings, and above all with oneself. A great discovery does not leap completely achieved from the brain of the scientist, as Minerva sprang … from the head of Jupiter."[1] Inspired by that video, I thought it would be interesting to write a book that explained how electricity was discovered through the personal history of the men and women who discovered it. Something that described not only how electricity works but how we got electricity to work. However, it was only several years after I had this idea when I had the time to try my hand at this project.

While researching the history of electricity, I made three important realizations. The first discovery I had was that Faraday wasn't the only one who had an interesting life story. Every scientist I encountered had a fascinating life with twists and turns and amusing anecdotes. Despite our image of a scientist being only a certain type, I found a wide range of personalities: some were quiet and studious, while others were flamboyant, artistic, cruel, romantic, or even totally insane!

The second surprising realization I made from my investigations is that no discovery, no matter how much it changed our understanding or our daily lives, was dramatically different from what was known before. For example, a shoemaker and retired soldier named William Sturgeon discovered the electromagnet in 1824 when he put current in a wire wrapped around an iron bar and found that it acted like a strong bar magnet. However, Sturgeon only did that because he was copying a French scientist named André-Marie Ampère who had discovered that wires could work like weak magnets if they were wrapped in a spiral around a glass bar.

Similarly, Ampère only conducted that experiment because a Danish scientist and philosopher named Hans Christian Oersted discovered that current in a wire would move a magnet, which made Ampère believe that he could make magnets out of electricity. Of course, Oersted was only able to conduct his experiment because Volta invented the battery first. Following the pattern, Volta only invented the battery because he was in a philosophical debate about the nature of "electrical fire" with a doctor named Galvani who discovered that two different metals would make a dead frog jump, and on and on. Every idea, every invention, is linked in a human chain of discovery. Nothing is completely new.

The third surprising realization I made as I read about these discoveries was that the words of the original scientists led me to have a deeper understanding of the science itself. I feel honored to have "met" all the great scientists and inventors in this book and am grateful to have learned more about the science of electricity from them.

My hope is that you, irrespective of your scientific background, learn something new from the amazing, delightful, and at times, infuriating people who are profiled in this book.

Chapter 1

Small Beginnings

(1600–1733)

[Do not] despise the small beginnings—they precede
of necessity all great things. Vesicles make clouds;
they are trifles light as air, but then they make drops,
and drops make showers, rain makes torrents and
rivers, and these can alter the face of a country.

– Michael Faraday (1858)[2]

There used to be an odd commercial on late-night television for "the amazing static duster." What made it so amazing, and why I was a little obsessed with it, was how, after you removed a plastic sleeve, dust would fly toward the duster. The people in the commercial would gasp with amazement as dirt, stray paper, feathers, and even parts of their hair would zoom toward the duster like magic (although I still don't know why you want your duster to attract the hair on your own head).

Of course, the people who sold these devices were aware that this was static electricity in action, which is why they named it "the amazing *static* duster." What they might not have known was that the first glimpses of modern electricity started with the study of this same strange, amazing power. It was this seemingly inconsequential study that was to form the foundation of our electric universe.

Ready to learn about folks rubbing objects and then staring intently at floating feathers and pieces of fluff? Let's go!

1.1 The Doctor Who Named Electricity

I would like to start with an Elizabethan doctor named William Gilbert (1544–1603), who is often referred to as the "Father of Electricity."[3] Gilbert was the first person whom we know of who scientifically studied electricity, and his studies made him famous. In the painting below, you can see him demonstrating static cling to Queen Elizabeth. But what, you might ask, inspired a medical doctor like Gilbert to study static cling, and why would that interest the queen of England?

The first part of the answer is that neither Gilbert nor the queen was particularly interested in electricity—they were actually interested in magnets and compasses, and Gilbert only studied electricity to see if it was a form of magnetism or not. So, why would a doctor and a queen be interested in magnets? The answer can be found accidentally in the painting. See the man behind the table leaning over to get a better view? That's a depiction of the explorer, slave trader, state-sanctioned pirate, and politician Sir Francis Drake.[4]

Drake's rise to fame and fortune occurred on September 26, 1580, when he hobbled back to England from three years at sea, having lost four out of five ships and 105 of his original 164 crew members.[5] However, that one remaining ship was full of spices from Asia and gold stolen from the Spanish, and Elizabeth's cut was more than she earned from taxes for the year. Drake was immediately knighted and given every honor that Elizabeth could bestow upon him. At the time, William Gilbert was an up-and-coming 36-year-old surgeon who was an expert on tropical diseases[6] and known to practice medicine to "great success and applause,"[7] which is why he came into contact with Drake and his surviving crew.

Possibly while "curing" Drake or one of the crewmen with magnetic cures (basically waving a magnet over them), Gilbert learned a fact that was known to long-distance sailors for a while—compasses don't always point exactly toward the North Star. Gilbert must have been shocked since he'd been taught differently at medical school. However, it wasn't surprising that there were no previous public writings about experiments on magnetic forces since medical doctors didn't typically investigate the physics of their medical

Figure 1: Painting from 1902 depicting William Gilbert demonstrating electrical attraction to Queen Elizabeth while Sir Francis Drake leans in for a better look from behind the table

tools and sailors typically held their magnetic observations as state secrets. With this new knowledge, Gilbert was inspired to start an informal club to investigate all things magnetic.

Gilbert didn't like the typical method of studying science at the time, complaining that most people "treat the subject [of magnets] esoterically, miracle-mongeringly, abstrusely, reconditely, [and] mystically."[8] Gilbert claimed that in all of the other books he'd read there was "never a proof from experiments, never a demonstration do you find in them."[9] Instead, Gilbert declared that he would start with an experiment and see what happened, which was a method, according to Gilbert, that was "almost a new thing, unheard-of before."[10] (Gilbert studied magnets almost 40 years before Francis Bacon published his highly influential book on the scientific method, *Novum Organum*, which is widely considered the origin of the scientific method.)[11]

For the next 16 years, Gilbert and his friends diligently studied every aspect of magnets that they could think of. He even made a mini-Earth by taking a natural magnet and smoothing it into a sphere, concluding that Earth *itself* is a magnet and must be full of iron (which we still think is true today).[12] In addition, he found that his mini-Earths, if free to rotate, would revolve around their axes every 24 hours. Gilbert bravely speculated that "the earth therefore rotates, and by an energy that is innate ... revolves in a circle toward the sun."[13]

ɔ was some 50 years after Copernicus's theory of heliocentrism was
.shed, but Gilbert's statement was still considered heresy among most
religious leaders, Catholic and Protestant alike. Gilbert also named the ends,
or poles, of the magnets the "north" and "south" poles after the geographic
directions, which is why the uppermost point of the globe is called the North
Pole, even though it's in no way a point or a pole.[14]

In the midst of all of these magnetic studies, Gilbert also devoted a little
time toward the study of electric forces. Doctors at the time regarded these
two things as identical because magnets would attract small pieces of metal
from a distance and certain materials, like amber jewelry, would attract pieces
of fluff from a distance if they were rubbed first. Some doctors believed they
could remove bad spirits with sparks from electrified amber or magnets. But
is static electric attraction the same phenomenon as magnetic attraction?

There were some obvious differences as electric objects had to be rubbed
first and could produce sparks, while the effects from magnets were permanent and didn't produce sparks. The more Gilbert looked, the more differences he found. Magnets could only attract specific types of metal, but an
electrically charged object could attract *any* light object. Also, static electricity
does *not* work in humidity or when the rubbed object is submerged in water,
while magnets are unaffected by these conditions. It would be another 230
years before scientists found a relationship between electricity and magnets.
However, we still think that static electric attraction is different from magnetic forces for mostly the same reasons that Gilbert did.

Figure 2: A natural magnet with nails stuck to it (left); amber jewelry with feathers
stuck to it (right)

Gilbert wondered if electric attraction was a special property of amber or could be found more widely, and he began to rub every object he could get his hands on. To his surprise, a whole host of objects could attract feathers if they were rubbed. It was not, as he put it, "a rare property possessed by one object or two (as commonly supposed), but evidently belongs to a multitude of objects, both simple and compound."[15] Because this property was common in many objects but different from magnetism, it needed its own name. As static electricity was first noticed by the ancient Greeks with rubbed amber jewelry, and the ancient Greek word for amber was *elektron*, he called this phenomenon an "electrius" force (or Latin for amber-like), which was translated into English as an "electric force." Gilbert's book was so popular the name quickly became commonplace.[16]

Perhaps from the successes of his magnetic research, Gilbert quickly moved up the ranks of the Royal College of Physicians, a prestigious group started 55 years earlier under King Henry VIII, he of the many wives, as a mark of a quality doctor. By 1600 Gilbert was elected as president of the college.[17] That same year Gilbert was also made Queen Elizabeth's personal physician, which was basically a ceremonial position as Elizabeth "detested doctors and would have none of their drugs."[18] For this reason, Gilbert wasn't blamed in 1603 when Queen Elizabeth died. In fact, he was hired as the personal physician for the new king, James. Unfortunately, the new gig didn't last long as Gilbert died eight months after Queen Elizabeth, most likely from the dreaded bubonic plague.[19]

Despite all of Gilbert's careful measurements, he made one significant mistake. He noticed that magnets could attract or repel, but he didn't realize that "electrics" could repel too. It would take another 60 years or so before anyone noticed this effect. This brings us to a German politician with some ridiculously awful theories about gravity who found a way to chase feathers with a stinky ball on a stick.

1.2 The Stinky Ball

In 1660 a German politician and amateur scientist named Otto von Guericke noticed that electricity could repel as well as attract when he observed that feathers move toward and away from a charged stinky ball of sulfur on a stick.[20] * Why was Guericke playing with a ball of sulfur? Well, Guericke was the kind of scientist that Gilbert detested, a person who used science to demonstrate his philosophies concerning the nature of the heavens and Earth. In this case, the ball of sulfur was a model of Earth and static electricity was a model of gravity.

Otto von Guericke was the mayor of his hometown of Magdeburg, in what is modern-day Germany. Guericke thought politics was a "grim and soul-destroying business,"[21] and was desperate to quit and focus on science. You might ask how Guericke got stuck in politics in the first place. First, Guericke came from a political family, as both his father and grandfathers were mayors, so it was considered natural for him to be a politician as well. Second, he'd survived turbulent times and felt it was his patriotic duty to protect his town.

From 1618 to 1648 there was a terrible religious war between Catholics and Protestants in Europe, now known as the Thirty Years' War.[22] In 1631 the Protestant town of Magdeburg was sacked, burned to the ground, and 25,000 out of 30,000 inhabitants perished. According to Guericke, "Many thousands of innocent men, women and children were … wretchedly executed in manifold ways, so that no words can sufficiently describe it, nor tears bemoan it."[23] Guericke and his family barely escaped the attack. However, his infant son was mortally wounded in the process, and all of his servants were slaughtered in front of his young family. The next year, Guericke was invited to return as an engineer and leader to help reconstruct "his" city.[24] Thus, even after the war had ended, Guericke was still stuck with politics. In fact, he was only allowed to retire in 1677 when he was 75 years old.

Meanwhile, he tried his best to be a scientist in his free time. Guericke was fascinated by the barometer, which had been invented in 1643 to demonstrate that air has weight and pressure. Guericke was actually the first person to think of using a barometer to predict storms.[25] He then created the first vacuum pump, which removes air to create a vacuum. Amusingly, he made dramatic demonstrations by taking two hemispheres and evacuating

---

* Chemists say that pure sulfur doesn't smell, but my friend Jeff Behary of the Electrotherapy Museum actually tried it. He said his lab stunk for three weeks, and I believe him because 1) he actually did the experiment; and 2) it's funnier if it smells bad.

the air between. The air pressure would hold them together, and then he'd have teams of horses try to pull them apart.

The vacuum pump and the barometer would turn out to be very practical devices, and his work on the vacuum pump led directly to the steam engine. But Guericke wasn't interested in practicality—he was interested in theory. He used the vacuum pump to model the vacuum of space and the barometer to model the atmosphere in the air. What he needed was an experiment to model Earth, and for that reason he came up with a truly strange idea. He represented Earth with a ball of sulfur on a stick and modeled gravity with static electricity. Guericke never said why he used sulfur instead of glass, as it is difficult to work with and commonly smells like rotten eggs. The only thing I can think of is that volcanoes can sometimes smell sulfuric (which is due to a compound of sulfur called hydrogen sulfide), so maybe he felt that the interior of the earth was sulfuric.

Guericke placed ground sulfur in a glass vial attached to a wooden stick that he used to hold it. He heated the sulfur until it melted, cooled it, and then broke the glass. Voilà, a very stinky yellow ball on a stick. He rubbed the sphere with his hand to electrically charge it and watched as feathers stuck to the surface, using static electricity as an analogy for gravity. Fascinatingly, the equation for static electricity *is* of a similar form to the equation for gravity (depending on the two charges or masses divided by the distance squared), but that has nothing to do with Guericke nor his stinky model. After a while, Guericke noticed that small objects fell off the sphere. Guericke then realized that small objects didn't just fall off the stinky sphere—they were repelled off the sphere. He spent many hours chasing feathers "about the whole room with the globe wherever one wishes."[26] This is the first mention that electric forces can repel as well as attract.[27]

Guericke published his theories and experiments as a book in 1672. His magnum opus was very popular and inspired the study of vacuums in Europe. Although several people were interested in his reports on electric repulsion, very few tried to recreate his self-described "wonderful globe," probably due to the difficulty in creating it—not to mention its *lovely* odor.[28] However, it was his experiments with vacuums and the barometer that led to the next great development in electricity, the first electric light.

Figure 3: Guericke's drawing of chasing feathers (labeled a) around with electrostatic repulsion

1.3 The Glowing Ball

Now we leave Germany and return to William Gilbert's hometown of Colchester, England, where Francis Hauksbee was born in May 1660.[29] Francis was the youngest of five sons and an undetermined number of sisters (as no historian paid any attention to such unimportant things as sisters) of a solidly middle-class family. His father, Richard, was a draper, a person who sells cloth, as well as a local low-level politician. By his teens, Francis was following in his father's and brothers' footsteps to a life as a draper.

However, he was fascinated with mechanical devices and started to tinker with them in his free time. By 1701 Hauksbee figured out how to build sophisticated machines and started to sell air pumps and pneumatic engines as a side job.[30] At the time, a draper was good enough to sell devices, but science was reserved for the upper class. It was through his side hustle of selling mechanical devices that Hauksbee met Isaac Newton, and through this relationship that he became sufficiently famous—and connected—to write a book.

To understand Hauksbee a little better, perhaps a little backstory is needed. In 1649, the king of England, Charles I (James I's son), was beheaded by radical Protestants (or Puritans) who took over the government.[31] About the time of Hauksbee's birth, England reinstated Charles's son (also named

Charles) as the king in an action called the Restoration. Charles II was invested in undoing the restrictive rules of the Puritans. He supported the arts, sciences, and, apparently, every attractive woman in London. (Charles II had at least 12 illegitimate children.)[32]

In 1662 King Charles II approved of the creation of a science "club" called the Royal Society to promote scientific research. The Royal Society was the world's first independent science academy, and today its journal is the world's oldest continuously published science journal.[33] On one hand, the society and its journal were a major font of scientific development, emphasizing the scientific method, peer review, and a desire for knowledge for its own sake. Their motto "*Nullius in verba*" roughly translates to "take nobody's word for it."[34] On the other hand, the society was relentlessly classist and sexist, as was common for everyone in power at the time. For example, for hundreds of years, many of the members were elected based on their social standing alone without having to demonstrate any scientific merit or ability. Also, to be published in their journal, one needed to be a member or have approval from a member of the academy. For this reason, it took over 120 years before they published the first article by a woman and 282 years before they elected their first female member.[35]

In 1687 the Royal Society published Isaac Newton's *Philosophæ Naturalis Principia Mathematica*.[36] Publication had been delayed because the publishing house was broke due to the disappointing sale of a book on fish. Newton's notoriously unpleasant personality and personal miserliness had not hastened its publication either.* Newton's book is ridiculously difficult to read and has been called "one of the most inaccessible books ever written."[37] However, as the years passed, the brilliance hidden in the text became more and more clear, and following Newton and Newtonian physics became basically a sign of English patriotism.

In 1703, 16 years after publishing his book, Newton's rival Robert Hooke died, and Newton was nominated to be the president of the Royal Society. After surreptitiously destroying all portraits of Hooke at the Royal Society, Newton turned to improving the Royal Society and refocusing on scientific research and discussion.[38] For that reason Newton decided

---

* If you want to know more about this fascinating story, I highly recommend the description in Bill Bryson's *A Short History of Nearly Everything* (New York: Crown, 2010).

to start a series of weekly science demonstrations to emphasize the sci-entific nature of his position and hired Hauksbee to be his assistant and run the demonstrations. Alas for poor Hauksbee, Newton's personality had not improved with fame, as he was still notoriously temperamental and aloof. He was described by a contemporary as having "the most fear-ful, cautious, and suspicious temper that I ever knew."[39] Newton made Hauksbee's income both meager and inconsistent. His yearly pay was determined by his productivity and was doled out, according to Royal Society notes, "as he deserves."[40]

At first Hauksbee performed experiments using vacuums, which included making superior vacuum pumps. Then, he learned that years earlier a French astronomer named Jean Picard had moved a mercury barometer in the dark, and the vacuum at the top produced a faint glow. When Picard had carefully shaken it up and down, it glowed even more.[41] Hauksbee did everything he could to kick this experiment up a notch. (Remember, his pay depended on the quality and entertainment value of his demonstrations.) When Hauksbee added a splash of mercury to an evacuated glass globe and shook it, to his satisfaction he found that it glowed moderately bright.

Next, he put the glass globe on a table with a handle to spin it instead of shaking it, which made it look like a strange sewing machine (see figure 4). He found that when he touched the globe with his hand, the globe would glow, emitting a "curious purple light," which was, according to Hauksbee, bright enough to read large print.[42] Hauksbee realized, from his reading of Guericke, that by rubbing the spinning tube he was creat-ing a lot of static charge. As the electric charge made the mercury vapor glow, Hauksbee actually recognized that he'd invented the first electric light bulb.

Not only had Hauksbee created the first electric light bulb, he'd also cre-ated the first powerful static electricity machine, even without the vacuum and the splash of mercury. Hauksbee made a new machine without a vacuum and studied the electrical effects of adding a semicircle of wire with threads in order to see how the electrical forces worked. However, the results were confusing to him, so he quickly moved on to work on surface tension and didn't experiment much more with electricity or electric lights. He published a compilation of his experiments as a book in 1709 and died four years later

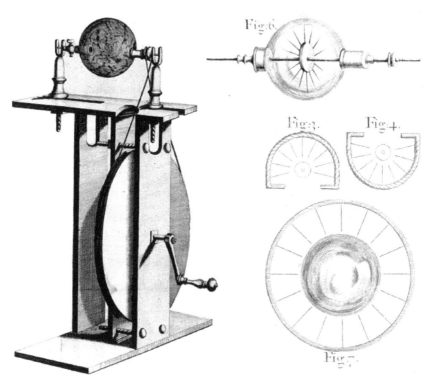

Figure 4: Hauksbee machine that glowed (left); Hauksbee's drawings of how the machine would create static electricity even without mercury or a vacuum (right)

from an unknown cause at the age of 52. The Royal Society gave his widow so little money that she was forced to live in an almshouse and go back to being a draper.[43]

Hauksbee's death was obviously a tragedy to his friends and family, while Newton, of course, simply found another assistant—an immigrant from France named John Desaguliers. Desaguliers wasn't directly of much significance in terms of electricity, but indirectly, he was of utmost importance. See, Newton had a long list of enemies and used Hauksbee to keep these people from power or publication.[44] Upon Hauksbee's death, Newton's new assistant decided to just ignore or pretend not to understand Newton's long-standing rivalries and, in fact, started to help some of them. One of these now-lucky individuals was a clothing dyer named Stephen Gray, who would change the course of electrical history with a single feather.

1.4 The Feather That Changed History

Stephen Gray's early life was similar to Hauksbee's. He was born around the same time (in 1666 instead of 1660) in the town of Canterbury, which is located 60 miles from London (whereas Hauksbee's hometown of Colchester is around 55 miles away).[45] Gray, too, was not from the upper class, and his family was involved with clothing. However, Gray came from a lower social status than Hauksbee as Gray's family were clothing dyers, which was back-breaking work with little profit. Like Hauksbee, Gray went into his family business even though he was fascinated with science. Gray then completed self-funded research on a wide variety of topics, including telescopes, microscopes, and a detailed attempt to capture the Canterbury ghost.[46]

In 1698, Gray's research (which was mainly in astronomy) brought him to the attention of a very powerful scientist named John Flamsteed, who was the first royal astronomer (a post created in 1675 by the busy King Charles II to work on more accurate measures of the stars for navigation).[47] However, Flamsteed partook in heated and angry battles over star maps with Newton, after which Newton basically blackballed Flamsteed and anyone connected to him from publishing at the Royal Society.[48]

For example, between 1696 and 1703, Gray published nine papers at the Royal Society, but after Newton became president of the society in 1703, Gray fell silent for 18 years. In addition, Gray found his day job of dying cloth to be difficult, physically onerous, and deeply distracting from his desire to study science. In 1705 Gray apologized to Flamsteed. "I have very little time and am so fatigued that I can make but a few Astronomical observations."[49] Poor Stephen Gray then threw his back out and, in July 1711, wrote a friend: "Now being in the 45th year of my age think it time to consider how I shall procure a comfortable subsistence, being already so infirm as to be able to follow my employ without much more difficulty and pain than in former years, caused by a strain I received in my back some years ago."[50] Although this friend was the secretary of the Royal Society, he could not seem to help Gray.

Gray's finances only started to improve when Hauksbee died in 1713, when, as I said before, Newton's new assistant, John Desaguliers, was able to manage the notoriously prickly Newton while being quietly friendly to his "enemies," which included Gray. For a while Desaguliers even let Gray live for free as a scientist-in-residence at a hotel for visiting tourists with scientific interests. Unfortunately for Gray, the house was torn down to make a bridge, landing him once again in financial trouble.[51] Finally, in 1719, Flamsteed and Desaguliers (and other friends) helped Gray to get a position at the Charterhouse, a boarding house for poor, retired, and deserving soldiers. Gray was never a soldier but skirted this issue by stating that his astronomy studies were for the betterment of Britain, and so, in a way, he had served his country. Gray wrote that he was delighted to "have time enough to make a further progress than I have yet done in some inquiries relating to Astronomy and navigation and might happily find out something that might be of use."[52] For the next 10 years, Gray did various experiments, including several on static electricity. But aside from finding that a few more items would attract small objects if rubbed or were "electric," nothing of note came from the Charterhouse.[53]

That brings us to July 8, 1729, when 63-year-old Gray made a surprising discovery with a feather. Gray had a glass tube with corks inside to keep out the dust. One day, Gray removed the corks to experiment with the glass and wondered if the glass would still attract feathers after rubbing if the corks remained in the tube. He found that it worked fine. He then pondered whether the corks affected the power of the tube. First, he studied the static attraction of the tube with and without the corks and found the difference to be negligible. Then, he charged the tube by rubbing it and observed if a feather behaved differently if it was released near the center of the tube as opposed to the ends. To his surprise, the feather released near the end attached to the cork instead of the glass even though he had never rubbed the cork. Gray had discovered electric communication, or as he put it, "There was certainly an attractive virtue communicated to the cork by the excited tube."[54]

Before this date, no one knew that electricity could flow at all. Gray quickly extended the experiment to see how *far* it could flow. He placed a small stick in the cork along with an ivory ball at the end of the stick and found that the ball could be electrified by rubbing the glass tube without touching the ball at all.

Gray then tried thick twine called packthread instead of a stick in a strange pantomime of fishing, where he rubbed a glass tube with his bare hands and picked up feathers with a ball hanging off the end of his tube. However, he noticed that if the twine touched the ground, the experiment stopped working. He tried tying the twine off the ground with other pieces of twine, but that did not work. Finally, Gray climbed the highest tower of the Charterhouse. With a glass tube and 34 feet (10.4 meters) of packthread tied to an ivory ball, he threw the ball over a balcony and attracted feathers to the ball by rubbing the tube in the tower. Following this success, he went in search of a higher tower.[55]

Luckily for Gray and for science, he sought the help of another wealthy friend named Granville Wheler. As a distant relative of Flamsteed, Wheler was happy to give over his large estate to these strange studies. According to Gray, "Mr. Wheler was desirous to try whether we could not carry the electric virtue horizontally. I then told him of the attempt I had made … but without success."[56] Wheler then suggested that they use silk thread to hold up the packthread, which Gray thought was a wonderful idea, as silk is much thinner than twine and, he thought, might prevent the loss of "electric virtue." The silk string *did* work well. They threaded twine (held up by silk strings) for 765 feet (233 meters) through Mr. Wheler's hallways and ballrooms with one end of the twine connected to a glass tube and the other to an ivory ball.[57]

Several experiments later, Gray and Wheler became frustrated by how many times the thin silk lines broke.[58] Gray thus tried to replace the silk with thin metal wires since metal is stronger, but they were surprised to find that the thin metal wires conducted the electricity away from the packthread. They correctly deduced that it was not the thickness of the material that mattered as much as what it was made of. Thus, they discovered that all materials could be placed into two categories: materials that would allow the "electric virtue" to flow (conductors) and materials that would prevent the "electric virtue" from flowing (insulators). Note that the terms "insulator" and "conductor" were actually created a few years after Gray's experiments by his friend John Desaguliers, although their meanings took a few years to settle into our current definitions.[59]

Since Gilbert in 1600, scientists believed that metal was not an "electric" and that if you rub a metal, it wouldn't attract feathers. However, Gray found that it was possible to "electrify" metal objects as long as they are kept from touching the earth by hanging them on an insulator. In other words, electricity is *in* things equally but does not *flow* in things equally. Therefore, if you try to electrify an object on the ground it's possible that the electricity will just flow into the ground, making it seem like that object is "nonelectric."

However, if you keep the object electrically isolated (insulated), then metals can attract feathers just as well as any other object.

On August 5, 1729, Gray noticed that the experiment worked even when the charged glass tube didn't touch the packthread and was simply placed near it. In other words, the electricity would be *induced* to move without actually touching. For this reason, the process was called induction (charging without touching), and Gray was the first person to discover this effect.

Gray and Wheler then spent the next 30 months electrocuting basically any object they could think of, including a large map, a tablecloth, a hot poker, and an umbrella. Gray wrote that Wheler even "suspended a large chicken upon the tube by the legs, and found that the breast of the chick was strongly electrical."[60] They happily found that everything they played with would fit neatly into one of these categories (insulator or conductor).

On April 8, 1730, Gray decided to move from live chickens to live children! In this experiment, Gray took a small volunteer, "between eight and nine years of age,"[61] and hung him from a wooden structure with silk threads as if he were flying (see figure 5). Gray then charged his glass tube and made his hair stand on end. He also got sparks to jump from the boy's hand or nose to the tube and found that if he placed the charged rod near the boy's feet, little feathers and fluff would be attracted to the boy's hands and head. Although this sounds torturous, this trick doesn't hurt. If you've ever played with electricity equipment in a physics classroom (like a Van de Graaff generator), you've likely experienced a similar effect. This strange demonstration of induction became a popular parlor trick for years afterward.

Figure 5: Gray's flying boy

In 1730 Gray wrote a long letter describing all of these events to his friend, and recently named secretary of the Royal Society, Cromwell Mortimer. Isaac Newton had died three years earlier, so Mortimer was free to publish the letters in the Royal Society magazine where they attracted a bit of attention. Meanwhile, Gray became convinced, like Guericke before him, that gravity was somehow electrical. On February 14, 1735, Mortimer visited Gray on his sick bed. Gray told Mortimer that "he hoped, if God would spare his life but a little longer, he should … bring his electrical experiments to the greatest perfection."[62] Instead, he died the very next day. Although Gray was widely read at the time and even won a few awards, Gray's contributions were largely overshadowed by the burgeoning Newtonian theory that was the biggest thing in science at the time. Gray is buried in a common grave with no marker or monument. However, just a few months before Gray's death, his words inspired a well-connected Frenchman to play with electricity and move it from obscurity into the mainstream.

1.5 Du Fay's Laws

The most important person to read Gray's 1731 paper on conduction was a 33-year-old wealthy Frenchman with the elegantly cumbersome name of Charles François de Cisternay Du Fay. Du Fay came from a long line of wealthy diplomats and generals. In fact, he became a soldier at the tender age of 14 but retired early to focus on diplomacy and science. Du Fay was interested and excelled in basically everything scientific: chemistry, anatomy, botany, geometry, astronomy, engineering, and physics.[63] A charming, tasteful, and witty man, Du Fay's real gift was in studying all who came before him, improving on their experiments and then condensing the observations into concise laws.

In December 1733, Du Fay sent a letter to his friend the Duke of Richmond (one of Charles II's many recognized illegitimate children) to be published in the same Royal Academy journal that Gray was published in. Du Fay wrote that he had made "some extraordinary discoveries … in the electricity of bodies."[64] In fact, Du Fay specifically wanted to be published in English in that journal because "the writing of Mr. Gray, and the late Mr. Hauksbee, both of that society, first put me upon the subject [of electricity], and furnished me with the hints that led me to the following discoveries."[65] Du Fay then proceeded to explain the first complete theory of electricity in just 10 pages. More astonishingly, these experiments and theories were conducted in a single, stunningly productive year.

First, Du Fay tried to determine whether electricity was really in everything or only in certain objects. Remember, at the time, an object was "electric" if, when you rubbed it, small objects were attracted to it. With his knowledge of electrical conduction from reading Gray's papers, Du Fay found that *every* solid object he experimented with would attract small objects after rubbing or heating and rubbing (aside from those objects that melted or were too soft) as long as they were on an insulated stand. Du Fay then placed a charged glass tube near a container of water that was on a wooden stand and found that even *water* attracted objects. He found "upon trial, that the same thing happened to all bodies without exception, whether solid of fluid."[66] In other words, Du Fay demonstrated that electricity is in all objects—not a select few. Du Fay's exhaustive work on this stopped other scientists from publishing new "electrics" every few years since everything is electric, or everything contains electricity.

Du Fay then began to study the act of electric repulsion. He read about Otto von Guericke chasing feathers with a stinky ball of sulfur and wanted to recreate it without sulfur. Du Fay then found that this electric repulsion happened after a neutral object was in contact *with any* charged object for a set amount of time. Du Fay then came up with his first "simple principle" to explain how electricity works. This was not only Du Fay's first theory, it's actually the first theory of electricity *ever*, and we still believe this theory to be correct over 280 years later.[67]

In his own words, Du Fay states, "Electric bodies attract all those that are not so, and repel them as soon as they become electric … by contact with the electric body."[68] This is what happened with Guericke and the stinky ball. When he rubbed the sphere, it became electrified and the neutral feathers were attracted to the electrified ball. However, after they stuck to the ball for a while, some electricity was transferred from the ball to the feather so that the feather was repelled and could be chased around the countryside.

This theory also explains why electrical experiments only work well on dry days. On humid days, the water in the air is attracted to the charged object, but once in contact, the water becomes charged and is repelled, taking some of the charge with it. This continues with multiple water droplets until the charged object loses all of its charge and no electrical experiments can be conducted. As Du Fay himself said, "Applying this principle to the various experiments of electricity, one will be surprised at the number of obscure and puzzling facts it clears up."[69]

Du Fay came up with an ingenious method for verifying his theory. If the small object is repelled off a charged object because it gains some of its charge through contact, any charged object should repel the small object too. Therefore, Du Fay took two tubes and charged them both by rubbing them. He then placed gold leaf near one of the tubes and noticed how it was attracted and repelled. (Gold leaves are a preferred item to use for experiments if you have the money, as they are conductive and can be made very light; Du Fay had the money.) In his theory, the gold leaf is repelled because it has taken some of the "electrical fire" from the tube, and therefore, the second tube should repel the gold leaf too.[70]

Du Fay was flabbergasted when he tried the experiment and the gold leaf was repelled by the first tube but strongly attracted to the second. Du Fay determined that the gold leaf behaved this way because one tube was made of glass and another of sealing wax.[71] In other words, Du Fay realized that there's more than one type of electricity. "Chance has thrown in my way another principle, more universal and remarkable than the preceding one, and which casts a new light on the subject of electricity. This principle is, that there are two distinct electricities, very different from one another, one of which I call vitreous electricity, and the other resinous electricity."[72] Note that "vitreous" refers to things made of glass, and "resinous" refers to things made of resin or wax; Du Fay was stating that there are two kinds of electricity: glass-like and wax-like. Du Fay determined that the neutral gold leaf was attracted to the glass tube and gained some of the glass's charge. It then was repelled by the glass but even more attracted to the wax, as the wax had the opposite charge, and opposites attract.

Du Fay discovered the basic law of "electrics," which we still believe today: "opposites attract, like repels, and charged attracts neutral."* Despite discovering a law of electricity that has withstood the test of time, Du Fay

---

* Confusingly, charged attracts neutral *because* opposites attract and like repel. That is because neutral objects that are bigger than a neutron are not 100% neutral but instead have equal amounts of positive and negative charges. When a neutral is near a charged object, the opposite charges in the neutral object are attracted and move closer to the charged object, and the like charges move away. As the electric force increases as distance decreases, the attractive force is greater than the repelling force and the neutral object has a net force toward the charged object.

misunderstood something vital. Du Fay thought that by rubbing objects he was *creating* electricity and that different types of material created different electricities instead of the idea that all materials contain electricity and that by rubbing them you are *moving* electric particles.

After Du Fay's letter of 1733, he wrote 17 additional papers on electricity for the French Royal Academy. Most of his theories in the later papers didn't advance the understanding of electricity, and some of them actually contradicted his original statements. Prophetically, however, he stated in his last paper that electricity "influences the mechanism of the universe far more than we think."[73] Tragically, Du Fay died from smallpox at the age of 41 in the summer of 1739. His theories were popular enough to travel all the way to Germany, where a flamboyant scientist used them (and Hauksbee's spinning electricity machine) to make electricity into a party.

Chapter Summary

✧ **1600:** William Gilbert publishes *De Magnete* (*On Magnets*) and states that static electricity is different from magnetism. He names electricity after the Greek word for amber.

✧ **1672:** Otto von Guericke publishes *Experimento Nuevo* (*New Experiments*) where he describes his experiments with the barometer, creating the vacuum pump, and rubbing a-stinky ball of sulfur, which shows that electricity can repel.

✧ **1705:** Newton's assistant, Francis Hauksbee, publishes his book on spinning a globe and getting it to glow. He also notes that rubbing a spinning glass bulb creates a lot of static electricity.

✧ **1729:** Steven Gray determines that electricity flows, that some materials conduct well (conductors) and some do not (insulators), and that one can get electricity to move without contact (induction). Gray suspends a boy in the air to demonstrate.

✧ **1733:** Cisterney Du Fay discovers that everything contains electricity. He also finds that there are two kinds of electricity and determines the like-repel-and-opposites-attract law for "electrics." Du Fay concludes incorrectly that rubbing creates electricity instead of moving it.

Chapter 2

Electricity Party

(1736–1792)

Electricity … that pleasing astonishment, which has such charms for all mankind; we shall not wonder at the eagerness with which persons of both sexes, and of every age and condition, run to see electrical experiments … so far are philosophers from laughing to see the astonishment of the vulgar at these experiments, that they cannot help viewing them with equal, if not greater astonishment themselves.

– Joseph Priestley,
The History and Present State of Electricity (1767)[74]

As a teacher, one of my favorite days is when I break out the Van der Graff machine, an electrical machine that looks like a large metal mushroom. When it's plugged in, a belt in the stalk of the "mushroom" spins and rubs against a brush to create a significant charge on the top. This can be used to create bright sparks or to make my students' hair stand up. I often spend weeks examining my students' hair with devilish glee, scheming about whose hair would be the most impressive electrified. It turns out that I was a little late to the development of this festivity, as in the 1700s the upper crust of Europe would do far more spectacular electrical demonstrations. These crazy

Figure 1: My hair doing its thing while touching a Van der Graff machine at the Exploratorium in San Francisco

"electricity parties" turned out to be not just wild and amusing, but also vital for the development of electricity.

2.1 Electricity for Fun and Entertainment

Now we come to one of the most flamboyant, self-aggrandizing, and generally kooky scientists of all time, Georg Matthias Bose. Matthias (he was known by his middle name) gave demonstrations to nobility and commoners alike and ignited an electricity craze in Europe, "which swiftly reached a stage of feverish enthusiasm."[75]

Bose was born in Leipzig, in what is now Germany, in 1710 and was a bit of a prodigy, lecturing in physics, mathematics, and medicine by the time he was 17. In 1736 Bose read a report from a Dutch man named Johann Schilling who conducted experiments by making a glass ornament move around on water by waving a charged rod above it. Bose said that it "almost drove me mad with delight [to find] the cause of the antics of the swimming glass balls."[76]

Matthias Bose was hooked. He replicated all of the electrical experiments he could find, including Hauksbee's rotating glowing sphere. Then, in September of 1737, Bose read Du Fay's papers and repeated all of his experiments with, as he put it, "incredible patience."[77] However, Bose found it irritating to generate all of the electricity by rubbing a glass tube by hand and decided to use Hauksbee's electricity machine to make it easier to create static electricity. Matthias Bose was so pleased with the results that he wrote an appalling poem and ode to himself (where he referred to Du Fay as Cisternay, as Cisternay was one of Du Fay's many names):

> Immortal Cisternay, you who preceded me ...
> so long as I live, Bose will praise you
> But everything you did was done with hollow tubes
> which are good, but make slow and heavy work,

I was first to take—how convenient!
the sphere of Hauksbee. In a time as short as you please
everything becomes stronger, surpassing all belief.
The tube was slower, feeble, insipid.[78]

Bose then realized that he could do dramatic and strange electrical tricks on humans, like Gray's flying boy, in a simpler manner by having the person stand on an insulating stand. He could make it even more dramatic by electrifying them with Hauksbee's machine. Bose made his machine even better than Hauksbee's by adding what he called a "prime conductor" to his electricity machine (see figure 2). The prime conductor was a large metal object (an iron bar, cannon barrel, or sword) that was held between the rotating sphere and a person on a wax stand. In this way, the prime conductor would store extra charge (or as he would put it, electrical fire) that could be used for a more dramatic experiment.

Bose did not contribute much to physics theory—he was mostly interested in show. In this regard he was unparalleled, even labeling himself a "modern wizard."[79] Bose quickly created an assortment of quirky demonstrations

Figure 2: Woman standing on a wax stand holding a prime conductor while the man spins a Hauksbee machine so that she can attract gold to her hand

that he exhibited to the nobility in England, France, and Turkey as well as to the pope, which got him into a bit of trouble with the strict Lutherans in Germany. According to a contemporary, Bose "seemed to have had a singular affection for something mysterious and marvelous in his experiments."[80]

For example, Bose would invite guests to an elegant dinner and then wire forks at a dining table to his machine (hidden in the other room) so that sparks flew off them to the delighted glee of the diners.[81] One of his more dramatic demonstrations was with a homemade "crown" made of glass adorned with metal embellishments that was sealed and evacuated. A person would then sit on a chair under a metal plate connected to the prime conductor, and the candles would be blown out. When an assistant spun the electrical machine, the sphere would charge up the prime conductor, which would charge up the plate above the person's head. Sparks would then fly between his crown and the plate above. The crown would also sometimes glow, looking like the halo from a religious painting where "a continual radiance or corona of light appear encircling his head."[82]

Another favorite was to ask an attractive woman to stand on an insulating stool and touch the prime conductor. The electric machine was then run to give the lady a strong charge so that when she kissed a brave volunteer, they both got a pretty strong shock. He called it *Venus electrificata*, or Venus, the goddess of love, electrified. Of course, Matthias penned more bad poetry on the subject. "I kissed Venus, standing on pitch. / It pained me to the quick. My lips trembled / my mouth quivered, my teeth almost broke." He also added that "anyone scandalized by the experiment is advised to throw himself into the ocean."[83]

Note that for the first time, women were involved in science experiments—and not just the ones with kisses. This was the age of enlightenment, when all of upper-class Europe was debating the rights of man, which sometimes even included the rights of women. Women ran the salons where science was demonstrated and are in almost every picture of electricity from the time. Although they were appreciated as attractive assistants and noble patronesses of the sciences, their opinion on how electricity worked was suppressed.

Bose's most popular and influential experiment was to create fire out of alcohol and electricity. Bose would stand on an insulating sphere with one hand on the prime conductor. He would then have the machine run until he was electrified and his hair stood on end. Then, when he placed either his

Figure 3: The assistant in the background (B) is turning a crank. The assistant on the right (D) is touching the sphere as it is rotating. The "prime conductor" is the long bar (E) that the man on the left is holding on to. The man at point G (Bose?) is standing on insulating stand and the electricity runs through him and his sword to create a spark and ignite the alcohol in the woman's spoon (I).

finger or a sword near a bowl of alcohol, sparks would jump to the alcohol and light it on fire!

This particular experiment seemed like so much fun that I had to recreate it. I made an electricity machine by spinning a large plastic lid and had my assistant rub it with fur. I then stood on a plastic stool and held a large aluminum baking pan on the lid with my left hand as my prime conductor. Finally, I leaned over a pan of rubbing alcohol and lit it on fire with a spark from my bare finger. (See figure 4 for proof.)

Bose stated a desire to "die by the electric shock, that the account of his death might furnish an article for the memoirs of the French Academy of Sciences."[84] Instead, his fame led to his kidnapping as a "strategic asset" during the Seven Years' War, and he died in captivity in 1761. (Strangely enough, poor Bose was held and died in Magdeburg, the same town where Guericke electrified his stinky ball some 100 years before.)[85] In a cruel twist of fate, Bose was famous enough to be kidnapped but isn't recognized for his contributions today.

Why is Bose not more celebrated? I suggest three possible reasons. The

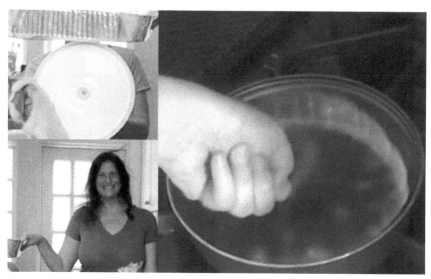

Figure 4: My static electricity machine made from a plastic lid spun by an electric drill and rubbed with fur, where the prime conductor is an aluminum pan (left-top); my hair becoming electrified (left-bottom); a spark from my bare hand lighting alcohol on fire (right)

first is that he was a showman who was very nervous about others stealing his thunder. For that reason, he refused to publish the details of his research so that other people were often credited with his discoveries. The second reason is that he really, really, disliked Newton's theories and "English" science. This made him particularly unpopular in England but also with anyone who liked Newton, which is basically everyone in physics. The third reason is that we have changed the history of science to try to make it dignified and logical, with men in white coats studying diligently with a specific goal in mind. Real science that's messy and fashionable with electric kisses and bad poetry violates that idea. It's unfortunate that Bose isn't more famous because he was so much fun and was in fact responsible for making electricity popular. Once all the cool kids were playing with electricity, all sorts of new discoveries were possible.

2.2 The Shocking Leyden Jar

It all started in 1745 when a German man named Ewald Georg von Kleist heard about Matthias Bose's demonstration using a spark to light alcohol on fire. Kleist didn't know how Bose achieved this feat, so he decided to connect the alcohol directly to the electricity machine. On October 11, 1745, Kleist got a bottle, filled it halfway with alcohol, and put a cork in it. He then put a nail through the cork into the alcohol and held it up to the prime conductor of his electric generator. For a long time, not much happened. Then, Kleist touched the nail with his free hand and was thrown across the room. It was such a large jolt that he wrote, "Bose would never dare brave the kiss of a Venus so armed."[86]

Let me explain how a Kleist's jar worked, as it's a little confusing. When Kleist's assistant rubbed a glass sphere on an electricity machine, it collected electrons from the hands of the person rubbing it. Electrons are negatively charged and repelled by each other and flow through the "prime conductor" into the liquid in the bottle and spread out on the inner surface of the jar. However, since glass is an insulator, the electrons don't escape the jar.

But electricity works at a distance, so, as Kleist was holding the glass with his bare hands, some of the electrons in his hands were repelled by the electrons on the inside of the jar. These electrons then flow away from the outside of the jar and into Kleist's body and eventually to the ground, which left the outside of the jar with a positive charge. The positive charge on the outside of the jar then attracted more negative electrons to the inner surface of the jar, repelling even more electrons off the outside of the jar to create a stronger positive charge on the outside. This continued until it reached its maximum charge capacity with equal and opposite charges on both surfaces of the glass. These charges on each side of the glass were attracted to each other but are prevented from moving toward each other by the insulating glass. However, when Kleist touched both surfaces with his bare hands, there was a conductive path for the electrons to travel. The electrons on the inner surface raced through Kleist to get to the positively charged outer surface all at once, giving him that terrible shock. (A shock is just our body reacting to the flow of electrons, and a spark is the quick flow of electrons in the air.)

Of course, Kleist knew none of this. He only knew that he had found a new way to get shocked. He then wrote to several friends about his traumatic experience, and they were eager to copy it. It's difficult when studying these people not to conclude that they were masochistic adrenaline junkies. However, even though Kleist reported that his device worked when being held by bare hands, Kleist's friends experimented with a jar insulated on the *outside* and reported back that the device didn't work. The problem was that "qualified" scientists knew about Du Fay, who stated that you could electrify conductive fluids (like alcohol) as long as it was insulated. This method was even called the rule of Du Fay. However, these scientists did not know that if the glass is insulated, no electrons can leave from the outside of the jar—meaning you can't store extra electrons on the inside of the jar. The jar will be slightly electrified on the inside from the electricity machine but not enough to give a great shock. Since Kleist was not famous in any way and his work was not repeatable, it looked as if nothing would come of his discovery.

Now we come to a famous physics professor in the town of Leyden, Denmark, named Pieter van Musschenbroek. Van Musschenbroek was so famous that a contemporary claimed that "kings vied with one another for the possession of him."[87] One day, a local lawyer named Andreas Cuneus came to van Musschenbroek with his story of how he'd given himself a terrible shock with a jar full of water. Either Cuneus read Kleist or happened to come up with a strikingly similar experiment on his own. Either way, Cuneus used the same setup as Kleist but with water instead of alcohol. (It works the same as long as the liquid is conductive.) Cuneus must have demonstrated the jar to van Musschenbroek, because van Musschenbroek wrote about his adventures in a letter on January 20, 1846.

Amusingly, van Musschenbroek didn't think the experiment was worthy of a paper or even an entire letter, but after he informed his friend about meteorological observations, he added, "As I see that this sheet is not completely filled, I would like to tell you about a new but terrible experiment, which I advise you never to try yourself, nor would I, who have experienced and survived by the grace of God, do it again for all the kingdom of France … the arm and the entire body are affected so terribly I can't describe it. I thought I was done for."[88]

A French clergyman named Jean-Antoine Nollet, who was a former assistant of Du Fay's, read the letter and was intrigued. (Remember: masochists.) Nollet quickly repeated the experiment whereby it "bent him double and knocked out his wind."[89] Nollet read van Musschenbroek's letter to the Paris Academy in April 1746, and pretty soon everyone was torturing each other with these jars. Quickly, Nollet began to sell jars that he called "Leyden

Figure 5: Drawing of Cuneus demonstrating a shocking jar of water to van Musschenbroek

jars," as van Musschenbroek was from the town of Leyden (and presumedly, he thought that calling them van Musschenbroek jars would be a mouthful). One of the intriguing features of this jar is that it stores charge for future use. You can charge it up with an electrical machine (or with a modern battery) and then safely move it by only touching either the outside or the nail. As long as the air is not conductive (like on a humid day), the jar will keep its charge for hours or even days.

In 1767, the Leyden jar experiments were described as the following: "It was this astonishing experiment that gave éclat to electricity ... Everybody was eager to see, and notwithstanding the terrible account that was reported of it, to *feel* the experiment; and in the same year in which it was discovered, numbers of persons, in almost every country in Europe, got a livelihood by going about and showing it."[90] Amusingly, an Englishman named Benjamin Wilson was so fond of turning things into Leyden jars that a contemporary wrote that "I hear that all Mr. Wilson's kitchen utensils are converted into Leyden bottles. If so, I should not much care to dine with him."[91]

Figure 6: A woman, thought to be Madame du Barry (King Louis XV's mistress), using herself as a human conduit to charge up a Leyden jar before a young boy electrifies himself with it

One of the favorite uses of Leyden jars was to electrocute large groups of people, either by holding hands or holding onto metal bars. Nollet entertained Louis XV, the king of France, by simultaneously shocking 180 soldiers, over 200 monks in their robes at a monastery, and as many as 600 people in a giant circle at the College de Navarre.[92] Nollet noted with glee that "it is singular to see the multitude of different gestures, and to hear the instantaneous exclamation of those surprised by the shock."[93]

Perhaps my favorite story about Leyden jars involves Nollet's assistant and eventual successor Joseph-Aignan Sigaud de Lafond, who was described as an "inexact a maker ... of scientific instruments as [he is] a mediocre physicist."[94] Lafond tried to electrocute a large group of people without making sure they were insulated from the ground first and was surprised to find that only the people closest to the jar were shocked.

Instead of concluding that the current went through the ground, Lafond assumed it was due to the lack of manly vigor of the first person to not be shocked—or as he put it, they were "not possessing everything that constitutes the distinctive character of a man."[95] To validate his theory, Lafond redid the experiment with three of the King's castrati (singers who had been castrated at puberty). To Lafond's disappointment, they all jumped despite obviously lacking in "the distinctive character of a man." It was only after Lafond conducted an experiment where the last man on the circle to be shocked complained that his leg hurt as well as his arm that Lafond realized that the current ran to the ground, irrespective of the victims' genitalia.

Despite the power of the original Leyden jar, scientists immediately attempted to increase it. In 1746, an Englishman named William Watson found that the jars were more efficient with metal (basically tin foil) on the inside and the outside of the jars by removing the water. That same year, a German physicist named Daniel Gralath realized that you could use multiple jars at the same time to get an even bigger punch, which he used to kill birds and small animals.[96]

Although many people liked using the Leyden jar, the famous scientists at the time couldn't seem to figure out how it worked. As van Musschenbroek said at the end of his letter about the discovery of the jar, "I've found out so much about electricity that I've reached the point where I understand nothing and can explain nothing."[97] Gray found that you could rub one object and get electrical attraction in a different object. But neither Gray, Du Fay, Bose, or any other previous electric wizard realized that electricity moves in a circle.

However, it was quickly discovered that in order to discharge a Leyden jar, you needed to have the electricity flow in a closed circle—or closed circuit, as it was called by 1747.[98] The Leyden jar was a key discovery that helped to unlock the mysteries of how electricity works. Strangely enough, the person who managed to figure it out and who intuitively saw what was going on electrically, did not live in Germany, France, or England. Instead, he lived in one of the last places scientists from Europe would expect: Philadelphia.

2.3 Enter Benjamin Franklin

In 1746, an Englishman named Peter Collinson read an article in a magazine about some "wonderful" German experiments with electricity, which were mostly about Bose. Collinson, who was a Quaker merchant and amateur scientist, thought these "electricity parties" would interest his good friend Benjamin Franklin in Philadelphia. (Yes, that Franklin, the one who helped write the Declaration of Independence and is frowning on the $100 bill.) Collinson sent Franklin a glass tube as well as a copy of the magazine with a shipment of other materials for Franklin's library.

Like Bose before him, Franklin was immediately hooked, writing back, "For my part, I never was before engaged in any study that so totally engrossed my attention and my time as this has lately done [and] my friends … come continually in crowds to see them, I have, during some month's past, had little leisure for anything else."[99]

By the time Franklin was 40 years old, he had a successful printing company, post office and stationary shop, and just two children to support—a 15-year-old named William and a three-year-old named Sally.[100] This was a very small family for the time. In comparison, Franklin was from a family of 17 children—seven from his father's first wife, who died in childbirth, and 10 from Ben's mother who survived bearing 10 children and raising 17.[101] Collinson had very good timing, as Franklin had just hired a manager for his businesses and wrote to a friend about his new phase in life. "I am in a fair way of having no other tasks than such as I shall like to give myself, and of enjoying what I look upon as a great happiness, leisure to read, make experiments, and converse at large with such ingenious and worthy men as are pleased to honor me with their acquaintance."[102] Benjamin Franklin was also of a near perfect disposition to study electricity. He was physically dexterous and observant like Gray, had an ability to develop the deeper ideas like Du Fay, and was equipped with a good dose of Bose's showmanship and whimsy to boot. Added to all that was Franklin's desire to create items "of use to mankind."[103]

Franklin built his own electrical machine, but unlike other machines at the time that required one person to spin the wheel and a separate person to rub the wheel with their bare hand, Franklin's had a brush rub against the glass (see figure 7. Interestingly, Franklin soon found that with his new electricity machine, he could charge up a person by putting them on an insulated wax stand and having them touch either the spinning glass or the brush but not both. He also found that if one person was charged by touching the glass and another person was charged by touching the brush, they could give each other a big shock. However, once they shocked each other, they were no longer electrified.

Figure 7: Franklin in 1746 (left); Franklin's electricity machine (right)

Because of this, Franklin quickly came to the supposition that, contrary to the thinking of all those before him, rubbing a material does not *create* charge but instead *moves* charge. In other words, all things contain charge, and you cannot create or destroy it, only move it. This is called conservation of charge, and it's still believed true today. As he put it, "We had for some time been of [the] opinion, that the electrical fire was not created by friction, but collected, being really an element diffused among [all] matter."[104]

Franklin gave these processes a name that we use today. If an object had too much "electrical fire," he said it was electrified positively, too little was electrified negatively, and uncharged objects were called neutral.[105] It was decidedly a shopkeeper's physics, with all of the pluses and minuses of an accountant's ledger, and it was almost correct. One of the difficulties is that when you see (or experience) a spark, it's impossible to tell which direction it's going in. It's just as painful to lose electrons as it is to gain electrons. Franklin decided that since brooms collect dust, they should also collect "electrical fire," which is why he assigned the charge of the broom "positive," assuming that the positive charges moved. It took an additional 150 years to realize that the "electrical fire" that was flowing in Franklin's experiments were electrons, and they went from the broom to the glass, so, according to Franklin's nomenclature, they were negative. In other words, Franklin thought electricity flowed one way, when it really flowed the other way. We're still stuck with this mistake today. It's common to say that "conventional current" flows from positive to negative, when we know that what's really going on is that tiny negative electrons are flowing the other way.* Still, despite that mistake, the idea that all objects contain charges and that we merely move them was a brilliant observation that changed how people understood electricity.

Meanwhile, Franklin wasn't only creating new rules for electricity, he was also having a lot of fun. Franklin came up with many ingenious demonstrations. For example, he would tell people that a piece of burnt cork with linen thread was a dead spider, and then he would terrify them by reanimating the dead spider by having it "fly" between charged rods.[106] Franklin also discharged a Leyden jar through gold leaves in a book and said when he did it, the gold glowed with "a vivid flame, like the sharpest lightning," which is possibly the first example of electric incandescence.[107]

Franklin was having so much fun that on April 29, 1749, he decided to have an electrical "party of pleasure" where he killed a turkey by electric shock, roasted it with electrically, toasted to electricity with drinks that would give small electric shocks, then ended the party with "the discharge of guns from an *electrical battery*."[108] This party was to have a lasting impact, as after the story of this party was recalled in a book, Leyden jars started to be sometimes referred to as electric batteries even though Franklin was just referring to a battery of toy electric guns powered by Leyden jars.

While playing with his electricity machines and electrifying turkeys, Franklin started to think about lightning. He became convinced that it was the same as the sparks he got at home but on a larger scale. Franklin started by building a model of an electrically charged cloud. Now he couldn't make a thundercloud in a room, but he wanted to make an object that he could hang off the ground and could contain a lot of charge, regardless of whether it actually resembled a cloud or not. Therefore, he made a thin cardboard tube 10-feet long and one-foot wide (three meters by 30 centimeters) that was coated in gold. He proceeded to hang it with silk chords and charge it with

---

* It is even more confusing because sometimes what is moving is not the negative electron, but positive ions (atoms missing an electron). However, as electrons are so much lighter than ions, typically electricity is just the flow of electrons which moves from negative to positive.

his spinning static electric machine. If he approached the charged "cloud" with a blunt instrument, the cloud would discharge with a loud crack and a flash. If he approached with a thin tapered needle, the spark would be far less dramatic.

He then turned the experiment around. This time, he had one person hold a thin metal needle close to the cloud before he charged it up. When he ran the static electricity machine, the stick would get a steady stream of quiet sparks, and he could not charge up his cloud. Franklin thus wondered if pointed rods could "draw the electrical fire silently out of a cloud ... and thereby secure us from that most sudden and terrible mischief?"[109] But first, Franklin felt that he had to demonstrate with an actual lightning cloud that lightning was the same as the electrical sparks in his home.

On July 29, 1750, Franklin came up with a completely terrifying experiment to test his theory.[110] He proposed that you could put a large iron rod in a tiny house, or what he called a sentry box. The rod would be put on an insulating stand so that the electricity couldn't flow into the ground, and the rod would have a kink in it, as he knew that sparks were easier to get from a bent or pointed piece of metal. Since the roof would protect the "soldier" from getting wet, Franklin thought that if an electrified storm cloud passed by, the rod would silently draw electricity from the cloud and provide sparks from the kink without flowing around in the wet room.

It turns out that Franklin was wrong. Clouds are far too high in the air to "silently drain" into a metal pole in the ground. However, electricity works at a distance, so that if a rod was *near* an electrified cloud, the electrons at the top would move toward the bottom and could provide sparks. This was lucky for Franklin (and others), because if the rod was actually hit with lightning, it would've killed any poor person in the guardhouse. Nonetheless, it was the soldier in the box experiment that thrust Franklin into international fame.

2.4 Franklin's Kite and a French Rivalry

The invention of the lightning rod might not have occurred without an astonishingly petty and long-standing rivalry between two Frenchmen: a religious electrical scientist named Jean-Antoine Nollet and a biologist who had no interest in electricity named Georges-Louis Leclerc, compte de Buffon.

In the 1700s, Jean-Antoine Nollet was considered France's premier electrician.[111] Nollet came from an impoverished background and joined the church as a young man. He then switched to science but insisted on being called Abbé Nollet (*Abbé* is French for *abbot*) for the social distinction and to remind everyone of his deep religious beliefs. He quickly moved up the social ladder due to his charm, wit, and delight in "shocking" experiments. According to a historian in 1895, "there was no startling experiment of Hauksbee, Gray, Du Fay, or Bose which Nollet did not repeat, and in many instances on a scale greater than the originator had ever attempted."[112]

Soon Nollet became a palace favorite, so much so that the king of France made him the tutor to his son. Nollet was also Du Fay's former assistant, which made him the standard bearer for Du Fay's legacy after Du Fay died from smallpox in July of 1739. Du Fay had also been the curator of the king's gardens called the Jardin du Roi (called simply the King's Garden). Nollet thought that he would gain the position upon his mentor's death. Instead, a rich nobleman, freethinker, drinker, womanizer, and sophisticate named Buffon got the position. It was the beginning of their lifetime rivalry and acrimony.

Georges-Louis Leclerc, compte de Buffon was in many ways, the epitome of the French Enlightenment. He was a brilliant writer, a lover of money, fame, popularity, and disturbingly young girls.[113] Unlike the highly religious Nollet, Buffon was indifferent to religion and "did not fight religion, he ignored it."[114] His circle of friends included Voltaire and Denis Diderot. Surprisingly, Buffon had no interest in electricity, and instead was mostly known as a naturalist, studying plants and animals. He published the first volume of his eventual 36-volume treatise on natural history in 1749. In this book he explained theories that today (and even then) seem a little bizarre. For one, he thought that America was a land full of "noxious vapors" where the animals were all small and the native people lacked virility with "small and feeble" penises. (Buffon was quite racist but not unusually so for his time period.)[115] Despite, or perhaps because of these oddities, the book was an international success and "was read … by every educated person in Europe."[116]

This leads us back to Benjamin Franklin and electricity. In 1750, Collinson convinced Franklin to publish his letters to him about electricity as a book, as he told Franklin, "We thought it a great pity that the public should be deprived the benefit of so many curious experiments."[117] It took

Collinson a little while to get it published in England, and at first, he had little luck sparking interest from the intellectual elite. The leaders in electricity were loath to read new ideas in the field—especially from an upstart colonist. Franklin decided that the lesson he learned with England was not going to be repeated in France. This time, he decided to send his book to the *rival* of the leading authority in electricity. Instead of sending his book to Nollet, he "asked Mr. Collinson to send one of the first copies to Mr. Buffon."[118]

Buffon was delighted to get the book. Although Franklin was never rude or insulting to anyone, Franklin's theories were a direct contradiction of Du Fay's theories (who, remember, was Nollet's former mentor). Buffon asked a friend named Thomas Dalibard to translate it into French, probably because Dalibard was fluent in English. Dalibard then translated Franklin's book into French with an "Abridged History of Electricity" in the preface. It was so abridged, in fact, that "Nollet's name did not even figure in it."[119] Buffon then decided to promote the ideas in Franklin's book so that everyone could learn that Nollet's physics was outdated. For that reason, Buffon hired a public demonstrator of electricity with the stage name Delor to conduct Franklin-inspired "Philadelphia Experiments" for the king.

Nollet, as expected, was furious. "Mr. de Buffon is the promoter of the whole business. He does not appear openly himself, because he knows too little about the subject; he has two tradesmen in his service [Dalibard and Delor] who take care of everything."[120] Nollet even wondered if Franklin might have been invented whole cloth by his enemies just to embarrass him.

On February 3, 1752, Delor demonstrated Franklin's theories to King Louis XV, and to Nollet's frustration, soon the court was brimming with talk of Franklin.[121] Encouraged, Buffon, Dalibard, and Delor began scouring Franklin's book for even more dramatic demonstrations. This is the primary reason they rashly decided to try the "sentry box" lightning experiment, or as they put it, they gained "a desire of verifying the conjectures of Mr. Franklin upon the analogy of thunder and electricity."[122]

Dalibard placed a large metal pole on an insulated stand sticking out of a tent in his home in Paris as well as near his country house in the town of Marly-la-Ville 15 miles away. As he never knew when or where a thunderstorm would appear, Dalibard obtained the services of a retired soldier named Coiffier to manage the apparatus in Marly-la-Ville for times when Dalibard was in the city. On the afternoon of Wednesday, May 10, 1752, Coiffier heard thunder and ran to the tent "armed" with a Leyden jar and a brass wire sticking out of it. Coiffier managed to get a couple of good sparks to go to the jar and called for his neighbors to fetch the local parish priest who was also an amateur scientist interested in the experiment.

This is how Dalibard dramatically described what happened next to the Paris Academy three days later: "The priest ran with all his might, and the parishioners seeing the haste of their spiritual guide, imagined that poor Coiffier had been killed with lightning. The alarm spreads through the village, and the hail storming down did not prevent the flock from following their shepherd. The honest ecclesiastic, arriving at the machine, and seeing there was no danger, took the wire into his own hand and immediately drew several strong sparks, which were most evidently of an electrical nature, and completed the discovery for which the machine was erected."[123]

When Dalibard reported the experiment to the Paris Academy, Nollet objected to the paper and insisted that more research needed to be done, especially by "qualified" electricians before publication. Nollet thus inspired every scientist in Paris to repeat the experiment, up to and including even poor Mr. Nollet, who was "dying of chagrin from it all" as the ever-gallant Buffon put it.[124] Buffon and his "crew" had thoroughly defeated Nollet on the issue of Benjamin Franklin, making Franklin the toast of Paris. Benjamin Franklin, the shrewd politician, used his fame when he went to France for aid during the American Revolution. After such unprecedented success in humiliating his rival, Buffon went back to his natural history studies and never dealt with electricity again.

Meanwhile, in October of 1752, Franklin wrote that he had heard of the "success of the Philadelphia experiment" in papers from Europe and that he had had similar success "made in a different and more easy manner" with a kite.[125] Here's how Franklin described how he performed the famous kite experiment. First, he made a silk kite with a sharp wire sticking out the top of it. He used a line made of twine (tied to the wire) with a bit of nonconducting silk near the hand of the person flying the kite. Finally at the juncture between the silk and the twine, he tied a metal key. Even though the kite was flown in the rain, the person and the silk rope and the key were under a doorway and kept dry so that no electricity would flow to the person holding

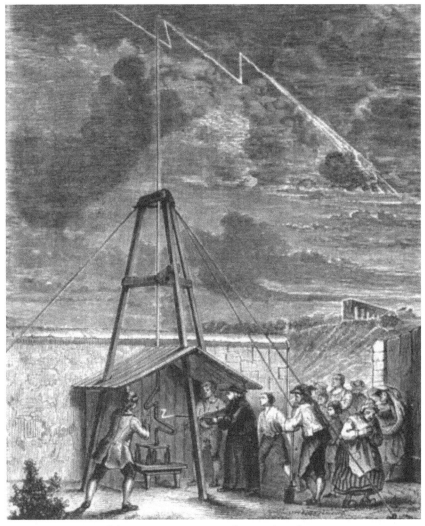

Figure 8: Painting of the priest capturing sparks in a thunderstorm

the kite. Notice that, just like the previous experiment, the experiment works *without* the kite being struck by lightning. The idea is that if the clouds are electrified, then the kite (and the wire and the twine and the key) will be electrified too. Franklin found that it worked very well. The sparks "stream out plentifully from the key on the approach of your knuckle. At this key the vial [Leyden jar] may be charged; and from electric fire thus obtained, spirits may be kindled, and all other electric experiments be performed, which are usually done by the help of a rubbed glass globe or tube, and thereby the sameness of the electric matter with that of lightening completely demonstrated."[126]

Benjamin Franklin had literally captured lightning in a bottle, and it made him famous. It's hard to fathom today how influential Franklin's experiment was at the time. In 1769, a historian described Franklin's discovery as "the greatest, perhaps, that has been made in the whole compass of philosophy, since the time of Sir Isaac Newton."[127]

Years later, many people erroneously thought that since Franklin claimed he was draining electricity from a cloud, he meant that his kite was actually hit by lighting, rather than flying it on a stormy day without getting hit. This has caused many, many (many) people to mistakenly think that Franklin didn't conduct the experiment at all. If it was a fake, it was an odd one, as he said that he had completed it *after* the French experiment, and his report contained a lot of detail. Also, Franklin had no history of making up experiments or not taking science seriously.

Keep in mind that just because it is possible to play with metal poles or fly a kite in a thunderstorm, it remains a very dangerous experiment. In fact, on August 6, 1753, a German man named Georg Wilhelm Richman in St. Petersburg was killed by a Franklin-style sentry box device when it was struck by lightning.[128] His death was widely reported and remarked upon, and it was taken as the conclusive proof that lightning was a form of static electricity. It certainly put a damper on doing lightning-capture experiments, although some, like the author and scientist Joseph Priestly in 1767, thought it was wonderful and said, "It is not given to every electrician to die the death of the justly envied Richman."[129]

With this successful proof that lightning clouds were electric, it was clear that Franklin's idea of pointed sticks stuck to the ground would protect cities from lightning. In fact, when Dalibard wrote about the success of his lightning experiments, he ended with the thought that "perhaps a hundred or so iron rods ... would suffice to preserve the entire city of Paris from thunderstorms."[130] Despite the fact that Franklin's original idea was flawed, an iron rod connected to the ground with a wire is exactly what a lightning rod is composed of. However, it never worked to drain the electricity "silently" from a thundercloud, as a thundercloud is farther up in the sky than Franklin realized. For electricity to jump the gap between the clouds and items on a building on the ground, they must have tremendous charge, which means they strike with terrible power.

So, if the lightning rod doesn't work, why do we use it? We use lightning rods because, although they don't prevent lightning strikes from happening, they still prevent lightning from their "terrible mischief." This is because electricity flows easily through metal but doesn't travel easily through wood or glass. So, when lightning strikes a lightning rod, the electricity safely and easily flows through the wire and into the ground. By 1755, Franklin realized that even if he was wrong about lightning rods draining the clouds of electricity, it would still help, and he wrote to Dalibard that "pointed rods erected on buildings and connected with wire with the earth, would either prevent a stroke of lightning, or if not prevented, would conduct it so that the building should suffer no damage."[131]

Back in 1752, two months after his kite experiment, Franklin constructed a lightning rod on his house with a small gap with bells and a clapper to warn him when the rod was electrified. Through this device, he determined that the charge from lightning was negative. As he was incorrectly convinced that only positive charges move, he determined that lightning must be going *up* from the ground to the clouds instead of what we think now—that in lightning, it is mostly negative charges that strike the earth.* Meanwhile, Franklin installed lightning rods without bells at the church at the University of Pennsylvania and in the Pennsylvania State House (later renamed Independence Hall with the Liberty Bell).

By the next year, Franklin published in his *Poor Richard's Almanack* the details of how to "secure buildings from mischief by thunder and lightning [with] a small iron rod."[132] In South Carolina, a doctor managed to recreate Franklin's kite experiment but was restrained from installing a lightning rod by his nervous neighbors. Why were they scared of a rod of metal?

The first and most powerful reason was religious. Lightning was God's judgment on man, and it was the height of hubris to get in the way of God's plan. Franklin tried to quiet their nerves by saying that "surely the thunder of heaven is no more supernatural than the rain, hail, or sunshine of heaven," and there were no qualms about roofs or umbrellas. He also thought that

---

* Like most natural phenomena, lightning is complicated. Basically, a positively charged plasma leaks upward and meets a stream of negatively charged plasma, which makes a conductive path for the electrons to strike the earth.

his newfound conclusion that lightning flowed upward might calm people: "I can now ease [people from their] apprehension because it is not lightning from the clouds that strikes the earth, but lightning from the earth that strikes the clouds."[133]

That did not quell the anxiety. Back in France, Abbé Nollet said it was "as impious to ward off Heaven's lightnings as for a child to ward off the chastening rod of its father."[134] In 1755, a terrible and unusual earthquake hit Boston and a reverend blamed it on the "iron points invented by the 'clever' Mr. Franklin." He wailed, "Oh! There is no getting out of the mighty hand of God."[135] (By the way, lightning rods do not cause earthquakes.)

Ironically, as churches tended to be the tallest buildings at the time, and with a nice pointy cross on top, they were often struck by lightning, leaving other nearby structures—a brothel for example—untouched. Ringing bells were supposed to help, but that just tended to be dangerous for the bell ringer. However, the fight against the lightning rod was a losing battle, especially after terrible lightning accidents. For example, in 1769, lightning hit a church in Breccia, Italy, which was storing over 200,000 pounds of gunpowder, and blew it to smithereens. Over 3,000 people died, and one-fifth of the town was destroyed.[136] The tower of St. Mark's in nearby Venice had a lightning rod installed the previous year and was undamaged. Despite this, progress in putting lightning rods on buildings was very slow. The first public building in England to have a lightning rod was only in 1769 after the previous steeple was obliterated by a lightning strike in 1764.[137]

Despite the conflict over the lightning rod, most people from every level of society loved and admired Benjamin Franklin due to his work on electricity. People fawned over him and had his image on every item imaginable. Supposedly, the new king of France, Louis XVI, became so irritated with hearing people gush over Franklin that he gave out chamber pots with Franklin's image on the bottom, especially to Franklin's many female admirers.[138] Twenty years after Franklin's death, John Adams, a man who personally disliked Franklin, wrote that "the invention of the lightning rod was one of the most sublime that ever entered a human imagination" and that Franklin's "reputation was more universal than that of Leibnitz or Newton or Frederick or Voltaire, and his character more beloved and esteemed than any or all of them ... there was scarcely a peasant or a citizen, a valet de chambre, coachman or footman, a lady's chambermaid or a scullion in a kitchen, who was not familiar with [him], and who did not consider him as a friend to human kind."[139]

By the 1760s, Franklin's attention was diverted from science to politics, although he continued to work on science for the remainder of his life. At the end of his life, Franklin was described as follows: "He snatched lightning from the sky and the scepter from tyrants."[140]

2.5 Coulomb Lays Down the Law

While Benjamin Franklin's interests turned to politics, Abbé Nollet continued to teach his view of electricity. In 1760 Nollet taught a 24-year-old student named Charles Augustin Coulomb in the country's top military engineering school.[141] Coulomb was born in 1736 to a middle-class aristocratic family with a bit of family drama. His father, Henry Coulomb, who was described by a contemporary as "good natured and unsuspecting,"[142] had a distant and acrimonious relationship with his wife, even before Charles's father lost all of the family money in the stock market when Charles was a late teen.[143] Frustrated, Charles's mother, Catherine, kicked her husband out, and Henry Coulomb left Paris and went back to his hometown of Montpellier, in the South of France.

Catherine, who had some money that she'd inherited, tried to bribe Charles into becoming a doctor, but he rebelled and went to live with his father in Montpellier. When Coulomb was 21, he joined the Montpellier Society of Sciences, which was a small group of men dedicated to studying mathematics, anatomy, chemistry, botany, and physics.[144] Although the group was impressed with Coulomb's mathematics skills, it didn't really pay the bills. Coulomb had very few options: he could become a priest, or he could join the military as an engineer. He chose the latter, which is how he ended up in Paris learning about the two kinds of electricity from Abbé Nollet himself.

After about a year of instruction, Coulomb became a lieutenant in the military engineering corps. After a couple of years doing geological mapping, he was transferred to the island of Martinique in the West Indies, some 6,800 km away. Twenty-eight-year-old Coulomb ended up becoming a lead engineer designing Fort Bourbon, a six-million-livre project with 600 workers.[145]

Coulomb was a superb engineer and ended up being promoted to captain after just six years of work. Unfortunately, he also got very ill with a tropical disease and asked his superior, named Le Beuf, to let him return to France. Le Beuf agreed, and in 1770 wrote to Versailles asking for Coulomb to be transferred for the "future value to the state."[146] Then, five days later, Le Beuf had a change of heart and realized that this would be a good way to get home himself. Le Beuf then wrote another letter to Versailles saying that actually he, Le Beuf, was the ill one and needed to come home but the government didn't need to be concerned as Coulomb wasn't really that sick and could take care of things. Le Beuf wrote that Coulomb "has been in charge of the work at Fort Bourbon since the beginning, and whom I have decided to keep here for the next year."[147] Poor Coulomb took another two years to return to France. According to a biographer, "Coulomb's health was so affected by his illness during the eight-year tour of duty in Martinique that he was never again a well man."[148]

Back in France, Coulomb wrote some papers on using calculus to optimize building stability, which had a lasting impact on engineering. A 1971 textbook noted that "in this one memoire of 1773, there is almost an embarrassment of riches [including a] theory of soil mechanics that remains in use today in basic engineering practice."[149]

In 1777 the Paris Academy had a competition to create a very sensitive compass with incredibly low friction to measure variations in Earth's magnetic field during the day.[150] Coulomb worked on it for a year and co-won the prize for a thin magnet held up by a thin silk string. That also inspired Coulomb to study the physics of friction, which he published in 1781. This report includes an equation for friction that's still taught to this day. An article in 1956 claimed "Coulomb's contribution to the science of friction were exceptionally great. Without exaggeration, one can say that he created this science."[151]

The Paris Academy was impressed with Coulomb's compass and installed a version of it at their observatory. Unfortunately, it turned out to be so sensitive that, as a historian put it, the compass "twitched when an assistant sneezed, or when the door opened, and trembled when carriages passed the street."[152] Coulomb attempted to isolate the needle in a chamber from drafts or other disturbances, but it would still often move when an assistant touched the outside. Coulomb eventually determined that while walking to the compass, the person who was going to measure the compass would often gain a little bit of electric charge, which would make the needle sway electrically, not magnetically. Eventually, Coulomb grounded the outside of the compass and the needle, which solved the problem.

The "twitchy" needle gave Coulomb an idea: maybe he could use a similar setup to measure the electrostatic force. One of the difficulties with any study of static electricity is that the forces are usually so slight that you can only see movement of little pieces of fluff or a feather (or if wealthy, gold foil). Most scales and balances cannot measure such minute forces. Coulomb knew from his needle that twisting can be very sensitive, but in order to use it as a scale, he needed a mathematical model for the force of twisting. Coulomb therefore wondered if the torsional force had similar equations as the law for vibrating springs, called Hooke's law.

Hooke's law is named after its inventor Robert Hooke, who was an English scientist 100 years earlier and a rival of Newton's.[153] In fact, Hooke claimed that he'd proven that the force of gravity depends on one over the distance squared *before* Newton did but didn't want to share it, claiming that he would "conceal it for some time, that others trying and failing, might know how to value it."[154] (Hooke never revealed it.) One of the reasons we know of Hooke is that he made some important discoveries about springs, which it seems he was willing to share, even if people wouldn't value it.

First, Hooke found that for moderate disturbances, the amount springs compress or stretch is in direct proportion to the force on the spring. So, if you double the force, you double the amount the spring stretches. How much a spring stretches with a given force depends on the strength of the spring, called the spring constant. Therefore, if you know the spring constant, and you know the amount of displacement, then you can know the force on a spring. This is how most simple spring scales in people's bathrooms work today. Hooke also determined that if you pulled a spring and let go, it would oscillate up and down at a steady rate until it stopped. Therefore, the time for the spring to vibrate back and forth is solely due to the mass on the spring and the spring constant, not the amount you pull on the mass. This means you can use the vibration time to determine the spring constant.

Coulomb therefore took piano wires and twisted them to measure how they vibrated. He was pleased to find that the wires twisted back and forth isochronously—at a constant rate. This implied that twisted wires followed Hooke's law and that the twist is proportional to the force. In addition, Coulomb used the time it took for the wire to vibrate back and forth to measure the "twisting" spring constant.

Now all Coulomb needed was a bar on a piano wire, and the amount it moved would tell him the force on the bar. He'd just invented the world's most precise measuring device, where a degree on the scale was equivalent to 1/100,000[th] of the weight of a single grain of sand.[155] Of course, I call it simple, but the actual experiment was incredibly difficult to complete or recreate, and the machine was described by a contemporary as an "all too unsteady twisting machine."[156] Still, the torsion machine was then used for all kinds of scientific experiments (including by the quirky Englishman Henry Cavendish in 1798 to determine the gravitational constant and thus the mass of Earth).[157] In fact, torsional balances are *still* used for scientific experiments.

Amazingly, Coulomb accomplished all of this while his life was quite chaotic. In 1783 he was commissioned to determine the feasibility of canal and harbor improvements in Brittany. However, when he stated that the plan was ill conceived, the people hoping to profit off the scheme actually had Coulomb imprisoned for his actions![158] He ended up being freed within a week, and the incident improved his reputation and standing with the government despite it being in chaos.

Coulomb decided to focus on his electrical experiments. By 1785 Coulomb used his torsional balance on electric charges and experimentally determined that electrical repulsion force is proportional to one over the distance squared, which he declared to be a "Fundamental law of Electricity."[159] It was a bit more difficult to measure attractive forces, but the following year, Coulomb determined that the attractive force of different charges follows the same relationship and that the electric force was linearly dependent on the size of the charge.

Unfortunately, Coulomb couldn't directly measure the amount of charge. Instead, he touched a charged ball in the balance with a neutral ball of the same size and then removed the outside ball to reduce the charge on the ball in the balance by two. He found that the force would then also be reduced by two. Coulomb wasn't the first person to predict that the electric forces look like gravitational forces, but he was the first to experimentally validate it. The law is justly named Coulomb's law, the constant, or Coulomb's constant, and the value of a charge is measured in Coulombs in his honor. However, at the time, few people were interested in electrical forces as electricity parties seemed decidedly passé.

There were bigger issues for Coulomb than the public reception to his law. The French Revolution began in 1789, and his supporters were thrown out of power—and sometimes, like his friend Lavoisier, they lost their heads. At first the new leaders were not very happy with a semi-aristocratic scientist like Coulomb. By 1791 he quit his position in the military and, for a while, hid in the countryside with his very young girlfriend, Louise, and their baby, Charles (who was born in 1790). By 1795 the new leaders had a change of heart, and Coulomb was invited back to Paris to be an experimental physicist at the new Institute of France. In 1802 Coulomb was made the inspector general of public instruction. With his new important position, he decided to marry Louise and legitimize their now two children. (He and Louise had another son in 1797.) By 1806 Coulomb's illnesses from his time in Martinique caught up with him, and he died of a "slow fever" at the ripe age of 70.[160]

At around the same time that Coulomb was discovering the laws of electricity, an Italian doctor and biologist accidentally discovered the link between life and electricity and galvanized us onto a new electric era: the age of the battery.

Chapter Summary

✧ **1737:** Matthias Bose recreates Du Fay's experiments with Hauksbee's spinning globe to start an "electricity party" craze in Germany and lights alcohol with a spark.

✧ **1746:** Pieter van Musschenbroek of Leyden, Denmark, writes his friend in Paris about the terrible jar that can store charges and give them a jolt. Abbé Nollet sells them as "Leyden jars."

✧ **1746:** Forty-year-old Benjamin Franklin receives an article about Bose's electricity antics in Germany; he decides that electricity is moved, not created or destroyed, and names electrical forces positive and negative. Franklin determines that electric charges are on surfaces and erroneously thinks that the positive "fire" is what moves.

✧ **1749:** Franklin hosts an electric "party of pleasure" where he fires cannons of "electric batteries." Soon after, powerful Leyden jars are commonly referred to as "electric batteries."

✧ **1751:** Franklin's letters are published as a book, which includes his reasoning on why lightning is electric and a proposed electrical experiment with a metal pole sticking out of a sentry box to test his theory.

✧ **1752:** In France, Dalibard gets sparks from a pole in a storm and makes Franklin famous in order to humiliate his rival, Abbé Nollet. A few months later, Franklin does the same experiment with a kite. Franklin publishes how to make lightning rods.

✧ **1785:** Charles Coulomb discovers that the laws of electric attraction and repulsion are similar to the law of gravity, dependent on the magnitude of their charges and one over the square of the distance.

Chapter 3

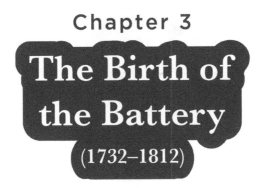

The Birth of the Battery

(1732–1812)

*Could not the **Annalen** [German Scientific Journal], in consideration of its object, be a little more varied? Galvanism, interesting as it is, is still only a very small part of physics.*

– Dr. Benzenberg (1801)[161]

Volta has presented us a key which promises to lay open some of the most mysterious recesses of nature.

– Humphry Davy (1807)[162]

When I was a teacher, I had my students attempt to make a battery from household objects. It isn't that hard, as a battery is only composed of two different metals and an acid or a base. In fact, a coworker of mine used to tell his students this whole dramatic tale where the students were supposed to imagine that they found themselves on a deserted island and had to use iron nails, copper pennies, and lemons (which they picked on the island) to electrify a tiny LED light and try to signal for help. Admittedly, it was pretty silly, and I didn't have the courage to repeat it to my students. Also, it took about four lemons connected with wires to make the LED faintly glow, so the theatrical story broke down a bit.

Still, it always felt magical to make electric light powered from nature. However, it turns out that the real story of how the battery was developed and created electric light is even more dramatic than my colleague's LED lemon story. Starting with a genius who earned their PhD to attract visitors to a struggling town, we travel through jumping dead frogs (and even dead jumping criminals) to poetic drug parties and a giant stinky battery. In addition, the first electric light powered by a battery wasn't a tiny, dim LED light, but a startling, brilliant torch "so intense as to resemble that of the sun."[163] No wonder this happens to be one of my favorite stories.

3.1 A Most Unusual Professor

There was an influential meeting that occurred in 1732, four years before Matthias Bose read about electricity and started electricity parties, when the leaders of the town of Bologna (in modern-day Italy) gathered to discuss a terrible problem. The town and the university were in severe decline. Plague had reduced the population by almost half, the silk industry had moved to other towns, and the university was struggling to retain students and staff. And since the church controlled what university students could study and say, they had difficulty attracting foreign visitors—especially those who believed that the Earth goes around the sun. What makes this meeting so influential was that a leader of the university and the local archbishop had a radical idea to award a doctorate to a person who was known locally as a genius. This was a drastic idea, because as it turns out the local intellect was a 20-year-old woman named Laura Bassi.[164]

Bassi was the only child of a local lawyer named Giuseppe Bassi and his wife, Rosa Cesari. When Bassi was five, her adult cousin Father Lorenzo Stegani was so impressed with her intelligence that he taught her French and arithmetic. Early in 1732, Laura's father and cousin decided that Bassi should put on a demonstration to a select group of elite Bolognese gentlemen, which included the secretary of the Institute of Bologna and the new archbishop, Prospero Lambertini. Soon news of her brilliance was the talk of the town, and she "found herself constrained to make almost a continuous spectacle of herself in the city."[165] It was these "performances" that led to the revolutionary idea of giving Bassi a doctorate. Bassi was not the first woman in the world to earn a university degree—she was the second. Over 50 years earlier, a woman named Elena Piscopia received a degree in philosophy from the University of Padua. Over 20,000 people came to see Piscopia, so the leaders of Bologna had a good inkling of what this action could do for their city and school.[166]

By April 17, 1732, Laura Bassi earned her degree by writing a series of papers on philosophy and physics and defending them publicly. However, unlike all previous applicants, her defense was made into a public show of epic proportions, where even her dress was preordained by the powers that be. She was given a silver crown, a ring, an ermine mantle, and endless poems and accolades. They even printed special medals in her honor. A local poet wrote his friend that "all the gentlemen of Bologna make a great display of this girl, and depict her everywhere as the miracle of our age."[167]

In October, she had a second round of defenses, which she passed easily and was then awarded a lectureship at Bologna with a 500-lira-a-year paycheck. Bassi was ecstatic, proclaiming, "The magnanimity of the Senate raised me, beyond what I asked for and dreamed of, to the highest dignity of speaking in public."[168] It turns out she had spoken too soon, because then the Senate decided that they didn't want to "burden" her with too much actual teaching, declaring that Bassi "should not read in the public schools [teach] except on those occasions when her Superiors commanded her, because of her sex."[169]

Despite not teaching often, one advantage of Bassi's position was in regard to what she could read. The Vatican decided that the works of Galileo, Descartes, Kepler, Copernicus, and more were too dangerous for public consumption and were to be kept in a special library where only doctors of philosophy who were 24 years old or older were allowed. In 1735, the second she

Figure 1: Laura Bassi with her ermine coat

turned 24, Laura Bassi became the only woman in all of the papal state who could legally read these books.[170] Despite this, most of the men in power would've preferred if she limited herself to the feminine arts of poetry and be trotted out a few times a year as a symbol of virginal intelligence. Bassi wasn't interested in that, and by February of 1737, she was writing to a friend that she had no desire "to compose poetry ever again."[171]

Bassi tried to get permission to teach more, either in the university or at home. However, she couldn't get permission to teach at the university, and at the time, it was considered scandalous for a single woman to have a bunch of men enter her home. What to do? In 1737, Laura Bassi decided that what she needed to do was to get married. She chose a fellow professor named Giovanni Veratti, who was a 30-year-old biology and physics professor who had just obtained a position as a lecturer of physics at the University of Bologna.[172] Bassi wrote to a friend that "my domestic circumstances have induced me to change my mind and make this decision ... I had hoped quietly to pursue [science studies] in this life; therefore, I have chosen a person who walks my path in the arts and who, through long experience, I was certain would not impede me from following mine."[173]

Despite her protestations that she would continue to study and teach after marriage, most of the town hated that she wanted to get married, for they felt that her virginity was symbolic of her "extraordinary feminine ability."[174] A local historian (who was a supporter of education for women) published that Bassi had "changed the virginal decency into conjugal bonding" and cried, "you have stained your glory."[175]

Despite all the objections, Laura Bassi married Giovanni Veratti in February of 1738. Bassi was correct in that her marriage freed her to start a teaching and research institute in her home and to go to more meetings protected by her new status. Bassi was also correct in her assessment of her husband, for he supported his wife as a scientist. Laura Bassi then diligently taught, wrote, conducted original experiments, and even wrote dreaded poetry while she dealt with as many as twelve pregnancies, which resulted in eight births and five children who lived past infancy. In addition, the Bassi-Veratti home was a must-stop for any visiting scholar, from Abbé Nollet to Voltaire, and was considered, according to a visiting scientist, "the most open and welcoming in Bologna."[176]

In 1740 Bassi's prospects improved when her benefactor Cardinal Lambertini was elected pope. In 1745 the new pope (now called Benedict XIV) was interested in promoting science at the University of Bologna, so he created a group of learned scientists called the Benedettina who got more money and prestige but were required to publish one original work a year and attend three-quarters of all meetings.[177] Bassi was distressed to find that the original group of Benedettina included her husband but not her. Boldly, Bassi asked the new pope if he could raise the number of Benedettina from 24 to 25 to include her, and he agreed. The authorities tried to fight Bassi on this appointment, but with the pope on her side, she prevailed. She presented dissertations for the next 31 years until her death.[178]

In 1747 Bassi's husband was asked to study the medical uses of electricity and to conduct experiments. They became the first private people in Bologna to own an electricity machine. This was such a coup that when Bassi's husband was on vacation, he wrote to his bride. "Remember the electrical machine, the love I feel for my children and to yourself, who are the greatest wealth I possess on this Earth."[179] In 1752 Bassi and Veratti heard about the electrical experiments in France getting sparks from a kinked metal pole in a thunderstorm (to validate Benjamin Franklin's theory that lightning was electric), and they quickly reproduced it at the observatory tower. However, when they tried to install lightning rods, there were mass protests, and they quickly took them down. Eighteen years later, Bassi bemoaned that despite their best efforts, "no lightning rods have been erected in this town."[180]

Meanwhile, Bassi started teaching more and more students at home. One of her first students was her much younger cousin Lazzaro Spallanzani, who went to school to be a lawyer but was convinced to switch to science by Laura. Later on, Spallanzani described Bassi as "my venerable teacher, of whom I will always remember as long as I have spirit and life. I can truthfully say that what little I know originated from her intelligent teachings."[181] Spallanzani ended up being a pioneering biologist. He became the first person to do in vitro fertilization (on a frog) and artificial insemination (on a dog), the first to say that bats don't use their eyes to see, and to determine that digestion was a chemical process.[182] Remarkably, he's possibly most famous for being the first to determine that microbes don't spontaneously exist but actually fly through the air and can be destroyed by boiling (and he did this almost 100 years before Louis Pasteur).[183]

By the 1750s, Bassi noted to a friend, "The classes have gathered such momentum that they are now attended by people of considerable education, including foreigners, rather than by youths."[184] In a way, being restrained from teaching at a university freed her to teach without restrictions. This included "modern" ideas like those from Newton and Franklin as well as other experiments that were largely absent in the traditional classroom.

In fact, according to a friend, Bassi did "not dislike good reasons but never [tired] of experiments."[185] Unfortunately, her experiments were expensive, and she wrote that unless she received some form of financial assistance, she couldn't conduct them well, crying, "I am almost in despair."[186] Luckily, her classes were so popular and her demands for money so frequent (and supported by powerful people) that by 1759, the Senate gave Bassi a significant salary increase to cover the equipment. She earned 1,200 lira a year, which was as much as the head of the science department.[187] Eventually, Bassi would receive the highest salary given at the University of Bologna.[188]

In 1752 a Swiss scientist named Albrecht von Haller published an anatomy book that described the nerves as being "sensible" because you were always aware when they sent a signal, and muscles were "irritable" in that they could contract if you irritated them without the person or animal noticing.[189] That may not seem very interesting or profound to modern ears, but in the 1700s, it was revolutionary. You could actually experimentally study how the muscles and nerves worked, and according to a modern historian, "Haller's theory became a central debate in Europe with several famous persons on both sides of the argument."[190] Laura and Giovanni were firm believers in Hallerism, and their home was the site of many electrified animals (as electricity was found to be an excellent stimulant and they still had the only private electricity machine around).

It was in the 1760s that Laura Bassi, independently of her husband, began researching the physics of Franklin's electricity theories. One of the big arguments against Franklin's idea of positive and negative "fluids" is how negatively charged objects repel each other. If they're both lacking in "electrical fire," how do they push against each other? According to a contemporary of Franklin's named Priestley, "Dr. Franklin himself ingenuously acknowledges, that he was a long time puzzled to account for bodies that were negatively electrified repelling one another."[191] It seemed a real weakness of the Franklin philosophy of electricity. Tragically, none of Bassi's papers on electricity have survived, so there's no way of identifying the validity of her arguments. Fortunately, a fellow scientist wrote her in 1775 and explained. "You have expressed in most ingenious and subtle terms of physics a defense of the Franklinian system."[192] To enable her investigations into electricity, Bassi set up an outside observatory in 1774 to "experiment on atmospheric electricity" that was so popular that they had to find a larger venue to deal with the crowd.[193]

In 1770 the head of the science department retired, and the new head was a man named Paolo Balbi. Giovanni Veratti, Bassi's husband, became Balbi's assistant. Then, two years after attaining the position as head of the science department, Paulo Balbi suddenly became ill and died. There was talk of replacing Balbi with Giovanni Veratti. However, there were concerns that Veratti was lacking the mathematical skills required, and perhaps more importantly, a respectable public reputation. Instead, there was a person who was very good at advanced mathematics and was possibly the most famous scientist in all of Italy—Laura Bassi. So, in May of 1776, Bassi, at the age of 65, became the first woman to have a professorship and the first female university chair, with her husband as her assistant.[194] Then, tragedy struck. Less than two years after finally becoming a professor, Bassi felt ill after a day of teaching and died, probably from a heart attack, at the age of 66. The entire city mourned. Her body was buried in the Church of Corpus Domini with full honor. She was the first scientist buried there.

Although Laura Bassi was easily the most famous woman in Italy at the time, her gravestone is currently overlooked, and most visitors pass by her marker to view the grave of one of her former students, Luigi Galvani, who is buried at the same church. Galvani, who learned of electricity and atmospheric electricity from Bassi, was to discover a shocking thing about frogs, and it would lead directly to the development of the battery.

3.2 The Frog Battery

Luigi Galvani was born in 1737 and was the son of a prosperous goldsmith.[195] When he was 18, he flirted with the idea of becoming a priest, but instead went to the University of Bologna. This is how he became Laura

Bassi's student while she was busy investigating the electrical effects on nerves—though Galvani mostly focused on traditional medicine and surgery. In fact, Galvani had a particularly close connection to Gusmano Galeazzi, his anatomy professor and head of the science department who encouraged his interest in biology.[196]

It was through this teacher that Galvani met the love of his life, Galeazzi's talented daughter Lucia. Lucia Galeazzi was also a brilliant scientist who had been instructed in anatomy and surgery by her father and worked in hospitals as a doctor and midwife. I can find no documents that state that Lucia Galeazzi studied under Laura Bassi. However, as Lucia was another female science genius from Bologna, it defies logic that Lucia wouldn't at least have attended Laura's public talks and possibly attended some of her classes. However, as Lucia's father was a famous scientist instead of a lawyer and Bologna already had a female scientist, there was no talk of awarding Lucia any degree, and instead she assisted her father in his research.

Galvani graduated in 1759 and applied to be a lecturer at the university, which he was granted with Galeazzi's help. By 1762 Luigi and Lucia married, and, at the request of Lucia's father, moved into the Galeazzi household.[197] Luigi and Lucia spent the next eight years assisting Gusmano Galeazzi in his biological systems research while also working together at a local hospital. According to contemporaries, Luigi and Lucia had a very happy life together, although they both felt sad that they never had any children and that Lucia's health remained poor from severe asthma.[198]

In 1770 Galvani's father-in-law, Gusmano Galeazzi, retired due to poor health. Luigi Galvani took over his classes without taking over his position as the head of the science department (which eventually led to Bassi taking over the position). Gusmano Galeazzi passed away in 1775, and the following year Galvani was nominated to be a "Benedettina" with the stipulation that he submit a research paper every year.[199] For the next four years, Galvani published work on the hearing of various animals, which Lucia edited. However, in 1780, their work was "poached" by a rival named Antonio Scarpa in an act so blatant that they decided to give up on that research entirely.[200] They needed a new topic quickly and decided on electricity.

While they never said why they started to experiment with electricity, it seems clear that they at least learned a few things from Laura Bassi and her electricity machine. Unfortunately, Bassi died two years earlier in 1778, so the Galvanis could not turn to her for assistance. As the Galvanis had never personally experimented with electricity before, they sought the aid of several assistants and hoped to find something to publish.

One day Luigi Galvani happened to place a dissected frog on the table while his assistants were conducting electrical experiments. There isn't much of a consensus as to why Galvani was cutting up frogs that day. What we do know is that Galvani said that it was unrelated to electricity or electrical experiments.[201] Some authors state with unsupported conviction that Galvani was using frog skin in electrical experiments, while others state that Galvani was making frog soup as medicine for Lucia.[202] To me it seems more likely that he was dissecting the frog for a lecture since he was an anatomy professor.

This is how Galvani described what happened next: "It happened by chance that one of my assistants touched the inner nerve of the frog with the point of [an electrified] scalpel; whereupon at once the muscles of the limbs went into violent convulsions."[203] Galvani was astonished to see a decapitated frog jumping on his table and proceeded to electrocute every dead animal he could find. He discovered that all animals would respond physically to

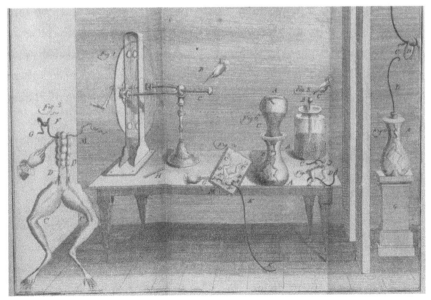

Figure 2: Galvani's drawings. "Fig 1" is a static electricity machine.

electricity, although frog legs seemed to have the greatest dramatic effect with their powerful leg muscles.[204] Galvani also noticed that the convulsions were the most pronounced when the electricity was placed on an animal's nerves or muscles.

After conducting frog experiments in the lab for several months, Luigi and Lucia Galvani decided to move the experiment outdoors to see if the frogs would jump similarly during a thunderstorm. This was around 40 years after Benjamin Franklin demonstrated that lightning was electric and around 15 years after Bassi setup her outdoor electrical demonstrations, so they were not surprised to find that the frogs jumped theatrically in thunderstorms. However, they noticed something quite strange: the frogs "exhibited convulsions not only during thunderstorms, but sometimes even when the sky was quite serene."[205]

At first, they wondered if the frog had collected atmospheric electricity from past storms. They quickly realized it had nothing to do with the weather but rather had to do with the outdoor gate. The frogs had been attached to the iron railings surrounding the garden, and brass hooks were used to transport the frogs. It was this combination of iron and brass that caused the frogs to convulse. When the frog was taken inside, they could make a frog dance by simply placing a piece of brass and iron on a dead frog's leg. This was a major discovery. By putting both brass and iron into a frog's body, you could *produce* electricity with no spinning machines or thunderstorms in sight. The Galvanis postulated that all animals had what they called "animal electricity" inside them, which is what makes them (and us) alive, and it was the metal that somehow brought out this latent life force.[206]

In the middle of all of this exciting research, Lucia Galvani became very ill, and despite Luigi's devoted care, she died from complications of her asthma in 1788. Luigi Galvani was overcome with grief and did not publish their work on electricity, titled *De Viribus Electricitatis*, until 1791.[207] When he finally did publish, his work became an international sensation, especially among anatomists.[208] Suddenly, there was a new way of examining how muscles move and nerves communicate. There was also a new hope of using electricity in medicine in a more scientific manner as opposed to receiving magic jolts from a traveling entertainer. Finally, Galvani's theory of

Figure 3: Luigi and Lucia Galvani—notice that Luigi Galvani is experimenting with a dead frog while Lucia is reading a book (to show she was educated) with the company of a dog (to show she was loyal).

"animal electricity" created a link between electricity and what makes things alive. While we don't think of it exactly the way that Galvani did, modern biologists do share similar beliefs as it relates to "animal electricity." Muscles contract with electricity, our hearts pump with electricity, and we think, hear, see, smell, and feel with electric signals. Luigi and Lucia Galvani had made the spark of life literal.

Galvani didn't know it, but he had also inadvertently invented the first battery. Though he imagined that he was bringing the frog back to life with his copper and iron, what was actually happening was less sensational. The acid in the frog's leg reacted with the brass to add electrons and then reacted with the iron to remove electrons. The electrons flowed through the frog's leg from the brass back to the iron, making the frog leg jump. In terms of physics, it was a completely useless battery, as it discharged inside itself. In other words, it was a battery that could not create external current, which is why most people do not consider Galvani's "invention" to be a battery. However, Galvani's useless battery led directly to the invention of the first useful battery by another Italian named Alessandro Giuseppe Antonio Anastasio Volta.

3.3 Volta's Artificial Electric Organ

Alessandro Volta lived in the beautiful mountain town of Como, Italy, about 180 miles away from Galvani, and was known at the time as Europe's greatest electrical scientist. He was a loud and boisterous man, a world traveler who spoke many languages, and was, according to a contemporary, "a genius who swore and cackled over his experiments, guzzled and disputed over his dinner, electrified the ladies ... and understood more of electricity than anyone else in Europe."[209]

Figure 4: Alessandro Volta

In 1792 Volta began to replicate Galvani's work and found the results "unbelievable" and "miraculous."[210] Then, while experimenting with frogs, Volta got a *live* frog to jump by attaching two different metals to the frog's leg and back. As a result, Volta concluded that the electricity came from the different metals and that the frog was merely responding to the electricity they produced, just as it jumped in response to the electricity from machines and from lightning bolts.[211] He argued that his findings destroyed Galvani's claim that animals have electricity within them.[212]

Galvani didn't want to respond. Galvani was a quiet, soft-spoken, religious man who didn't like conflict, and at the time, he was still mourning his wife's passing. Galvani's young nephew Giovanni Aldini, however, was rearing for a fight—especially after Galvani had just nursed him through an illness. This is how Aldini described what happened in 1794: "[Galvani] was treating me for a deadly fever. After having escaped, thanks to his generous care and efforts, a nearly unavoidable death, I started to work zealously to bring support to a doctrine that I trusted, despite the attacks under which it came. I felt at ease to be able to pay a tribute to the truth and, at the same time, to provide Galvani with a public account of my gratitude."[213] Aldini began writing and traveling throughout Europe electrocuting animals and promoting his uncle's theories. From this time on, Aldini was the face of galvanism.

The debate between the Voltists and the Galvanists became widespread in academic circles. Was the frog jumping because it had once been, or was currently, alive? Or was the frog jumping because two different metals created electricity? What both sides of the debate missed was that a chemical (an acid or a base) was needed to interact with the metals and move electrical charges.

In 1797 Galvani refused to sign a paper acknowledging Napoleon's conquest of Italy, and he lost his job as a result. Depressed and impoverished, he died the next year from unknown causes.[214] Meanwhile, Volta, who did not object to Napoleon, did well politically and scientifically. Despite his friendliness with Napoleon, Volta won a prestigious British award from the Royal Society for explaining Galvani's experiment.[215] Yet Volta remained unsatisfied. Volta didn't want awards for explaining other people's work—he wanted an award just for himself. Volta needed a decisive experiment that would prove that electricity came from the metals and not the frog.

The first thing Volta did was to determine which metals worked best on the frog and found that silver and zinc seemed to have the greatest effect. He then put a piece of silver and zinc in his own mouth and noticed that he felt a slight tingle. (You might have experienced the same feeling if you accidentally bite on aluminum foil if you already have another metal in a filling or crown in your mouth.) Volta then found that if he put the silver and zinc together on a table and connected the metal with wires on his tongue, he felt nothing. Volta wondered if the metals had to be wet to create electricity and put the metals in a cup of water and connected them to his tongue with wires. Suddenly, there was a tiny tingle on his tongue. This sensation became more dramatic when Volta recalled that saliva is salty and added salt to his cup of water.

Volta then turned the experiment on its side by stacking pieces of silver and zinc with thin, wet cardboard between them into a pile. When he attached the pile to his tongue with wires, he felt a relatively strong tingle. He experienced an even greater tingling sensation by adding more disks (see figure 5). Volta found that if he wet his hands and touched the pile, he could even feel a shock run through his whole body. With no rubbing required, the electricity continuously flowed between the terminals. Volta had just invented the battery! This was an entirely new phenomenon, and Volta published his work in 1800 to tremendous acclaim.[216]

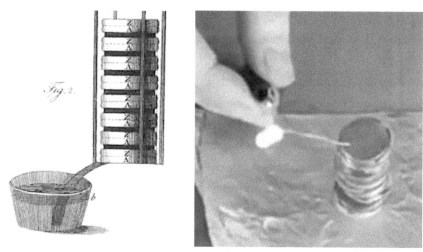

Figure 5: Volta's diagram of his pile (the A is silver; the Z is zinc) (left) and a photograph of a battery made of copper pennies and zinc washers (with vinegar-soaked paper) lighting an LED bulb (right)

Volta's battery, like all batteries, works with chemistry. The acid of the saltwater reacts with the zinc and the silver and removes electrons from the silver to leave it positively charged, while adding electrons to the zinc leave it negatively charged. This continues until the voltage, or the electrical pressure, is the same as the chemical strength. When the ends are connected with a conductive material, like a metal wire or Volta's wet hands, the electrons in the negative zinc flow through the conductive material (or person) and into the positive silver. At this point, the chemical reaction happens, as more electrons are taken from the silver and are deposited on the zinc. This continues until the circuit is broken or the saltwater runs out of acidity (which was usually within an hour or so with Volta's pile).

Surprisingly, Volta's battery could create a significant voltage, or electrical pressure, around 0.75 volts per cell of two disks, so a typical pile would have between 5 and 30 volts, and it gave a good shock.[217] However, because of something called internal resistance, it could only produce a small amount of current, or a small number of electrons flowing per second, which is only enough to light an LED bulb (see figure 5). A common analogy for the difference between voltage and current is water pressure in pipes. Voltage is like the power in a water pump that adds pressure to pipes, and the current is like the amount of water flow you can get from the pipes.

Back in 1800, Volta didn't know about current, voltage, or LED bulbs. In fact, Volta didn't even call his device a battery, preferring the title of "artificial electric organ,"[218] a name that appealed to no one else. For that reason, many people referred to it as a "galvanic pile," or "Volta's galvanic apparatus." In fact, a battery is often called a *pile* in French, Italian (*pila*), and Spanish (*pila*) to this very day.[219] However, as this was over 50 years after Benjamin Franklin discharged his "electric battery" of guns at an "electricity party,"[220] the term "electric battery" was a common term for a set of multiple Leyden jars, which was the most powerful electrical device available at the time. Volta knew that his device was very different from a bunch of Leyden jars, but he was trying to inflate his accomplishment, so he repeatedly referred to his discovery as "resembling an electric battery."[221] Thus, you can see how the name was established.

Volta's victory was complete. Napoleon gave Volta the title of count as a reward for his accomplishments. The potential of a battery is measured in volts and is referred to as voltage in his honor. Volta retired a wealthy man, never to do anything else worthy of publishing. Interestingly, in his famous paper of 1800, he still found time to insult Galvani who had died two years earlier, writing that his research was initiated because "I found myself obliged to combat the pretended animal electricity of Galvani."[222]

Galvani's nephew, Giovani Aldini, wanted the world to acknowledge his late uncle's work and discoveries despite, as he put it, "the just tribute of applause [that] has been bestowed on the celebrated Professor Volta for his late discovery."[223] Note that Aldini was able to publish, as he wisely decided to accept Napoleon's reign to the point that he dedicated his book of 1803 to Bonaparte.

Aldini then used a battery, which he called a "Galvanic pile [discovered] by the celebrated Volta,"[224] to electrocute all sorts of animals in new ways. He even managed to manipulate the facial muscles of a decapitated ox by electrocuting parts of its brain. In 1802 Aldini experimented on several decapitated corpses of various criminals and, as with the ox, managed to manipulate their facial expressions by electrifying parts of their brains. He became the first person to realize that one side of the hemisphere of the brain controls the opposite side of the body.[225]

That year Aldini also became the first person to try electric shock therapy to cure depression. First Aldini conducted a "long series of painful and disagreeable experiments"[226] on his own head with a voltaic pile to gauge how powerful and useful electric jolts could be. Aldini then gave shocks to a 27-year-old farmer named Louis Lanzarini who was suffering from debilitating depression and was being held in an insane asylum. According to Aldini, after the first shock, the patient started to smile, and after several days of shocks, Lanzarini "not only got the better of his melancholy, but began to relish his food, and at length recovered so much strength that the physicians of the hospital thought nothing further was necessary to complete the cure."[227] Even though electroshock therapy was abused and misused in the 1950s and '60s, it's actually *still* considered one of the most effective treatments for severe depression that exists today.[228]

In the fall of 1802, Aldini went on a European tour where he inspired doctors and scientists in France and England with his macabre experiments. His most famous, or infamous, demonstration was on the lifeless body of an English murderer named George Foster. Aldini used a battery to get the dead man's jaw to shake and even opened his left eye. The highlight (so to speak) was when Aldini stuck one electrified probe in the corpse's ear and another one in his anus and made his legs kick and his right hand clench and pump in the air.[229] Aldini realized that electric shocks would be incredibly useful in getting the heart to beat, although he was never successful with his primitive batteries. It took well over 100 years, but you could argue that Aldini is the father of the defibrillator and the pacemaker.

Part of the reason that Aldini's work in England was so influential is because Aldini conducted his experiments on a prisoner from London's infamous Newgate Prison. That was important because, at the time, Newgate had a long history of publishing descriptions of criminals and their untimely

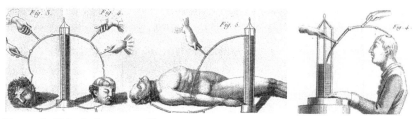

Figure 6: Aldini's drawings of his experiments on dead bodies (left) and on a depressed patient (right)

demises in a pamphlet sold to the public. This all started in 1676, when the chaplain of Newgate, Samuel Smith, decided to supplement his meager income by publishing lurid accounts of the lives and the deaths of the prisoners held there.[230] These pamphlets turned out to be profitable, and all of the following chaplains followed suit, with some even including advertisements.[231] *

Many of these periodicals have been lost. We do know, however, that at least one of them included a full description of George Foster's horrendous crimes and Aldini's electric experiments that were conducted on his body afterward, as it can be found in a compilation book called *The Newgate Calendar* published in 1825. *The Newgate Calendar* and its predecessors were quite popular, as parents hoped it would scare their children straight. It was easily the most popular book in England (second only to the Bible).[232] As far as I can tell, it didn't reduce crime in any way or form, but it gives an interesting background to the dark and gothic sensibilities of many English authors and poets in the 1800s.

As an amusing sidenote, 13 years after Aldini electrified Foster's dead body, an 18-year-old woman named Mary Godwin learned about galvanism. That is only important because Mary was vacationing with friends and her lover and future husband, Percy Shelley. Stuck inside with horrible weather, they tried to entertain each other by writing scary stories. After a discussion that "perhaps a corpse would be reanimated; galvanism had given token of such things," Mary Godwin had a "waking dream" about Galvanists and wrote a horror story about it called *Frankenstein: or, The Modern Prometheus*.[233]

In the early 1800s, the battery was not only interesting to biologists and resurrectionists—it also was an important tool for chemists. Back when Volta sent the first part of his paper about the battery to England in April of 1800, the secretary of the Royal Society let his friend Anthony Carlisle read it first. Carlisle was immediately fascinated and asked his friend William Nicholson to conduct experiments with the new device.[234] While playing with the battery, they used water to connect the plates to an electroscope, and Carlisle noticed that the water was forming bubbles. Nicolson smelled the bubbles

---

* According to Caroline Jowett's *The History of Newgate Prison* (Barnsley, UK: Pen and Sword Books, 2017), this publication led to criminal behavior on the part of the chaplains, including one particularly greedy chaplain named John Villette who attempted to negate the reprieve of a young boy so that he could profit from the report of his demise!

and felt like it was similar to the smell of hydrogen.[235]

When they put both ends into a container of water, they found that the zinc wire became oxidized while the silver wire produced bubbles of hydrogen. They then connected each wire separately into containers of water that were capped and connected to wires and found that the zinc produced 72 grams of oxygen and the silver produced 142 grams of hydrogen.[236] As 142 grams is almost exactly twice as much as 72 grams, and water is H_2O with two hydrogens and one oxygen, it seemed immediately clear that the battery worked chemically to separate the water into its elements in a process that was eventually called electrolysis.

As batteries were so useful for chemists, it should be no surprise that the next person to determine the use of the battery was a chemist: a charismatic Englishman named Humphry Davy.

3.4 The Influential Humphry Davy

In the early 1800s, Humphry Davy was a scientific superstar. He was so famous that when he gave science lectures, they had to make the street in front of the building one way to help with traffic.[237] A woman named Harriet Martineau recalled that Davy "was probably the most popular man of his time—so clear were his expositions, so beautiful his experiments, and so bewitching his ardent eloquence."[238] Which all raises the question—how did Davy, a middle-class man from the backwoods of southwest England with no pedigree and not much formal education end up as the toast of London? Humphry Davy's meteoritic success in life was due to his fierce intelligence, fortuitous timing, prolific writing, charming personality, good looks, and reckless experimentation. Oh, and drugs. Lots and lots of drugs.

Humphry Davy was born in Cornwall, England, in December of 1778 to a farmer and woodcarver.[239] Davy lived in genteel poverty, with enough money for him to go to the local school but not enough to advance his education without help from his godfather. His brother described their upbringing as having "little taste for literature, and still less for science, instead they all delighted in hunting, shooting, wrestling, cockfighting, all ending in drunkenness."[240] When Davy was 16 years old, his father died and his godfather got him a "job" as an indentured servant to a local surgeon and apothecary. The plan was for Davy to study to become a doctor himself.

Meanwhile, he self-taught and worked at the pharmacy. According to his brother, "[Davy] began the study of chemistry ... when he was entering his nineteenth year.... He appears to have entered this study merely as a branch of his professional knowledge."[241] Pretty soon he was hooked, causing his boss to complain, "This boy Humphry is incorrigible. He will blow us all into the air."[242]

Davy became friends with some local scientists, especially a man named Davies Giddy, a rich and influential man who let Davy play in his laboratory. Giddy also introduced Davy to his friend Thomas Beddoes who was starting a Pneumatic Institution to discover the medical effects of gasses like laughing gas on patients. Not, as you might expect, as a painkiller but to help with lung problems. (It wasn't used as an anesthetic until 1844.)[243] At the institution, Davy was so impressive that Giddy helped Davy get out of his indenture early so he could be a free man investigating science.

At the institution, Davy diligently conducted experiments with laughing gas on himself, his friends, and all types of animals. Pretty soon a group of doctors, patients, scientists, and poets were meeting at the institution every night to studiously "experiment" with this drug. It was especially popular with poets like Samuel Coleridge, Thomas Poole, Joseph Cottle, Thomas Wedgwood, and Robert Southey.[244] Southey ecstatically wrote his brother Tom: "Such a gas has Davy discovered! Oh Tom! I have had some, it makes me strong, and so happy! So gloriously happy! Oh excellent gas bag! Tom, I am sure the air of heaven must be this wonder working gas of delight."[245] (By the way, Davy didn't invent laughing gas, nor did he pretend to, but often people forgot, especially after using the drug.)

By 1800 Davy produced a 580-page behemoth research book on nitrous oxide and, almost immediately, nitrous oxide was used at "laughing gas" parties.[246] It continued to be a prominent feature in both upper-class events and traveling "science shows" for the masses for almost 100 years. For the upper crust of England, the handsome young Davy was the master of ceremonies (and a prolific practitioner) for an astonishing new drug. Bristol, and the Pneumatic Institution, was not big enough for this rising new star. It was time to go to London.

Luckily for Davy, in 1799, a wealthy American who had sided with the British in the American Revolution named Count Rumford had collaborated with his titled science friends to create a new science institute in London. The endless war with Napoleon in France landlocked many Englishmen from their international science pursuits, and Rumford wanted a place for research, to give talks, and for "exciting a taste for science amongst the higher ranks."[247] The original 58 members were dukes, barons, members of parliament, and, basically, every high-ranking man in England who was interested in science. Soon they had an opening for a chemist and lecturer. In 1800 Davy wrote his mother. "Count Rumford has made proposals to me to settle myself there [at the Royal Institution], with the present appointment of assistant lecturer on chemistry, and experimenter to the Institute ... an appointment as honorable as any scientific appointment in the kingdom."[248] Davy was only 22 years old.

Davy's most important job was to give interesting lectures. Davy brashly convinced Lord Rumford that in order to give exciting presentations, he needed a state-of-the-art laboratory. On April 25, 1801, Davy gave his first public lecture at the Royal Institution on the hot topic of the day: galvanism.[249] It was an instant success of grand proportions. A local paper gushed that "his youth, his simplicity, his natural eloquence, his chemical knowledge, his happy illustrations and well-conducted experiments, excited universal attention and unbounded applause. Compliments, invitations, and presents were showered upon him in abundance from all quarters; his society was courted by all, and all appeared proud of his acquaintance."[250] One can see the influence of Davy's popularity to this day in the English language, as Davy preferred to call Volta's device a battery instead of a pile.[251] It's quite possible that a battery is never referred to as a pile in English for this reason, although it remains common in many other languages.

Davy was not just lecturing—he was also a prolific researcher. He studied geology and agriculture with the same zeal as chemistry, publishing paper after paper (but was careful not to interrupt his busy social life, which required immense amounts of laughing gas and time for fly fishing). Frankly, it's exhausting just reading about him. By 1801, Davy determined that batteries work due to a chemical reaction, and that, therefore, Volta's battery could be vastly improved with a stronger acid.[252] Still, this stronger battery wasn't enough to complete the chemical experiments that Davy was hoping for, although he did find that "a thin slip of platina," a platinum alloy, glows with "a vivid light"[253] when he placed the current from his stronger battery

across it (which is why he is often credited with discovering
incandescence).

The next year, 1802, in
Scotland, a surgeon named
William Cruickshank used a
battery for biological experiments and found that his pile
kept falling down. To remedy
this, he placed the pile on its
side, which was called a trough
battery, as it was placed in
a rectangle that resembled a

Figure 7: Humphry Davy looking
Byronically handsome

trough to feed animals. This gave Davy an idea to make a huge battery that
filled over 880 square feet of the Royal Institution's basement with 2,000
plates of copper and zinc and unmeasured gallons of acid.[254] Supposedly, he
hid it in the basement because the chemical actions of the battery produced
waste gasses that smelled awful.

With this mammoth battery (the biggest in the world), Davy discovered
how to isolate new elements and, according to his brother, "he could not
contain his joy—he actually bounded about the room in ecstatic delight; and
that some little time was required for him to compose himself sufficiently to
continue the experiment."[255] Davy then quickly discovered a whole host of
new elements. His lectures on his new discoveries given in the end of 1806
till the beginning of 1807 cemented his place as one of the top scientists in
England. "Davy, not yet 32, in the opinion of all who could judge of such
labors, held the first rank among the chemists of this or of any other age."[256]

While experimenting with his giant battery, Davy noticed something
strange: if the current went between two carbon rods that were touching, it
would cause a spark. If the rods were then slowly separated the spark would
grow bigger and create a constant and brilliantly strong light. In this way, he
could get a four-inch-long, painfully bright lamp with electricity. Davy said
that his device produced "a most brilliant ascending arch of light."[257] This
lamp works because the carbon rods melt in the heat from the initial spark
and turn into carbon gas, which is what the current flows through. When

enough current travels through a carbon gas, it glows. Humphry Davy demonstrated his device on November 16, 1809, and the audience was enraptured.[258] Here was the first practical electric lamp, years before the invention of the generator. In 1820 Davy called this an "arc lamp," a name it retains to this day.[259] Although the arc lamp was the first practical electric light, Davy was mostly only interested in it for its dramatic display and to demonstrate the awesome power of his battery.

Davy was knighted and made a baron for his contribution to science in 1812. He then wooed and married a rich socialite named Jane Apreece, who he felt "refined many of my sentiments [and has] given me more correct principles of taste."[260] Davy then decided to stop lecturing at the institution and focus on research and his incredibly demanding social life. "If I lecture, it will be on some new series of discoveries.... I give up the *routine* of lecturing, merely that I may have more time to pursue original inquiries."[261] In February of 1812, Davy gave four last talks to a packed house of over 700 people at the institution and moved on to the next phase of his life.

In October of that same year, Davy had an accident in the laboratory. He was leaning over a container of chlorine and ammonia, which exploded and severely damaged his eye. According to his brother, it was surprising that he didn't incur more injuries. "[Davy's] boldness in experimenting was very remarkable: in the operations of the laboratory danger was very much forgotten, and exposure to danger was an everyday occurrence."[262] It took Davy a few months to recover, and in the meanwhile a friend of his recommended a young bookbinder and complete amateur named Michael Faraday to help him out. Davy didn't know it, but Faraday would soon eclipse him as one of the most innovative and influential scientists the world has ever known.

Chapter Summary

- ✧ **1732:** Laura Bassi becomes the second woman to earn a PhD.
- ✧ **1759:** Laura Bassi shows her student Luigi Galvani how electrical machines work.
- ✧ **1774:** Bassi demonstrates her atmospheric electrical equipment.
- ✧ **1780:** Luigi and Lucia Galvani's assistant notices that electric jolts can make a dead frog jump and discovers that all dead animals will respond to electricity, which he defines as "animal electricity."

- ✧ **1780s:** In experimenting with electrical storms on frogs, Galvani finds that two different metals will animate a frog.
- ✧ **1788:** Lucia Galvani dies.
- ✧ **1791:** Luigi Galvani publishes *De Viribus Electricitatis.*
- ✧ **1790s:** Alessandro Volta and Giovani Aldini (Galvani's nephew) debate whether electricity needs life.
- ✧ **1797:** Luigi Galvani dies.
- ✧ **1800:** Alessandro Volta publishes his proof against the "pretended animal electricity of Galvani," which is a pile of metals with salt water that produced continuous shocks. Soon this is called the electric battery or pile.
- ✧ **1800:** Anthony Carlisle and William Nicholson discover that a battery will electrically separate water into hydrogen and oxygen gas.
- ✧ **1801:** Humphry Davy proves that batteries work by chemical reactions and creates a better battery with a stronger acid.
- ✧ **1802:** Giovani Aldini electrifies dead prisoners in England.
- ✧ **1809:** Humphry Davy discovers that electricity can make a very bright lamp called the arc lamp.

Chapter 4

A Galvanized World

(1820–1867)

To what part of electrical science are we not indebted to Faraday? He has increased our knowledge of the hidden and unknown to such an extent, that all subsequent writers are compelled so frequently to mention his name and quote his papers, that the very repetition becomes monotonous.

– Alfred Smee,
Elements of Electro-Metallurgy (1851)[263]

There is no honor too great to pay to the memory of Michael Faraday, one of the greatest scientific discoverers of all time.

– Ernest Rutherford (1931)[264]

As I wrote in the preface, a video depicting Michael Faraday's life is part of the inspiration for this book. As I delved further into his story and his physics, I became even more enamored. Time and time again, Faraday just seemed to see nature in a new way, and almost all of his startling insights have withstood the test of time. Prophetically, John Tyndall wrote this in 1868: "Taking him for all and all, I think it will be conceded that Michael

Faraday was the greatest experimental philosopher the world has ever seen; and I will add the opinion, that the progress of future research will tend, not to dim or to diminish, but to enhance and glorify the labors of this mighty investigator."[265] As a woman who appreciates modern medicine and hygiene, I would not like to live in the past. Still, if I could travel in time, I would definitely like to visit Faraday—if only for a quick visit.

4.1 The Electric Life of Michael Faraday

Michael Faraday seemed an unlikely person to change the world. He was born in 1791 to a mostly out-of-work blacksmith in the slums of Surrey, outside of London. His rudimentary education was cut particularly short as his mother took him out of school after just a few months to keep him away from an abusive teacher.[266] His mother taught him to read and write but he never learned Latin or more than basic phrases in any languages other than English. Astonishingly, for a person who had such an amazing influence on physics and chemistry, he never learned mathematics (aside from maybe basic algebra).[267] He was also extremely poor in a time when it was incredibly difficult for a poor person to study science.

In addition, there were no free libraries available to Faraday.[268] Even if there were, many scientific books were written in Latin and assumed the reader had a formal education. Lectures were ridiculously expensive. Even a cheap lecture would cost a shilling (0.05 pounds), and a lecture by a famous scientist would routinely cost two pounds and sometimes as high as 20 pounds.[269] In addition, it was extremely hard to get materials and working-class jobs typically required seven days a week and 10- to 12-hour days. Finally, no one wanted to publish the work of an amateur scientist who didn't come from a "good" background. As an extra disincentive, Faraday's family was from an obscure religious sect called the Glassites or Sandemanians, further alienating him from the London elite.[270] Faraday's background was significantly more difficult than Davy's, as Davy at least had a connection to the upper class of society, albeit a tenuous one.

Fortunately, Faraday was very lucky. How lucky? Well, it's hard to imagine how he could have escaped poverty if it were not for a supportive boss, a helpful science book, a generous patron, a well-timed chemical explosion, a fistfight, and a conveniently timed outbreak of the plague.

It all started in 1814. When Faraday was 13 years old, he got a job as a delivery boy for a local bookseller named George Riebau. Riebau was impressed with the young boy and placed him in a seven-year apprenticeship program to be a bookbinder without requiring Faraday's family to pay for the service, as was usual at the time, as his family could not afford it.[271] In addition, Riebau was an incredibly generous and supportive boss for all his employees, especially for the time, and let his young employees read any of the books that floated through the shop. Faraday enjoyed fiction, but the science books were his favorite—and he especially liked to try to recreate any experiments he came across. Riebau then let the young Faraday set up a mini laboratory in the back of the bookshop, and Riebau said that Faraday spent all of his free time "searching for some Mineral or Vegetable curiosity ... his mind ever engaged."[272]

There were two books that, years later, Faraday credited for starting his journey into science. The first was the 1797 *Encyclopedia Britannica*, particularly with its 127 pages on the "latest" developments in electricity, which Faraday bound in 1810, when he was 19 years old.[273] The second was a book called *Conversations on Chemistry*, written in 1805 by a woman named Jane Marcet. A few years before, Marcet had gone to a talk by Humphry Davy, but found it confusing. When she asked around, she found that she wasn't alone. Most people were confused, especially the women who had no science backgrounds. After Marcet asked her husband to explain it to her, she found the lectures to be far more interesting. For that reason, she wrote a simple introduction to chemistry "especially for the female sex."[274] Despite the sexism of the period, this was the only book around that could explain chemistry on a simple level, so the book became a bestseller. Years later, Faraday stated:

> Do not suppose that I was a very deep thinker or was marked as a precocious person. I was a very lively, imaginative person, and could believe in the Arabian Nights as easily as in the Encyclopedia. But facts were important to me and saved me. I could trust a fact, but always cross-examined an assertion. So, when I questioned Mrs. Marcet's book by such little experiments as I could perform, and found it true to the facts as I could understand them, I felt that I had got hold of an anchor in chemical knowledge and clung fast to

it. Thence my deep veneration for Mrs. Marcet [as she] conveyed the truth which concern natural things to the young untaught and inquiring mind.[275]

In February of 1810, Faraday borrowed a shilling from his older brother and went to his first science lecture by a silversmith and amateur scientist named John Tatum. Tatum had created his own society of scientists called the City Philosophical Society. This was a working-class man's version of the Royal Institution, populated by clerks, painters, journeymen, and of course, as soon as he heard of it, an apprentice bookbinder. Faraday took copious notes from Tatum's talks, added his thoughts and experiments, and created a book of his own. He dedicated the book to his kind boss Riebau, adding that "to you … is to be attributed the rise and existence of that small portion of knowledge relating to the sciences which I possess."[276]

George Riebau was quite proud of his apprentice's accomplishment and prominently displayed Faraday's book in his bookshop. In the beginning of 1812, Riebau showed this manuscript to one of his patrons, a wealthy scientist named Mr. Dance. Dance was exceedingly impressed with this young man and his abilities and did an incredible service to Faraday: he gave the young man tickets to all of Humphry Davy's last lectures before Davy gave up "the *routine* of lecturing."[277]

As you might expect, Faraday was entranced by the talks, and he took extensive notes. It took him about five months to collect enough money to create his own battery. He wrote to his friend Benjamin Abbot from the City Philosophical Society about his adventures. "I, Sir, I my own self, cut out seven discs [of zinc] of the size of half-pennies each! I, Sir, covered them with seven halfpence and I interposed between [them] paper soaked in a solution of muriate of soda [saltwater]!!! But laugh no longer, dear A., rather wonder at the effects this trivial power produced."[278] Faraday placed the ends of battery in a solution of salts and took note: "A galvanic effect took place I am sure, for both wires became covered in a short time with bubbles of some gas."[279] Just as with Tatum's talks before, Faraday created a book of Davy's talks interspersed with his own experiments and observations. Faraday wrote to Davy, who said he was impressed with Faraday's "zeal, power of memory, and attention."[280] However, Davy didn't have a position for Faraday and recommended that he "stick to bookbinding."[281]

By October of 1812, Faraday had finished his apprenticeship with Riebau, and as he was unable to find a job in science, he took a job as a journeyman bookbinder to another French bookbinder named Henri de la Roche. La Roche had no desire to support Faraday's interests, refusing to let him peruse the books he was binding, let alone set up any ad hoc science experiments in the bookshop or even have Wednesday afternoons to go to his science meetings. Faraday morosely wrote a friend that "with respect to the progress of the sciences I know but little, and am now likely to know still less; indeed, as long as I stop in my present situation (and I see no chance of getting out of it just yet), I must resign philosophy entirely to those who are more fortunate in the possession of time and means."[282] Luckily for Faraday, Davy hurt his eye in a laboratory experiment, and Mr. Dance, who was the same helpful man who gave Faraday the tickets to see Davy, recommended Michael Faraday as an assistant to his idol for a few days until Davy recovered.

When Faraday was done assisting Davy, he sent a letter to Davy asking for a permanent job along with a copy of his book of notes from Davy's lectures. Davy responded with a short note of encouragement that Faraday kept until his death but then added that he didn't need any help at that time. Then, in late February 1813, one of Davy's assistants got into a fight with an instrument maker and was fired. By March 1, 1813, Faraday was hired as Davy's bottle washer and earned a full 25 shillings (£1.25) a week, as well as room and board.[283] Finally, Faraday was working in science.

Faraday quickly proved to be an able assistant, and Davy began to rely on him more and more. The messy and impulsive Davy was particularly pleased with Faraday for his organizational skills. In 1869 a Faraday biographer noted that "the most entangled and complicated matters fell into harmony in his hands."[284] At around the same time, Humphry Davy was so famous that Napoleon Bonaparte himself gave Davy and his entourage special passports to travel freely in Europe despite the 20-year-long war between England and France. When Davy's personal valet refused to go visit the enemy, Davy asked Faraday to join them as an assistant and a valet until he could get another valet in France. Faraday was nervous about the trip, having never seen the ocean, let alone traveled across it. With trepidation he decided to go and wrote in his diary: "This morning formed a new epoch of my life. I have never before, within my recollection, left London at a greater distance than 12 miles."[285]

Through Davy, Faraday met all of the important scientists of France and Italy. This included André-Marie Ampère, who showed them a crystal that he called *iode*. Davy determined this was a new element called iodine. In Italy, Davy and Faraday managed to set fire to a diamond, where it gave off "a beautiful vivid scarlet light,"[286] proving that it was composed of carbon. Faraday also made a fair number of friends among scientists in Europe, and it was said that "we admired Davy, but we loved Faraday."[287]

Faraday found his time with Davy to be endlessly educational, saying that "the constant presence of Sir Humphry Davy was a mine inexhaustible of knowledge and improvement."[288] Although Faraday got along very well with Davy, the same cannot be said of the aristocratic Mrs. Davy. Faraday complained to a friend: "She delights in making her inferiors feel her power [and she] endeavors to thwart me in all my views & to debase me in my occupations."[289] Once, when they were on a perilous sea voyage in the Gulf of Genoa, Mrs. Davy became too ill to speak. Faraday was so irritated with her that he wrote to a friend that it was worth the danger to their lives just to enjoy her silence.

Their relationship hit its lowest point in Genoa, Italy. That was where Davy and Faraday were invited to have dinner with Jane Marcet, the woman who wrote the book *Conversations on Chemistry* that Faraday credited with teaching him chemistry. However, when Faraday excitedly showed up to dinner to tell her how she influenced his life, Davy's wife refused to let Faraday join them for dinner, proclaiming in front of all the guests that he should eat dinner in the kitchen with the other "servants." After dinner, when the men were left to their cigars, Jane Marcet's husband, Alexander, tried to fix this injustice by announcing loudly, "And now, my dear sirs, let us go and join Mr. Faraday in the kitchen,"[290] but by this time Faraday was livid.

In November of 1814, Faraday wrote his friend Benjamin Abbot. "Alas! how foolish perhaps was I to leave home, to leave those whom I loved and who loved me."[291] Who knows what would have happened if the group had not heard that there was an outbreak of plague in their next stops, Greece and Turkey. Reluctantly, Humphry Davy decided to cut their trip short and return home. Faraday quickly jotted down a short note to his mother from

Brussels with the good news. "It is with no small pleasure I write you my last letter from a foreign country, and I hope it will be with as much pleasure you will hear I am within three days of England ... a spot of earth which I will never leave again" with the postscript that said, "'tis the shortest and (to me) the sweetest letter I ever wrote you."[292]

Despite the conflict between Faraday and Mrs. Davy, Faraday and Humphry Davy remained close. Back in England, Davy was promoted at the Royal Institution, and Davy arranged for Faraday to receive a promotion. Davy wrote Faraday: "Believe me there is no one more interested in your success & welfare than your sincere well wisher & friend, H. Davy."[293] In 1815 they worked together on a safety lamp with a wire mesh to keep the methane in the lamp from causing explosions if there were gasses outside the lamp. This was particularly important for minors digging for coal. With this lamp, called a Davy Lamp, Davy's fame increased along with Faraday's reputation. Faraday's issues with Mrs. Sarah Davy continued and convinced Faraday that marriage was a terrible thing for any scientist. In 1816 Faraday wrote a long (and frankly terrible) poem about marriage for his diary that began, "What is the pest and plague of human life? And what the curse that often brings a wife? 'Tis Love."[294]

Three years after decrying the "curse" of love, Michael Faraday met a young woman named Sarah Barnard at his small church and fell head over heels in love. When Sarah asked Michael Faraday to let her see his poem against marriage, he replied with a new poem and an apology for his earlier views pleading, "Do not ask for the proof that I once acted wrong, but direct me and guide me the way to amend."[295] By July of 1820, Faraday wrote Sarah. "You know me as well or better than I do myself. You know my former prejudices, and my present thoughts—you know my weaknesses, my vanity, my whole mind; you have converted me from one erroneous way, let me hope you will attempt to correct what others are wrong."[296] *

By May of 1821, Sarah agreed to marry Faraday, and with Davy's help, Michael Faraday got permission from the Royal Institution to have his new bride live with him there. He and Sarah, in the tradition of their religion, wanted a very simple ceremony. Faraday wrote, "There will be no bustle, no

---

* As far as I can tell, Faraday's "one erroneous way" was writing a bad poem against marriage.

noise, no hurry… In externals, that day will pass like all others, it is in the heart that we expect and look for pleasure."[297] Years later, he added to a book of certificates and awards the following entry: "Amongst these records and events, I here insert the date of one which, as a source of honour and happiness, far exceeds the rest. We were *married* on June 12, 1821."[298] Faraday's biographer and friend John Tyndall recalled that Michael Faraday adored his wife. "Never, I believe, existed a manlier, purer, steadier love. Like a burning diamond, it continued to shed, for six and 40 years, its white and smokeless glow."[299] One can see from the following letter from Michael Faraday to Sarah Faraday, written after the first year of marriage, that Tyndall saw the relationship clearly: "I am tired of the dull detail of things, and want to talk of love to you.… The theme was a cheerful and delightful one before we were married, but it is doubly so now.… The excess of pleasure which I feel in knowing you [are] mine is doubled by the consciousness that you feel equal joy in knowing me yours. Oh, my dear Sarah, poets may strive to describe and artists to delineate the happiness which is felt by two hearts truly and mutually loving each other; but it is beyond their efforts."[300]

At around the same time as Michael Faraday and Sarah Barnard were falling in love, Davy and Faraday and every other scientific person in England learned about an astonishing new experiment from Denmark. A man named Hans Christian Oersted had found a link between electricity and magnetism.

If you recall from the first chapter, William Gilbert (Queen Elizabeth's doctor) declared in 1600 that force from static electricity is different from magnetic force because they act on different objects with different rules. Over the next 200 years, several people tried to find a link between the two but to no avail. However, after Volta invented the battery in 1800, there was a renewed interest in finding a connection between electricity and magnetism. It seemed logical— magnets always have a north and a south, and batteries always have a positive and a negative. This leads us to Hans Christian Oersted.

Oersted was a philosopher whose beliefs, specifically in the philosophies of Immanuel Kant, meant that everything in nature was intertwined, so the forces in physics should also be connected. That was why in 1806, Oersted started experiments to try to find links between different physics forces. He wanted to "prove from empirical science how the laws of nature form a rational whole, and how nature itself is a revelation of the creating, living

Reason."[301] He must have been overjoyed when, in the spring of 1820, he put a compass underneath a wire and found that the compass needle turned when the current was running through the wire. Oersted knew that a compass is just a small magnet on a pivot so it can spin freely, which is why you can make a compass needle move by placing a magnet near it. Oersted knew that if the current in the wire moved the compass, that meant that electrical current creates a magnetic force. Oersted proved that electricity and magnetism were linked not through the battery but in the current from the battery.

Oersted was surprised, however, by the details of *how* electricity affected magnets. For when he put a compass near a wire connected to a battery, the magnet didn't move to point with the wire, toward the wire, or away from the wire. Instead, the magnet moved to point in a circle around the wire. This is why the experiment is so strange: the current flows *through* the wire and the magnet points *around* the wire. There are no other forces that work like this. Gravity pulls you toward the center of mass. Magnets and static electricity either pull toward or push away. Even directly pulling or pushing is either toward or away from the person pulling or pushing.

But compasses near current-carrying wires are pushed to point in a *circle* around the wire. No wonder it took Oersted 14 years to discover it—he and others were putting their magnets in the wrong orientation. Oersted knew his discovery was transformative. In fact, he successfully completed the experiment a month before he published his findings. But the battery was a little weak, so he repeated it with a stronger battery "considering the importance of the subject."[302] Unfortunately, many people who read this thought that Oersted's initial experiment was an accident. So, instead of Oersted being lauded for fulfilling a 14-year quest, he's most often rumored to have succeeded by chance.

Oersted was perturbed by the fact that the current goes one direction and the magnetic force moves in a circle around it. That seemed totally illogical to people used to Newton's laws. To "solve" his problem, he decided that the electricity wasn't moving straight down the wire. Instead, Oersted declared that the electricity was spiraling down the wire and dragging the magnets in a spiral direction too. In fact, he made it even more complicated because he believed that there were two types of current—a negative and a positive—that were mutually spiraling around each other, with each one pushing its own pole, writing, "negative electricity moves in a spiral line bent towards the right, and propels the north pole, but does not act on the south pole. The effects on the south pole are explained in a similar manner."[303]

Back in England, Humphry Davy heard about Oersted's experiment and became "deeply occupied in this."[304] He began to work with a friend named William Wollaston, and they had a conversation about getting a wire with current flowing in it to spin about its axis when pushed by a magnet—an idea that they were unable to realize but one that Faraday overheard.

Meanwhile, Michael Faraday was also thinking about Oersted's experiment. Faraday assumed that he had nothing to add to the results, writing, "I should have felt doubtful that anything I could do could be new or possess an interest."[305] But as he had been doing since he was a teen, he recreated all the experiments that he could. In this way, Faraday found something strange. It didn't seem to Faraday that the forces or the current were spiraling, nor did there seem to be a specific force on each pole of the magnet. As he wrote to a friend, "I find all the usual attractions of the magnetic needle by the [current-carrying] wire are deceptions, the motions being not attractions or repulsions … but the result of a force in the wire, which, instead of bringing the pole of the needle nearer to or further from the wire, endeavors to make it move round it in a never-ending circle."[306] But how to demonstrate this?

On September 3, 1821, with his 14-year-old brother-in-law George as his assistant, Faraday created a simple experiment in his laboratory. He had a wire drop down on a cup full of mercury (mercury is a conducting fluid) with a permanent bar magnet in the center. When he closed the switch, the wire spun continuously around the magnet. Later, Faraday made a version to allow the magnet to spin freely around a stationary wire (see figure 1). Once again, when current was put in the wire, the magnet would spin. In other words, electrical current and magnets push each other in a circle around each other. According to Faraday's young brother-in-law, when Faraday got his system to rotate, he shouted, "There they go! There they go! We have succeeded at last!"[307]

Technically, Faraday had just invented the electric motor—a device that changes electrical energy into motion. Of course, it wasn't a particularly practical motor as it didn't do any useful work (unless you want to electrically stir mercury). Luckily, Faraday didn't invent the motor to do any work—he

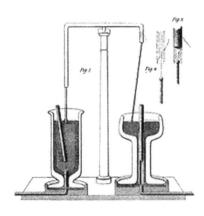

Figure 1: Faraday in the 1820s or early 1830s (Faraday apparently curled his hair for the painting) (left); diagram of Faraday's motor experiment (right)

invented it to demonstrate that the current moves straight down the wire and that the magnetic force is circular around the wire. As a motor, it was useless, but as a demonstration of the nature of magnetic fields, it was quite efficient.

Faraday published his work on October 1, 1821, to great acclaim. But within a week, he heard rumors that people were saying he plagiarized his material from Davy's colleague William Wollaston. Faraday wrote to Wollaston, "I am bold enough sir to beg the favor of a few minutes conversation [as] I am anxious to escape from unfounded impressions against me and if I have done any wrong that I may apologize for it."[308] Wollaston wrote back and claimed to be unoffended, saying, "You have no occasion to concern yourself much about the matter."[309] However, Wollaston didn't publicly defend Faraday, and Faraday was distressed to find his mentor Humphry Davy publicly attacking him over the issue.

While we cannot be sure of Davy's motivations, most modern researchers feel that Davy was jealous of his protégé's success and felt that Faraday was too low class and uneducated to be an independent researcher. That may well be the case. However, it's also possible that Davy felt justified in his anger. Faraday was a person whom Davy had plucked from obscurity, and he did not give credit to his benefactor. Contributing to Davy's feelings, I think, was a misunderstanding of Faraday's theory of electricity and magnetism.

Wollaston felt that a magnet could be used to twist a wire, whereas Faraday thought that the current went straight down the wire and that a wire could be made to circle a magnet or a magnet to circle a wire. In Davy's defense, not many people in 1821 understood Faraday's theories, let alone believed them. Davy's brother stated that his objections to Faraday were "an act of justice to Dr. Wollaston,"[310] and it's quite possible that Davy felt that way for the rest of his life.

Despite Davy's objections, Faraday was well respected by the other members of the Royal Institution. In fact, in May of 1823, Faraday was nominated to be a fellow of the Royal Institution. (The secret vote had only one dissenter, probably Davy.) Faraday was then offered a lucrative deal from the British government to try to make better optical glass that he felt he needed to accept in order to stay in research. Faraday also started giving and overseeing weekly science lectures at the same podium where he had watched Davy 15 years before. In 1825 Faraday started a tradition of giving a series of free science lectures to children, which was highly popular and continues even to this day.[311] In 1826 Davy fell very ill, possibly from the chemical gasses in his laboratory or from using too much laughing gas, and he resigned from the presidency of the Royal Institution. Davy passed away in 1829.

Faraday made few contributions to science between 1821 and 1831, as the optical glass experiments he conducted for the British government took up a lot of his time and were basically unproductive. He wrote that the only results were his own "nervous headaches and weakness," and he finally quit on July 4, 1831.[312] When Faraday was asked a year later to start a new project in the manufacture of iron, he wrote, "I had enough of endeavoring to improve a manufacture…. One such experiment in a man's life is enough."[313] However, before Faraday was waylaid by his work in optics, he had considerable influence on one of the most famous scientists of the era, the great French scientist André-Marie Ampère.

4.2 The Mighty Ampère

André-Marie Ampère was born in January of 1775 in Lyon, France, to a prosperous merchant and promoter of enlightenment ideas. Amazingly, his father did not believe in formal or even tutored education, and young Ampère seems to have taught himself all sorts of languages, history, and higher mathematics through reading books in their well-stocked library. In 1792 when Ampère was 18 years old, his father was beheaded in the Reign of Terror. Before he walked to the guillotine, he penned a note forgiving all people who had accused him of not loving his country and added "as for my son, there is nothing which I do not expect from him."[314]

Inspired, Ampère buried himself in the study of botany, mathematics, and even poetry, all in an attempt to become the polymath that his father had dreamed of. In later life he was known as a "living encyclopedia."[315] When he was 21, Ampère met a young woman named Julie Carron, and his diary began to show his feelings for her. "Monday, September 26, 1796: saw *her* in the garden, without daring to speak to her."[316] Finally, Ampère began to actually speak to the young woman, and by August of 1799, they were married. He supported the family by being a math tutor, and then in 1801, at the recommendation of a friend, as professor of natural philosophy and chemistry in Bourg-en-Bresse, France.[317] Ampère liked the position, but he was forced to spend time away from his beloved wife and new son, Jean-Jacques, and none of them enjoyed that at all. This separation, which was supposed to be temporary, became more tragic when his wife became ill. On April 17, 1803, Ampère wrote in his diary: "I returned from Bourg, in order to leave my Julie no more."[318] Tragically, Ampère's love and attention were not enough to save his wife, and she died on July 13, 1803. Ampère wrote, "God … wilt thou take from me all happiness here below? … O God of mercy, be pleased to grant that I may meet in heaven those thou allowedst me to love on Earth!"[319]

Ampère had no desire to stay in Lyon, the town where his father had been beheaded and his beloved wife had died, and he had quit his job in Bourg-en-Bresse. Luckily, a friend got him a job as a tutor at the prestigious École Polytechnique in Paris, where he impressed everyone so much that he was promoted from tutor to professor of mathematics in 1809. For the next 11 years, Ampère published papers in a dizzying array of subjects, and according to a biographer, "he was at home in every branch of science."[320] On September 11, 1820, when Ampère was 45 years old, a friend named François Arago demonstrated to the Paris Academy of Sciences Oersted's discovery of how current-carrying wires could move a magnet.[321] Ampère paid no attention to Oersted's views about spinning electric currents and instead focused on the whole idea of force. By the next meeting, only a week later, Ampère, who was inspired by Newton's laws, demonstrated that a magnet could move a current-carrying wire just as a wire could move a small magnet.[322]

Ampère immediately decided that Oersted's experiment could be "the explanation of magnetic phenomena" and assumed that Earth and bar magnetics were only magnetic due to internal electric currents.[323] He then wondered "how electricity might produce all phenomena presented by magnets."[324] Ampère noted that Oersted's discovery with straight current-carrying wires didn't act anything like a bar magnet, but wires aren't required to be in straight lines, so maybe some other orientation of wires *would* act like a bar magnet. He also might have been inspired by Oersted's description of twisted currents to create a pancake of wires (in what is called a planar spiral). To his delight he found that this "pancake" worked like a bar magnet, where one side of the pancake was a "north" and the other a "south," depending on the direction of the current. As one pancake spiral worked like a magnet, Ampère wondered if two spirals would work like magnets with each other, which they did. Ampère recalled that "in replacing the magnet by another spiral with its current in the same direction, the same attractions and repulsions occur. It is in this way that I discovered that two electric currents attract each other when they flow in the same direction and repel each other in the other case."[325]

Ampère continued to attempt to make magnets out of wires of current,

Figure 2: Ampère in 1825 and his pancakes of coils that repel or attract like magnets

and in order to model bar magnets repelling from their sides, he wrapped a wire around a glass cylinder in a helix, or in a solenoid (his term), and found it looked like a bar magnet, albeit a weak one. Mind you, all of this (and more) was conducted and published in under three months. However, in January of 1821, after that whirlwind of productivity, Ampère burned himself out and stopped researching due to illness and fatigue. In fact, it wasn't until seven months later, on October 18, 1821, when Faraday sent Ampère a copy of his paper on rotating wires with magnets and a version of his rotating "machine" that Ampère's interests once again turned to electromagnetism.[326] Although he didn't always agree with Faraday, Ampère found Faraday's experiment to be profound and they formed a close and strong friendship. Ampère recalled that for a while, "metaphysics occupied my thoughts; however, after Faraday's work, I think only of electric currents. This memoir [of Faraday's] contains very singular electromagnetic facts, which perfectly confirm my theory, although the author tries to fight against it by replacing it with a [theory] of his creation."[327]

One of the things that Ampère disagreed with Faraday about was that Ampère, almost as soon as he heard of Oersted's theory, wondered if "a magnet could be regarded as an assembly of electric currents."[328] Interestingly, by 1822, after discussing this with his friend Augustin-Jean Fresnel, Ampère realized that magnets couldn't be composed of macroscopic currents moving in circles as he first supposed, because if you cut a hole in the magnet, it would stop being magnetic. Instead, Ampère decided that the current in magnets had to be microscopic, or what he called "molecular currents."[329] Ampère's theory of magnetism, concocted far before the discovery of electrons that produce these "molecular currents" is, according to the 2015 science textbook *Ampère's Electrodynamics*, "accepted in its essence up to the present time."[330]

In 1824 Ampère's friend François Arago heard from an instrument maker that magnetic needles in compasses will vibrate less if the base is made of copper.[331] As Arago knew that wires were often made of copper, he wondered if the copper created a magnetic force even without a current from a battery. For that reason, Arago started to experiment with vibrating magnets above disks of different materials and counted how many rotations it took for a vibrating magnet to go from 45 to 10 degrees from horizontal and found that a thick copper disk would reduce the number of rotations by 77% compared to a similar wooden disk.[332] Within a few months, Arago had made a little device with a copper wheel with a separate magnet that was free to spin above it. When you spun the wheel, the separate magnet would spin too. This caused a lot of international interest, as copper is not magnetic. Magnets do not stick to copper, so why would spinning a nonmagnetic metal *near* a magnet cause the magnet to move? Scientists knew that copper was highly conductive, and electricity flows easily through it, so that current in a copper wheel would act like an electromagnet and move a magnet. But Arago's wheel had no battery, so no one, not even Ampère, could figure out why it worked.

That is not to say that Ampère was idle. In fact, after hearing about Oersted's discovery, Ampère published paper after paper on the subject: six publications about electricity or his term "electrodynamics" in 1820, six in 1821, an astonishing 26 papers in 1822, and a further 24 papers before his magnum opus, *Memoir on the Mathematical Theory of Electrodynamical Phenomena, Uniquely Deduced from Experience*, in 1827.[333] However, Ampère's health started to deteriorate almost right after that publication, and he died in June of 1836 to full national honors. François Arago gave his eulogy.

4.3 The Shoemaker Who Made the Electromagnet

Although Ampère was making steady progress toward equations and theories of this new branch of science, his results were very difficult to display, as they all tended to be incredibly subtle and delicate. That all changed in 1824 when an English shoemaker and retired soldier named William Sturgeon attempted Ampère's solenoid experiment with a piece of iron instead of a piece of glass and created the electromagnet.

William Sturgeon was born in 1783 in northern England to a poor shoemaker who treated him badly. When he was 10, his mother died, and a few years later, his father basically sold him to another shoemaker who also treated him cruelly. According to his biographer, he lived a life of "slavish drudgery."[334] When he was 19 years old, Sturgeon escaped by joining the army.

The army was good for Sturgeon. He found that the officers in particular were appreciative of his skill at fixing things, especially their shoes. He would also entertain the officers and fellow troops with amateur science demonstrations that he created himself. Sturgeon then traded his services to officers for lighter duties and to borrow their books. (Remember, at this time there were no libraries, and books were prohibitively expensive.) In this way, he actually taught himself math, Greek, Latin, French, German, Italian, optics, and lithography.[335]

After 18 years in the army, Sturgeon retired and moved to the Woolwich district of London. His plan was to start a shoe store. For that reason, he contacted some officers whom he knew from the military. Many of them were interested in the latest developments in science and asked Sturgeon for help with their scientific devices as well as their shoes. By 1824 Sturgeon's friends had helped him get a job giving science demonstrations at a military academy, and he gave up shoemaking to focus on science. That's how Sturgeon happened to read that André-Marie Ampère had discovered that a helix of wire with current in it will act like a weak bar magnet. One day, Sturgeon was recreating Ampère's coil by wrapping a coil of wire around an insulated iron bar. To his surprise, the iron bar significantly amplified the magnetic effects of the coil. Because the electricity in the wire makes the iron act like a magnet, this object is called an electromagnet.

Let us take a moment to go over the magnet versus the electromagnet. A permanent magnet always contains a north and a south. A north and a north will repel each other, a south and a south will repel, and a north and a south will attract. Permanent magnets can also attract certain metals like iron and steel. For example, if a magnet is placed near a metal paper clip, the paper clip

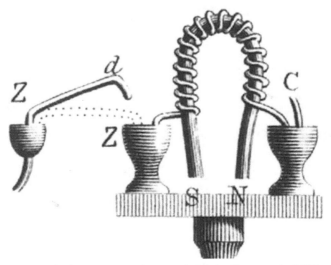

Figure 3: Sturgeon's electromagnet diagram drawn by Sturgeon in 1825

will be attracted to the magnet. This is because the paper clip is made of steel, and steel is composed of little magnets (or magnetic domains) that are randomly arranged. When the paper clip is near the magnet, the little magnetic domains line up, making the paper clip into a temporary magnet where the north of the paper clip is attracted to the south of the magnet. You know an object is a magnet if it attracts and aligns a metal paper clip.

Compare that to an electromagnet. An electromagnet is a coil of wire wrapped around an iron or steel bar. Without current, the bar will not attract paper clips or act like a magnet at all. However, if current runs through the wire, then the magnetic fields in the wire align the magnetic domains in the iron bar and make it act like a magnet with a north and a south. The bigger the current, the stronger the magnet. Amazingly, if the plus and minus connections to the battery are switched, the north and the south of the electromagnet switch as well. Also, once you disconnect the battery, the iron stops being a magnet (although sometimes the iron or steel will remain faintly magnetized after the current is removed).

Back in 1824, Sturgeon found that his electromagnet was so strong that even with the weak batteries at the time and with just a few turns of coil, his electromagnet could hold nine pounds (four kilograms) of weight and then drop it dramatically when the current was disconnected.[336] In 1825 Sturgeon was awarded a silver medal for this discovery as well as a well-needed 30 guineas.[337] Sturgeon wrote that he "considered that an apparatus for exhibiting the experiments on a large scale, and with easy management, would not only be well adapted to the lecture room, but absolutely valuable to the advancement of the science."[338] It turned out that Sturgeon was right, and one of the first people to discover something new from electromagnets was our friend Michael Faraday.

4.4 Electricity from Magnetism

On August 29, 1831, Michael Faraday started a new section in his laboratory notebook with the hopeful title "Experiments on the Production of Electricity from Magnetism."[339] After all, it had been 11 years since Oersted had shown that electricity pushes magnets. It seemed logical that magnets must affect electricity and even create electricity. For many years, Faraday tinkered with magnets and wires but never managed to create even the smallest current. Faraday wondered about the effect of the iron bar in Sturgeon's electromagnet. If a coil of wire with current in it becomes a stronger magnet when you added an iron bar, maybe iron could help transfer electricity from one object to another.

For that reason, Faraday made a little device with a six-inch iron ring and wrapped it with two separate coils of what looked like a strange artifact from a mummy's crypt, as the wires were insulated with cloth and twine (see figure 4). This was before it was easy to purchase insulated wire. Faraday then attached one set of insulated wires to a battery and connected the other side with wire only to a compass nearby to check if it had current in it.

When Faraday connected the battery to one of the coils, an amazing thing happened: the magnet next to the other coil twitched. Then, nothing. When he cut off the current, the magnet twitched again, in the other direction. Then, nothing again. Faraday repeated this experiment multiple times and found that he created current in the second wire *when* the first one was charging up or discharging but never when it was flowing steadily—even when it had an incredibly large current. In other words, an electromagnet only creates current in a separate coil when the magnetic strength is changing. If its strength is steady, nothing happens.

Faraday wrote to a friend about his accomplishment: "I am busy just now again on Electro-Magnetism and think I have got hold of a good thing but can't say; it may be a weed instead of a fish that after all my labour I may at last pull up."[340] He had managed to use electricity to create electricity, but he still hadn't managed to use magnets to create electricity. After

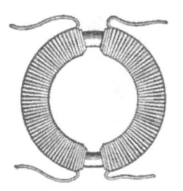 

Figure 4: Drawing of Faraday's ring (left); photograph of Faraday's actual ring (right)

several attempts, Faraday pushed a very strong magnet into a coil of wire and retrieved it again. When the magnet was moving, the compass moved, too, meaning that a magnet created current without any battery needed. Here was the "fish" that Faraday was hoping to catch. He had, briefly, created electricity with magnet and motion. He also noted that not only would it only work while the magnet was moving inside the coil (or the coil was moving relative to the magnet), but if the magnet moved outside the coil, no electricity was created.

Faraday realized that the current he had produced was in spurts and wondered if he could use magnets to make continuous electricity like a battery does. In this quest, he was inspired by Arago's wheel—a wheel of copper that when rotated near a magnet caused the separate magnet to turn too. Faraday postulated that Arago's wheel worked because turning the wheel moved the parts of the disk closer and farther from the magnet, which induced current in the disk. That current then acts as an electromagnet and pushes the original magnet. Faraday had a simple solution. He spun a copper disk near a fixed magnet and connected his leads between the axle of the disk and outer rim (see figure 5). As he spun the disk, the area between the leads was always moving toward the magnet and, therefore, he produced a constant current. Faraday calmly stated, "Here therefore was demonstrated the production of a

Figure 5: Faraday's generator: Part A is a magnet; B is connected to the center; B' to the outside of the disk D.

permanent current of electricity by ordinary magnets."[341]

Faraday himself felt particularly satisfied to have succeeded without using math. He told a friend that "it is quite comfortable to me to find that experiment need not quail before mathematics but is quite competent to rival it in discovery and I am amused to find that what high mathematicians have announced … has so little foundation."[342] He read his work on generating electricity on November 24, 1831, under the title *Experimental Researches in Electricity*. Faraday's discovery was so popular that the prime minister dropped by the laboratory to see it firsthand. When he asked Faraday about its uses, Faraday supposedly replied, "I know not, but I wager that one day your government will tax it."[343]

Faraday's discoveries were revolutionary. But his theories of why they happened were just as radical if not as appreciated at the time. For centuries people had noticed that if you sprinkle iron filings around a bar magnet, it creates patterns. In this paper, Faraday called them "magnetic curves" and described them as "lines of magnetic forces … which would be depicted by iron filings."[344] This is the first description of a magnetic field—an idea that Faraday invented. Faraday felt that these magnetic field lines were always present around magnets and around current-carrying wires. The iron filings just made them visible. Moreover, Faraday decided that current is created (or induced) when the lines of force are broken or "cut" by a coil of wire.

Think about pushing a bar magnet into a coil of wire. As you push the magnet, imagine the magnetic field lines passing through the coil. Faraday felt that it was this disturbance in the force (not to get too *Star Wars* about it) that created the current in the coil. All of Faraday's demonstrations worked with his new theory. As described above, moving a magnet into or out of a coil would cut the magnetic field lines. Also, charging up an electromagnet would create lines where there were none before. If there was another coil nearby, the new magnetic field lines would cut through the secondary coil creating current in the second coil. When the electromagnet was turned off, the magnetic field lines would collapse, and once again the secondary coil would have magnetic lines cut by the coil, and current would be induced in the secondary coil. As Faraday put it, "The law which governs the evolution of electricity by magneto-electric induction, is very simple although rather difficult to express [but it happens when you] cut the magnetic curves."[345]

Although we currently use different nomenclature (magnetic fields instead of magnetic curves or lines of force and we never talk about "cutting" magnetic fields), Faraday's law of induction is considered fundamentally accurate almost 200 years later.

However, Faraday was just getting started, and he produced paper after paper on electricity and magnetism, most of which did not even have descriptive titles besides the vague title of *Experimental Research in Electricity Part X.* (He ended up with 30 parts.) By 1835 Faraday wrote, "I had begun to imagine that I thought more about Electricity and Magnetism than it was worth [so that] I was perhaps only a *bore* to my friends."[346] Of course, Faraday wasn't boring people and was instead creating the science of electricity. In the 1830s, Michael Faraday realized that he was ill equipped to name everything that he had discovered. For that reason, he contacted a well-known mathematician, philosopher, linguist, and theologian named William Whewell who had already come up with many of the terms we use today, including the modern definitions of scientist and physicist.[347] With Whewell's help, Faraday created a list of new electrical names that we use to this day. For example, in a single paper in 1834, Faraday and Whewell came up with the names: *anode, cathode, electrolysis, electrolytes, anions, cations, ions* and *electrodes.*[348]

Faraday needed these terms, because in 1833 and 1834 he had discovered what is now called Faraday's laws of electrolysis, which are laws that relate the amount of chemicals that are decomposed by a battery to the charge and the molar mass of the substance.[349] These papers were very controversial at the time, especially as it was confusing to discuss electricity without distinguishing between current and voltage and with no units for total charge. For example, when Faraday wrote "chemical power … is in direct proportion to the absolute quantity of electricity which passes,"[350] in 1833, what did he mean by "the absolute quantity of electricity"? The more answers Faraday found, the more questions he created.

In 1837 Faraday decided to reexamine static electricity with his newfound knowledge of electricity. After conducting innumerable experiments, Faraday agreed with Franklin that charge is never created or destroyed but merely moved by any action, writing "as yet no means of communicating electricity to a conductor so as to relate its particles to one electricity, and not at the same time to the other in exactly equal amount, has been discovered."[351]

In addition, Faraday discovered, as Benjamin Franklin had done 100 years before, that all charges seemed to be "stuck" on the surface of objects and that metal objects seemed to shield the inside from electrical effects. For that reason, Faraday decided to do his experiments on a bigger scale and put himself in the middle of the experiment. He ended up building a giant cage for himself. "I had a chamber built, being a cube of twelve feet in the side … and copper wire passed along and across it in various directions, so as to make the sides a large net-work."[352]

When Faraday was inside his cage, he was protected from all electricity that happened outside. "I put a delicate gold-leaf electrometer within the cube, and then charged the whole by an outside communication, very strongly, for some time together; but neither during the charge [nor] after the discharge did the electrometer or air within show the least signs of electricity."[353] He even dramatically noted that he couldn't see any electric effects, "though all the time the outside of the cube was powerfully charged, and large sparks and brushes were darting off from every part of its outer surface."[354] One can do very theatrical (and scary looking) demonstrations where a person is nonchalantly standing in a cage totally undisturbed by artificial lightning bolts hitting the outside of the cage. This is currently called a Faraday cage and is an important feature of electrical safety in electronics today.[355]

After tackling static electricity, Faraday then decided to investigate the "nature of the electric current," which is when he heard that there was a 10-year-old theory by a German man named Georg Simon Ohm that could explain a lot of the experiments that he'd conducted. However, Faraday noted that "not understanding German, it is with extreme regret I confess I have not access, and cannot do justice to the many most valuable papers in experimental electricity published in that language."[356] In fact, it wasn't until 1841, 14 years after Ohm published his theory of electrical currents that Ohm's work was translated for the first time into English, and Faraday could finally read it. Which brings us to the story of Georg Ohm and why his famous equation took so long to be appreciated.

4.5 Ohm Finds Resistance, and Joule Heats It Up

Georg Simon Ohm, the son of a watchmaker, was born in March of 1789 in the town of Erlangen, which is now part of Germany. Ohm's father taught him the intricacies of machines and detailed devices, and along with his younger brother Martin, Ohm had been allowed to go to high school (which was unusual for the sons of tradesmen at the time who usually left school at age 11 or 12) only because their father liked mathematics and thought that this knowledge would give them a leg up in the business. However, Georg and Martin Ohm were so good at math that when Georg Ohm was 16 years old, a local mathematics professor heard about their skill and wrote their father that they would soon "emulate the brothers Bernoulli."[357] (Jacob and Johann Bernoulli were Swiss mathematical scientists who were famous for their influence on Bernoulli numbers, infinitesimal calculus, and more.) Georg Ohm's father was so impressed with this letter that he agreed to let his sons stay in academia and end the generational family business of locksmithing. Georg Ohm's younger brother Martin eventually became a prominent mathematician.

In 1804 Georg Ohm then went off to college at the University of Erlangen. However, after 18 months, he ran low on funds and went to Switzerland to become a math tutor. It took Ohm five years to finish his degree and another six years to obtain a permanent position as a math professor and physics teacher at a respected high school called the Great Gymnasium at Cologne.

Ohm read about Oersted's discovery of the force on a magnet from a current-carrying wire in 1820 but wasn't particularly motivated by it. Instead, Ohm was inspired by a book written by a French mathematician named Joseph Fourier who used advanced mathematics to study heat flow. As Ohm thought that heat flow was similar to electricity flow, it was logical for him to use Fourier's equations to study electricity.[358] In addition, Ohm also chose this topic because he felt that it had less competition from other researchers and that it was not a particularly popular subject in Germany (although it was quite popular in England and in France).[359]

In 1825 Ohm started with a simple experiment to study the effect of the length of the wire between terminals of a simple battery on the current. To measure the current, Ohm suspended a magnetized needle over a wire and used a tension-measuring machine (first invented by Charles Coulomb to measure the electric force) to determine the force between the wire and the magnet. As Ohm knew that his battery had a current that would quickly dissipate over time, he created a "standard conductor," which was a short and thick piece of metal that he alternated with the pieces he was experimenting with. He then took the average value of the "standard force" from the "standard conductor" and measured how much changed when a test sample was used. In this convoluted way, Ohm found a complicated equation that he admitted didn't work for long wires, but it was a start and clearly demonstrated that the length of the wire decreased the current. (Eventually Ohm's first, incorrect equation was found to work as an approximation with Ohm's laws as long as the external resistance is much smaller than the internal resistance.)[360]

Ohm's next experiment was conducted in a similar manner with wires of different material, where he experimentally determined the lengths of materials that would have equivalent currents and, thus, what's called the conductivity of different materials compared to each other. It was at this point that Ohm's former professor, the one who said he and his brother could have been like the brothers Bernoulli, suggested that he might have better luck with something called a thermocouple as his voltage source instead of a "wet" battery or hydroelectric battery because the "effects of this circuit [from a thermocouple] are by far more steady than those of the so called hydro-electric circuit."[361]

The thermocouple had been invented five years before when, in 1821, a German physicist named Thomas Seebeck discovered that if two metals were soldered together and kept at a temperature difference, and then the ends were connected to a wire, the wire would cause a magnet to turn. Seebeck thought it was a magnetic effect (as it moved a magnet), but within a year, Hans Christian Oersted (the same man who discovered the electromagnetic effect in 1820) suggested that the temperature difference with the two metals was creating a current in the wire, which was moving the magnet. Oersted called this a "thermoelectric" effect, a name we still use to this day. Then, in 1824, André-Marie Ampère and his friend Antoine Becquerel found that the "tension" of a thermocouple was a function of the temperature difference.[362] In 1826 Ohm tried out the thermocouple with the hot end under boiling water and the cold end in ice water and found to his delight that the current was steady and strong for over 30 minutes.

Ohm then repeated the experiment with a thermocouple source and measured the magnetic force from the wire for eight wires of different lengths.

Ohm found that the "strength of magnetic action" decreased with the length, x, according to the equation $a/(b + x)$.[363] Ohm instantly was quite sure that the values for a and b depended in some way on the "resistance of the other parts of the circuit" and what he called the "exciting force," although he needed more experiments to determine their dependence.[364] Ohm very cleverly redid the experiment with a reduced temperature difference and, thus, a reduced exciting force or tension of his thermocouple. In this case, only the numerator, a, changed. It seemed to Ohm that the current in a wire was related to a simple fraction, where the numerator had to do with the "strength" of the battery or thermocouple, and the denominator had to do with the length of the wires, or what Ohm called the "resistance length."[365]

Ohm made a profound deduction from these experiments, what he called a "pure law of nature."[366] He decided that the tension was from the battery or thermocouple that dissipated over the length of the circuit as the current flowed over the circuit. Ohm was quite happy with his conclusions but felt they were missing mathematics. So, he asked the Prussian minister of culture for a year off to create a mathematical formulation of his theories, which was accepted. Ohm then spent a year living with his younger brother on half pay, and by 1827, published his book, *The Galvanic Circuit Investigated Mathematically*.[367]

This book was not a success, to put it mildly. Critics called it "a web of naked fancies" and "the result of an incurable delusion, whose sole effort is to detract from the dignity of nature."[368] It is worthwhile to delve into why this work brought up such negative reactions. First, Ohm's mathematics were complex, and his ideas were not expressed well. For example, a translator of Ohm's book (written in 1891) added many sections from other scientists' papers and books that better explained the subject matter so that the reader might have a chance of understanding what Ohm meant. Even with 54 years of hindsight and acknowledgment of the correctness of his conclusions, it still isn't an easy read.

Second, Ohm's conclusions fell in opposition to what was considered established fact in the 1820s—namely, that the current produced by a battery is independent of the electric "force" from a battery. This all started with an experiment conducted by André-Marie Ampère in 1820. Ampère wanted to see the relationship between the strength of a battery and the current, so he measured the magnetic deflection from a wire connected to a battery. He then redid the experiment with several batteries in series and found that the accuracy of the galvanometer, the magnetic deflection, and therefore the current, were the same! As multiple batteries produced a bigger shock if one held the ends with wet hands, it was clear to Ampère that multiple batteries in series had more tension. Ampère therefore concluded that the tension of the battery was unrelated to the current in the wire. This experiment was repeated in different ways and was considered one of the few foundations of early electronics.[369]

However, what Ampère and other contemporaries didn't know was that batteries have something called internal resistance, and their batteries in particular had very high internal resistance. By using several batteries, you do get more tension or voltage, but you also get more internal resistance. As the total resistance in this experiment is mostly from the internal resistance, increasing the number of batteries in series increases the total resistance almost as much as it increases the voltage. Therefore, the current only increases by a minute amount, too small to be observed by their simple compasses.

Third, Ohm was talking about tension in a new way. At the time, tension came from the battery or the thermocouple, one did not talk about the tension (or what we now call the potential difference) between two points on a circuit. This is a difficult concept to appreciate, and as I said before, Ohm was brilliant enough to come up with it but not great at describing it in a convincing manner.

Fourthly, and possibly most damaging, Ohm's theories were opposed by a physicist and philosopher named Georg Friedrich Pohl. Pohl, who was supported by the philosopher Georg Hegel had just published his own work on the science of circuits and was unsurprisingly not too favorable to Ohm. In addition, Pohl believed in the Hegelian school of science, which, at least for Pohl, rejected using experiments to come to conclusions. Pohl called Ohm's results "an unmistakable failure."[370] Pohl convinced the German minister of education that "a physicist who professed such heresies was unworthy to teach science."[371] Ohm was devastated, especially by feeling that his superiors at the Gymnasium were offended by his work, and declared that it was impossible for him to retain his position there and quit his job, full of, as a biographer put it, "mortification and grief."[372] Ohm then spent the next several years struggling to find a position with room to experiment and mostly made a living as a tutor in a military school. It took until 1833, after continually sending entreaties to the king of Bavaria, for Ohm to find a new position as a professor at a polytechnic school in Nuremberg, although he still struggled with receiving recognition for his work.[373]

At around the same time in the mid-1830s, William Sturgeon, the shoemaker who invented the electromagnet, got into a fight with the people at the Royal Society of London. Frustrated and basically blackballed, in mid-1836 Sturgeon started his own newspaper where he promised that "every description of new experiment or instrument in Electricity, Magnetism, Electro-Magnetism, Magnetic Electricity, and Electro-Chemistry, will find a place in this work," which at first was very popular.[374] In his first magazine, in October of 1836, Sturgeon published a description of a motor he'd made and claimed was very powerful, "upon the same scale as we see pieces of machinery put into motion by the large models of steam engines,"[375] although it was obviously basically a spinning toy (see figure 6). Soon, many English tinkerers were attempting their own electric motor or device and scouring Sturgeon's magazine for advice.

In 1837 Sturgeon published a translation of an article written by a Russian architect living in Germany named Moritz von Jacobi who had invented his own motor three years earlier, which was clearly superior to Sturgeons (see figure 6).[376] In addition, Jacobi, whose brother was a mathematician, was a fan of Ohm and wrote a paper on the theory behind his devices. Jacobi clearly described Ohm's law, as he felt that "the theory established by Mr. Ohm … offers so much simplicity, and agrees so well with all the phenomena of the voltaic pile, that I have not hesitated to adopt it."[377] Within weeks, the articles in Sturgeon's magazine regularly referenced Ohm's law or at least Ohm's idea of resistance, although it was generally ignored by most scientists—especially at the Royal Society. (Jacobi also published his work in Germany and in France, but it did not make as big of an impression without Sturgeon's dramatic stories of the power of his motor.)

One person who was influenced by Sturgeon's and Jacobi's motors was a teenager named James Prescott Joule. Joule, whose family ran a popular brewery called Joule's Brewery (which still exists), worked at the brewery seven days a week from nine a.m. to six p.m. but still found time to tinker

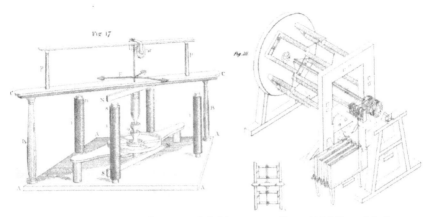

Figure 6: Sturgeon's motor from 1836 (left); a motor from 1834 from Moritz Jacobi (right)

with experiments in a spare room in his father's house.[378] By the time Joule was 19, in 1838, he published a paper on his improved electric motor in Sturgeon's magazine.[379] Joule was convinced that electric motors were going to be powerful soon, writing, "I can scarcely doubt that electro-magnetism will eventually be substituted for steam in propelling machinery."[380] Joule designed system after system, and to improve the motor, he created a new galvanometer. This motivated him to make precise experiments on electro-magnetic attraction, as he needed a galvanometer with readings "which could be depended on."[381]

It was these studies that led Joule to realize that he could use Faraday's laws of electrolysis to quantitatively measure how much electricity was produced in relation to how much hydrogen was decomposed. This meant that his or anyone else's galvanometer could be calibrated, as at this time there were no standard units for current.[382] With this more accurate device for measurement, Joule decided to systematically study how much heat electricity could produce. By the end of 1840, he'd determined that the heat produced by a wire "is proportional to the resistance of the conductor multiplied by the square of the electric intensity."[383] This equation, known as Joule's law, is an important factor toward how we distribute electricity, as the higher the current is in the wires, the more power will be lost to heat.[384]

Although this equation is used widely today, this was before most people had heard of Ohm's law or his definition of resistance, so it was mostly ignored. However, William Sturgeon was impressed and sent Joule a bound volume of his magazine in honor of his "valuable scientific labours"[385] and invited Joule to give his first public lecture in February of 1841. Joule's lecture went well, and he and Sturgeon became close friends. At the time, Sturgeon had been nominated as the director of a science museum hopefully named the Royal Victoria Gallery for the Encouragement of Practical Science. (The hopeful part was the wish that Queen Victoria would support it if it had her name on it; she didn't.) Unfortunately for Sturgeon, the Gallery closed less than two years after it opened.[386] Sturgeon attempted to open another museum that fell apart even faster, and he was left to eke out a living as a traveling electricity entertainer with his equipment in a cart.[387] In 1847 he suffered a severe attack of bronchitis and died at the age of 69 on December 4, 1850. James Joule wrote his obituary and made sure that Sturgeon's work—especially his discovery of the electromagnet—was known to the world.[388]

Meanwhile, in 1841 and 1842, Joule performed more experiments on the relationship between electricity and heat and realized that the amount of heat made by the current was proportional to the energy of chemical reactions inside the battery. Joule then became convinced that heat was not an indestructible "calorific" as most thought at the time, but instead something that could be created by work, or in reverse, heat could be used to do work.[389] By August of 1843, Joule was trying to convince anyone and everyone that "wherever mechanical force is expended, an exact equivalent of heat is always obtained."[390]

Joule's discussion of how heat transfers, eventually called thermodynamics, is a form of its first law: that heat is a form of energy, and energy is conserved.[391] Ironically, Joule's measurements were so accurate that scientists doubted his results. In addition, his theory that heat was just the motion of atoms was considered preposterous at the time. Also, few people at the time believed in Ohm's law, and without Ohm's law, Joule's law made no sense. As Joule was just a beer brewer, he was mostly ignored. It wasn't until Joule started to work with a young Irish scientist named William Thomson (who was later ennobled Lord Kelvin for his work on absolute temperature and for his opposition to Irish home rule) in the 1840s and 1850s that most scientists started to believe in Joule's results and the idea of energy conservation.

At around the same time that Joule was demonstrating to an initially unconvinced public the conservation of heat, an English engineer and scientist named Charles Wheatstone made Ohm's law famous, and eventually Joule's law as well. Wheatstone first became interested in sending acoustic signals when, as a teen in 1821, he invented an "enchanted lyre" as a gimmick to attract attention to his uncle's music shop. He accomplished this by causing a musical instrument to ring by playing a piano hidden in another room that was connected with wires.[392]

Wheatstone continued to study sound propagation and invent musical instruments for many years, which eventually led to his interest in electrical devices as well. In 1834 Wheatstone demonstrated a method of measuring the speed of electricity in a wire. The experiment turned out (eventually) to be erroneous but caused him to be quite famous in scientific circles. He was instantly hired as a professor at King's College of London, where he almost never lectured, as he had a terrible fear of public speaking.[393] Despite this, by 1836 Wheatstone was made a member of the Royal Society and became close friends with Faraday and other influential scientists.[394] Then, in February of 1837, a soldier named William Cooke met with Wheatstone for help with an idea of an electric telegraph. They soon formed a partnership, and Wheatstone scoured the papers for electric help. This is when he read Sturgeon's magazine and Jacobi's article and became an Ohm superfan.

In 1838 the British Association for the Advancement of Science decided to allocate 100 pounds for translating and publishing foreign scientific memoirs.[395] With Wheatstone's help and encouragement (he was a member of the committee), they decided to translate and publish Ohm's entire 1827 book[396] in the second volume of these scientific translations in 1841.[397] Suddenly, many of England's scientists became Ohm fans. That year, Ohm was awarded the Royal Society's highest honor, the Copley Medal for his "researches into the laws of electric currents."[398]

Soon, the scientific papers were full of scientists writing about Ohm's theories, and Wheatstone continued to promote Ohm's work, including asking his friend Ida Lovelace to make a better translation of Ohm's work in 1842. In 1843 Wheatstone became famous for introducing what is now called the Wheatstone bridge, where Wheatstone said that "the instruments and processes I am about to describe being all founded on the principles established by Ohm in his theory of the voltaic circuit, and this beautiful and comprehensive theory."[399]

Ohm felt indebted to Wheatstone and the people at the Royal Society and said that their support gave him courage, "which had previously been softened by disheartening treatment, to renewed efforts in the field of science." In 1849 Ohm published a book on molecular physics that he hoped would be the first of three books on the subject or, "if God gives me length of days for it," four.[400] However, when he found that his ideas had already been published, he gave up on the entire project.

Ohm died in July of 1854, at the age of 65, from an "attack of apoplexy."[401] Eventually, Ohm's results were called Ohm's law, and it is simply written as: Voltage = Resistance × Current. In 1864 the British Association for the Advancement of Science proposed a standard unit for resistance to be an "Ohmed" in Georg Ohm's honor (which was quickly shortened to Ohms) and given the Greek letter omega as the letter *O* looks too close to zero and was confusing; we use this nomenclature to this day.[402] As a side note, I was amused to learn that in 1883, William Thomson (Lord Kelvin) suggested measuring conductivity, or how easy it is for materials to measure how electricity flows, in mho in Ohm's honor (mho is Ohm backward).[403] *

Meanwhile, Michael Faraday suffered from stress, anxiety, and depression, possibly from mercury poisoning or from damage due to his work with heavy metals when he attempted to make glass in the 1820s. In the summer of 1840, 48-year-old Faraday had a serious breakdown, writing, "This is to declare … that I am not able to bear much talking … being at present rather weak in the head, and able to work no more."[404] For many years, he barely made it to the laboratory, writing a friend in 1843: "[my] memory is so treacherous that I cannot remember the beginning of a sentence to the end."[405] For that reason, Faraday had long periods where he could not do any research, and his experimental schedule slowed considerably.

That is not to say that Faraday stopped making important discoveries, as quite the opposite is true. The most impactful was in 1845, when Faraday found that a magnet could allow light to pass through polarizing filters and declared, "Thus is established, I think for the first time, a true, direct relation and dependence between light and the magnetic and electric forces."[406] Seven months later, on April 3, 1846, Faraday was supposed to introduce a talk

---

* The units of conductance were officially changed to siemens after Ernst Werner von Siemens in 1971, although some people still informally use mhos.

by his friend Charles Wheatstone (the same man who had promoted Ohm's work) when Wheatstone had a bout of stage fright and chickened out at the last moment.[407]

Faraday reluctantly stepped in and, to eat up the hour, ended up rambling on about light and electricity and magnetism, or as Faraday put it, "the vague impressions of my mind."[408] This is how Faraday postulated that it's possible that light is created by a vibrating electric charge that makes invisible waves in electric lines of force that cause another electric charge to vibrate in sympathy. In addition, as Oersted had found that moving charges create lines of magnetic force, this vibrating charge will create waves of magnetic lines of force too. So, according to Faraday's tentative thought, light is a wave of electric and magnetic lines of force, or an electromagnetic wave. As strange as that sounds, that's what we believe today!

Faraday conducted his last experiment on March 12, 1862, at the age of 70, on the magnetic influence on the light produced by a glowing gas.[409] Faraday was unable to determine any magnetic influence on the bands of light and retired from research altogether. (Years later, in 1902, a German man named Pieter Zeeman redid the experiment with more sensitive equipment and won a Nobel Prize for it.)[410] A few months later, Faraday wrote a friend about his deteriorating condition: "Again and again I tear up my letters, for I write nonsense. I cannot spell or write a line continuously. Whether I shall recover—this confusion—do not know."[411] Faraday wrote to his wife: "I long to see you, dearest, and to talk over things together, and call to mind all the kindness I have received. My head is full, and my heart also, but my recollection rapidly fails, even as regards the friends that are in the room with me."[412] Faraday died on August 25, 1867, at the age of 75 and, as was his wish, had "a plain simple funeral, attended by none but my own relatives, followed by a gravestone of the most ordinary kind, in the simplest earthly place."[413]

Faraday lived long enough to see for himself how his electrical ideas (as well as those of Oersted, Ampère, Sturgeon, Ohm, and more) led to the first major practical application of electricity. In 1866, a year before Faraday died, a newspaper breathlessly declared that this discovery had "done more to assist the progress of civilization and peace throughout the world than any other invention within the memory of man."[414] That invention? The electric telegraph.

Chapter Summary

- ✧ **1813:** Humphry Davy hires Michael Faraday as his assistant.

- ✧ **1820:** Hans Christian Oersted finds that electricity is related to magnetism by demonstrating that current will push a magnet to point in a circle around a wire. He erroneously thinks that both the current(s) and the force are spiraling.

- ✧ **1820:** Ampère creates a magnet out of a "pancake" coil with current and studies magnetic fields from a solenoid (spiral).

- ✧ **1821:** Faraday makes the first electric motor to demonstrate that the magnetic force from current is circular, not spiraling.

- ✧ **1825:** François Arago makes a magnet spin by spinning a copper disk below it. No one can figure out how it works.

- ✧ **1825:** William Sturgeon adds a metal bar to coils of wire and creates the electromagnet, which is more powerful than a permanent magnet, and is able to control the magnetism with electricity.

- ✧ **1827:** Ampère publishes his collected works on electrodynamics; much of it still holds up today.

- ✧ **1827:** Georg Ohm creates the idea of resistance and the relationship between the tension of the battery, the current, and the resistance, which is later called Ohm's law.

- ✧ **1831:** Faraday discovers how to create electricity with changing electromagnets and with moving magnets. He creates the first electric generator and also describes induction with the idea of "cutting" "magnetic lines of force."

- ✧ **1836:** William Sturgeon creates the magazine *Annals of Electricity, Magnetism, and Chemistry*. The first volume contains descriptions of Sturgeon's motor.

- ✧ **1837:** Faraday demonstrates how conductive material can shield one from electric fields by experimenting inside a metal cage, currently called a Faraday cage. Sturgeon's magazine includes a translation of Jacobi's motor and a description of Ohm's law. James Joule is inspired by Sturgeon to produce his own motor and decides to measure the power of electricity more accurately. Wheatstone and Cooke form a partnership to create an electric telegraph.

- ✧ **1840:** James Joule discovers the power equation for electrical devices—that power is equal to the current squared times the resistance.
- ✧ **1841:** Ohm's work is translated into English, and he is awarded the Royal Society's highest honor.
- ✧ **1845:** Faraday changes the polarization of light with a magnet and finds the first connection between light, electricity, and magnetism.
- ✧ **1846:** Faraday describes his strange idea that light might be a wave of electric and magnetic lines of force (fields).

Chapter 5

The Mighty Telegraph

(1826–1876)

As an answer to those who are in the habit of
saying to every new fact, "What is its use?"
Dr. Franklin says to such, "What is the use of
an infant?" The answer of the experimentalist
would be, "Endeavour to make it useful."

– Michael Faraday (1817)[415]

Although some people in the 1700s and the early 1800s made a small living out of running "electricity parties," selling items for home curiosities, "curing" aliments with shocking machines, or even installing lightning rods, electricity wasn't very profitable and certainly wasn't big business. All of that changed with the telegraph, and then the speaking telegraph (the telephone). In 1838 a congressman (who admittedly had a financial stake in the success of the telegraph) said that the telegraph was "a revolution unsurpassed in moral grandeur by any discovery that has been made in the arts and sciences. ... Space will be, to all practical purposes of information, completely annihilated."[416] Not only did the telegraph change the way we communicated and fought wars, but it also made several people a great deal of money. Suddenly, businesses were interested in electricity, and the world was never the same again.

5.1 The Teacher and the Telegraph

One day in 1816, a sick and bored teenager named Joseph Henry happened upon a book of science lectures at his mother's boarding house in the backwoods of Albany, New York, that would change his life and eventually lead to the telegraph. Before this point, Joseph Henry had shown no interest in learning or science. In fact, he had dropped out of school at 13 or 14 years old to work as an assistant to a watchmaker.[417] However, when the watchmaker quickly went out of business, Henry decided that a life on the stage would be his future. That was when Henry came down with a bad cold and, while convalescing, found one of his mother's boarder's science books. Years later, Henry wrote in the flyleaf, "This book, although by no means a profound work, has, under Providence, exerted a remarkable influence on my life … [it] was the first book I ever read with attention … [and it] fixed my mind on the study of nature, and caused me to resolve at the time of reading it that I would immediately commence to devote my life to the acquisition of knowledge."[418]

Joseph Henry meant it. He started to go to night school and voraciously read every science book he could find. When Henry was 19, he received a full scholarship to further his education at a high school called the Albany Academy. He studied mathematics, physics, and chemistry while supplementing his income with tutoring. Henry had a series of unrelated jobs, and by 1826, when he was 26 years old, he got a job as a math teacher at the same school he had attended seven years earlier. At first, Henry was glad of the offer to work at the academy. However, Henry really wanted to do research and quickly felt that "my duties in the Academy are not well suited to my taste. I am engaged on an average seven hours in a day … in the drudgery of instructing a class of sixty boys in the elements of Arithmetic."[419]

At that time, Joseph Henry, who had read Sturgeon's 1825 paper on making a magnet with electricity by wrapping wires around a soft iron bar, decided to make the strongest magnet he could with a single simple battery. His logic was that at the time it was hard to get or make a really good, strong battery, and that was what was keeping people from studying electricity in America:

The subject of electro-magnetism, although one of the most interesting branches of human knowledge, and presenting at this time the most fruitful field for discovery, is perhaps less generally understood in this country than almost any other department of natural science ... a principal cause of this inattention ... is the difficulty and expense which formerly attended the experiments—[i.e.] a large galvanic battery.[420]

Henry wrapped a thin wire as tightly as he could around a metal bar by insulating the wire with strips of his wife's petticoat. At first, he got a stronger magnet. But after a while, adding more wire didn't make the magnet stronger—it made it weaker. Henry realized that the battery was producing less and less current when he used a longer wire. (The longer the wire, the more resistance the wire had, and therefore less current.) Henry then got the idea of wrapping a bar of iron with nine separate coils of wire that he could connect individually or in groups to the same battery (see figure 1). He experimented with attaching different sections of the magnet to a simple battery (just zinc cylinders with copper in a half-pint of acid). He put a scale under the magnet and measured the maximum weight it could support. If only one coil was electrified, then it could support seven pounds (3 kg). If, however, he attached two to the same battery (in what we now call parallel) so that each coil was separately attached, he could get the magnet to hold up 145 pounds (66 kg). If he attached all nine coils, he managed to lift 650 pounds (295 kg). Henry crowed, "Our magnet [and battery] lifts more than 35 times its own weight; it is probably, therefore, the most powerful magnet ever constructed."[421]

Soon, Henry bested his own invention and made a magnet that held up to 1,500 pounds (680 kg). One of his favorite demonstrations was to lift a very heavy object, then remove the battery and have the object fall down with what must have been a terrifying bang. Henry recalled, "this never fails to produce a great sensation among the audience as before the fall they can scarcely believe that the magnet supports the weight."[422] It might seem like a cute parlor trick today, but at the time, this was considered the height of scientific achievement. As a biographer wrote, "The construction of electromagnets of great lifting power [was]... equivalent of our atom smashers, computers, and rockets—new, exciting extensions of human control of the unknown."[423]

Henry next tried attaching multiple batteries to a large coil in new ways, trying out one after the other (series) and all at the same time (parallel). When he attached 25 different batteries at the same time in a series circuit, he found to his disappointment that his batteries didn't make a particularly

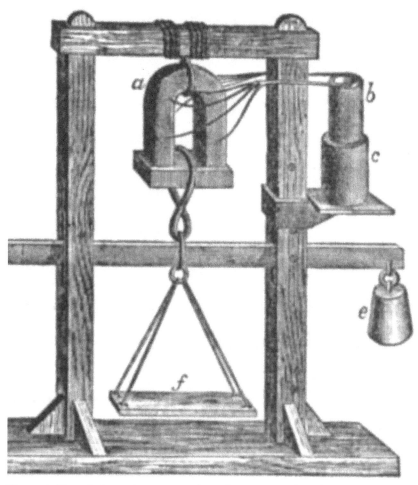

Figure 1: Henry's dramatic system to drop objects. Note that objects b and c are the battery and that the battery is connected in parallel to the electromagnet.

strong electromagnet. Henry then realized that he'd used a lot of wire, about a fifth of a mile, that he didn't need between the batteries and the coil. He speculated this might be the reason that so many batteries would provide so little magnetic force. However, when he removed the excess wire, the electromagnet still was very weak, perhaps even a little weaker. Henry realized that maybe the battery was running low but that with multiple batteries in series the length of a wire was "at least, not sensibly diminished by passing through a long wire."[424] In other words, serial batteries didn't produce very much electromagnetic power, but they could travel very far, whereas parallel batteries (or parallel coils) could produce a lot of current and therefore, a lot of magnetic force as long as the wires were short. Henry, who had not yet read Georg Ohm, called the serial batteries a "quantity" battery and the parallel batteries an "intensity" battery.[425]

The reason this works is the battery itself has resistance—internal resistance. If you place 25 batteries in a row, you get 25 times the voltage but also 25 times the internal resistance. This means that it's impossible to get a lot of current even if the external wires are very short and have almost no resistance. If you put 25 batteries in parallel, the voltage remains the same, but the internal resistance is reduced by 25 times, which makes it easier to produce a lot of current as long as the external resistance is small.

However, if the external resistance is very large, as is the case with very long wires, then the 25 batteries in series with their increased voltage are not as affected by the resistance as the batteries in parallel. For example, if the external resistance goes from equal to the internal resistance to 10 times the internal resistance, and you have 25 batteries in series, the current goes down by 25%, which sounds bad. But compare that to the 25 batteries in parallel, where, in the same situation, the current starts at the same number but goes down by 90%, down to a number similar to what you would get with a single battery (see figure 2).

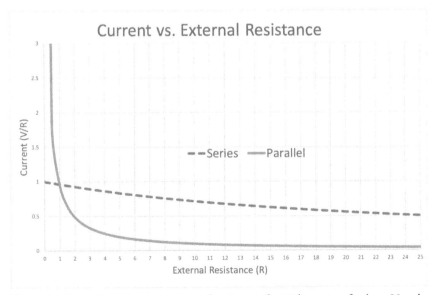

Figure 2: Chart of current versus external resistance for 25 batteries of voltage V and internal resistance R. Note that for low external resistance, the batteries in parallel produce more current, but for high resistance, the ones for series are superior.

Now that Henry could see that the magnetic effect of batteries in series wasn't altered much by long wires, he decided to see how far he could detect an electrical current. Henry thus scaled down his electromagnet to a simple bar that was tightly wound with insulated wire. He placed this electromagnet near a magnetic compass so that when the electromagnet was electrified it moved the compass, which rang a bell. Basically, it was the first doorbell. He then spooled out wire throughout the upper rooms of the academy and managed to make the bell ring with a signal from his series of batteries over a mile away! More than a doorbell, Henry immediately realized that this battery arrangement would be perfect for a telegraph.[426]

For 100 years, since Stephan Gray discovered that electricity could communicate over long distances in 1727, people had tried to use electricity to make a telegraph. But moving pieces of fluff just wasn't a very robust or repeatable method of long-distance communication. Then, when Oersted discovered in 1820 that a current-carrying wire would move a compass, there was renewed interest in an electromagnetic telegraph. My favorite was designed by William Cooke and Charles Wheatstone: five compass needles were used around a diamond of letters so that the operator would turn two compasses to point to each letter of the alphabet.[427] This device was popular in England for a while, but it took until the 1840s to get it off the ground.

When Sturgeon coiled wire around an iron bar to make the first electromagnet in 1824, his friend and mentor Peter Barlow tried to use it to make what he called an electromagnetic telegraph. Unfortunately, he found it didn't work beyond 200 feet and gave it up. Therefore, when Henry found that multiple batteries in series could send signals long distances, he wrote that it was "directly applicable to Mr. Barlow's project of forming an electromagnetic telegraph."[428]

It's important to take a moment to realize how influential these experiments were. At the time, very few people even knew about the difference between current and voltage, or the definition of resistance, let alone internal resistance. Despite that, Henry discovered how to make the world's most powerful electromagnet (with parallel coils tightly wound), how to wire batteries so that they could produce high current (parallel), and how to wire batteries so that they could produce some current that could travel over long distances (series). Henry's publication in 1831 won him acclaim, and he was offered a job working as a professor at Princeton University despite the fact that he admitted that he was not "a graduate of any college."[429]

At Princeton, Joseph Henry initially felt that the laboratory was far inferior to the one he'd built at his old high school, complaining that the school's equipment was "very deficient in quality … and in a very bad state of preservation."[430] Nevertheless, he built a combination of both his bell ringing and his heavy lifting demonstrations. He had a se-

Figure 3: Joseph Henry in the 1840s

ries battery connected for miles to a small coil. Instead of the coil ringing a bell, the coil pulled a switch that closed a circuit with *another* battery, this one in parallel, that was next to a large electromagnet. In this way, Henry could remotely lift and drop an astonishing weight from a large distance. Joseph Henry had not only invented the long-distance electromagnetic telegraph—he'd also invented the relay, which is an electromagnetic switch that would connect a new circuit and extend a telegraph for as long as one wished.

Henry also installed a telegraph where he draped wires on trees between his laboratory and his house to tell his wife when he wanted lunch. Henry's work was greatly aided when he was assigned an assistant—a free Black man named Sam Parker. (Mind you, slavery was still going strong in the 1830s and '40s but not in Princeton.) Parker was a bit of a campus character. He was known to sneak in late-night dinners to local students in exchange for old suits and was rumored to own over 100 suits that he changed multiple times a day.[431] Henry wrote often of his appreciation for Parker's work and said he was "indispensable."[432] In 1842 Henry wrote that his work was delayed for two weeks because Parker was sick.[433] However, like most White people at the time, he often treated his assistant like a child, and although Henry was antislavery, Henry would be considered racist by today's standards as Henry believed that Black people were biologically inferior.[434]

The students were even more racist. They loved to see Parker do electrical experiments, but it was a dangerous time to be Black in America—especially for someone who was known to "put on airs." We only know about Parker through a few comments in Henry's papers and the autobiography of a Princeton graduate named Edward Shippen. Shippen describes how Parker was considered by the students to be "one of the most important persons in Princeton,"[435] while he also mentions how he (and fellow students) disliked Parker's independence or "impudence." Years later, Shippen gleefully and maliciously described how Parker's behavior "improved" when Parker was (and these are Shippen's words) "thoroughly flailed by a stalwart north Jerseyman."[436]

Henry never patented his ideas on the telegraph. His friends actually encouraged him to do so as early as 1831, but he decided it was incompatible with "the dignity of science."[437] Or at least that is what he said years later once he realized how powerful, influential, and financially successful the telegraph would be. Sam Parker never patented anything either, but for different reasons. First, it is unclear exactly what Parker discovered, as no scientific journal at the time would publish the research of a Black assistant. Also, even if he did try to patent these ideas, he could never have afforded the $30 patent fee as he only earned $48 a year.[438] Instead, the patent, the money and the fame of the telegraph went to a painter with no scientific background named Samuel Morse.

5.2 The Painter Who Annihilated Space and Time

Samuel Finley Breese Morse was born on April 27, 1791, to an upper-crust family in Charlestown, Massachusetts, and had two interests—painting and xenophobia, which inadvertently led to his invention of the telegraph. Let me explain.

As a young adult, Morse went to the finest schools (Exeter and Yale) and got extra cash from doing small portraits of his classmates and with his inventions, which he was convinced were always going to make him rich but never went anywhere. After graduation, Morse moved to Europe to study painting. He wrote his mother: "Had I no higher thoughts than being a first-rate portrait painter, I would have chosen a far different profession. My ambition is to be among those who shall revive the splendor of the 15th century; to rival the genius of a Rafael, a Michelangelo, or a Titian."[439] Despite his ego, Morse was accepted into the Royal Academy of Art in 1811 and traveled as a successful painter both in England and in America. (He was quite talented; see figure 4.)

By 1816, 25-year-old Morse was an established portrait painter living in New Haven, Connecticut, where he fell in love with a 16-year-old girl named Lucretia Pickering Walker. They married in 1818, had two children in quick succession, and all seemed very happy. This is when tragedy struck. In 1825 Morse got a commission for $1,000 to travel to Washington, DC, to paint a portrait of the American Revolutionary hero Lafayette visiting from France. Morse was a little reluctant to go, as his wife was expecting their third child, but the honor of the commission (and the cash) was too much to refuse. Morse learned that his wife had delivered a son while he was painting and decided to finish working on the portrait, although he was eager to see his new child and wrote his wife, "I long to hear from you."[440] Lucretia Morse never received his letter, as she died from a heart attack due to complications from childbirth. She was only 25 years old. Sometime later Morse wrote to his daughter: "You cannot know the depth of the wound that was inflicted when I was deprived of your dear mother."[441] Morse felt bitter and angry toward the world, and he left his three children with his parents to focus on painting.

Figure 4: Samuel Morse's painting of his wife, Lucretia, and their oldest two children in 1824, a year before her tragic death in childbirth (left). Morse self portrait (right)

In 1832 Morse went on a trip to London to improve his mood and wrote to a friend: "My journey to England, change of scene and air, have restored me wonderfully."[442] This turned out to be a very important trip (and not just for Morse's mood). On the boat ride back on a ship called the Sully, he was seated with a doctor who informed the table about the interesting results of electromagnets from Sturgeon and that the electromagnet could be observed from a distance. Morse was immediately convinced that this device could be used to send messages long distances, telling the captain, "Should you hear of the telegraph one of these days as the wonder of the world, remember the discovery was made on board the good ship Sully."[443] Morse's older brother Sidney met Samuel when he arrived in New York and recalled that his brother "was full of the subject of the telegraph during the walk from the ship, and for some days afterwards could scarcely speak about anything else."[444]

Amazingly, one of the things that Morse came up with on the ship was the idea that you could use a system of dots and dashes with a *single* wire to send the signal. Initially though, his plan was to have the dots and dashes represent the numbers one to ten (with a dot and a space for one, two dots and a space for two, and so on) and then make a separate code for the letters represented by the numbers.[445]

His brother suggested that they just use 24 wires for (most of) the letters of the alphabet as "wire was cheap,"[446] but Morse was adamant that a single circuit was the way to go. Unfortunately for Morse, he didn't have the equipment, the knowledge, the money, or the physical place to conduct research. In fact, he moved into his brother Richard's house, and Richard's wife complained that Morse ruined a chair and carpet with his metalwork.

Meanwhile, Morse continued to paint in order to make money, fulfill his desire for fame, and promote his style of art. However, Morse's love of art flowed into a virulent hatred of Catholics and immigrants. To Morse, the purpose of art was to give "the highest moral and intellectual cultivation through every class," which he thought was desperately needed as "the democracy of our county [is tended] to low and vulgar pleasures and pursuits."[447] Morse decided that Catholic immigrants (especially ones from Italy and Ireland) were destroying "American" civilization and were doing so *because* they were indebted to the pope.

At the time, America was just forming public schools and there was fierce debate about funding religious schools for non-Protestants. Morse published a book supposedly from an anonymous French ex-priest railing, "Americans, when you shall have become tired with your liberty, when you shall envy the fate of Ireland, Spain and Italy; when you wish that your children and your descendants may become superstitious slaves, introduce Catholic schools."[448] In 1836 Morse decided that he should run for mayor of New York to save his country from this treachery. His friends were aghast. One wrote in an editorial that "Mr. Morse is a scholar and a gentleman ... and we should like on ninety-nine accounts to support him. But the hundredth forbids it. Somehow or other he has got warped in his politics."[449] His political foray was an abject failure, and he won only 400 votes out of the 35,000 votes cast.[450]

Despite his lack of popularity with the general public, Morse's political views were held by many people in power in the art world—particularly those in academia. In 1835 the year before his disastrous run for mayor, Morse was appointed the first professor of Art and Design at New York University. This gave him a little more financial security as well as a living space and workshop. Morse recalled that when he moved into this space, he "immediately commenced, with very limited means, to experiment upon my invention" which was made of "an old picture frame" and "the wheels of an old wooden clock."[451]

By the end of the year, Morse had put together a crude telegraph that would send signals about 40 feet. Morse showed it to a chemistry professor at New York University named Leonard Gale. Gale was aware of Joseph Henry's research on batteries and electromagnets and immediately set to improve Morse's device so that it used series batteries and wound the magnet tightly instead of loosely. Soon, Gale and Morse sent a signal a mile around (and around) Professor Gale's office. However, Morse was still distracted by his political attempts as well as his painting and did not have much time or money to work on the effort.

All of that changed in March 1837 when Morse learned that he wasn't going to be commissioned to make a painting for the Washington, DC, rotunda.[452] This was devastating to Morse as he had been publicly pushing for the gig for at least four years. In fact, Morse was so upset that he gave up painting altogether and instead focused on developing the telegraph. Seven years later, he wrote, "Painting has been a smiling mistress to many, but she has been a cruel jilt to me. I did not abandon her, she abandoned me ... I could wish that every picture I ever painted was destroyed."[453] There's disagreement about why a talented painter like Morse was overlooked for this important contract, but it very well could have been due to his embarrassing forays into politics. This loss turned out to be a windfall for the telegraph, as it's pretty clear that had Morse worked on painting, he never would have had the time to focus on the telegraph.

Six months after losing out on the commission, a 29-year-old graduate of New York University named Alfred Vail heard about Morse and Gale's experiments when on a visit his alma mater.[454] Vail, a machinist whose father owned a successful ironworks company, was instantly hooked on the idea of a telegraph. Within days, Vail convinced his father to support the endeavor for 25% of the future profits (where anything and everything that Vail discovered would be owned by Morse). Almost immediately, Vail was able to improve Morse's clunky device. By January 3, 1838, Vail sent a telegraph code over two miles with the words "a patient waiter is no loser."[455]

Vail and Morse also worked on the alphabet, and by February, Morse gave up on his two-step telegraph code and decided to simply have dots and dashes represent the letters. Vail wrote his father, "Professor Morse has invented a new plan of an alphabet, and has thrown aside the Dictionaries."[456] One interesting feature of Morse's first systems is that they were clearly based on the printing press. Morse actually went to a printer and had blocks made for the different letters and numbers with uneven upper surfaces (see figure 5). The word to be telegraphed was then created by placing the blocks into a trough and then the trough was pulled under a lever that made a key move up and down to produce the dots and dashes. It was only after Vail did so many experiments and demonstrations that he memorized the codes that he dropped this laborious process, and put the codes directly in the key instead.[457]

Soon, Vail, Morse, and Gale were demonstrating their miraculous device to everyone they could find, including members of Congress and the president. One congressman named Francis O. Smith agreed to help them for a cut of the profit. Morse then reduced Vail's cut by half to pay off the congressman. In April of 1838, Smith sponsored a bill to give Morse (and himself) $30,000 of government funds for a telegraph line. Needless to say,

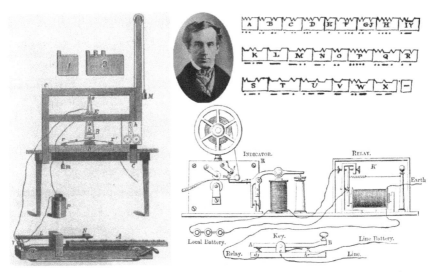

Figure 5: Diagram of Morse's first telegraph, 1835 (left), Samuel Morse in 1840 (top center), Morse's drawing of his original letter blocks (top right), and a Morse telegraph system from the early 1870s (bottom right)

Smith "forgot" to mention that he had a financial connection to Morse and his company in this attempt.[458]

With Congressman Smith working for them at home, Morse and Vail went to London and Paris to obtain international patents. Morse had patent trouble in London and wrote a friend that Charles Wheatstone and another inventor named Edward Davy, "were my oppressors [as] they have each very ingenious inventions of their own."[459] After seven wasted weeks in London, Morse and Vail moved to Paris, where they spent months impressing people without being able to get the patents that they wanted. Morse returned in April of 1839 to find that almost nothing positive had occurred in his absence. He wrote Congressman Smith: "I am quite disappointed in finding nothing done by Congress and nothing accomplished by way of [my] Company."[460]

Meanwhile, Joseph Henry also traveled to Europe and was disgusted to return to news that Morse had invented a telegraph without acknowledging Henry's influence, writing a friend that "the charlatanism of our country struck me much more disagreeably when I first returned [from Europe.] ... You probably heard of a great sensation [that] was produced by the Magnetic Telegraph of Professor Morse who first claimed ... the entire origin of the project."[461] Dr. Gale, the professor who had helped Morse with the physics of his telegraph, met with Henry and convinced Henry that Morse was just using the ideas, not pretending to have created them himself. (Gale also mollified Henry by loaning him a nice roll of wire.) Soon, Henry was feeling far more charitable toward Morse and wrote to him to say that he was "pleased to learn that you fully sanction the loan which I obtained from Dr. Gale, of your wire, and I shall be happy if any of the results are found to have a practical bearing on the Electrical Telegraph."[462]

For the next several years, Morse waited and waited for the money from Congress. In December of 1841, Morse dejectedly wrote, "If Congress would but pass the bill of thirty thousand dollars before them, there would be no difficulty. There is no difficulty in the scientific or mechanical part of the matter—*that is a problem solved.* The only difficulty that remains is, in obtaining the funds which Congress can furnish, to carry it into execution."[463] In February of 1842, Morse got a supportive letter from Joseph Henry saying that "I most sincerely hope you will succeed in convincing our representatives of the importance of the invention."[464]

Finally, in February of 1843, a congressman from Maryland named Mr. Kennedy initiated a bill to give Morse the $30,000 he had been seeking for five years. However, it was almost derailed when several congressmen joked that they wanted to use half the sum to build a railroad to the moon, and Morse only won by a margin of 90 to 82.[465] Morse wrote to the now-retired Congressman Smith that "the long agony (truly agony to me) is over."[466] In March of 1843, Morse, Vail, Gale, and others started a telegraph line between Washington, DC, and New York. While building his first telegraph line, Morse talked to Joseph Henry, who gave him advice on how to attach wires to poles with insulating material.

By May 24, 1844, Samuel Morse set up his telegraph key at the US Supreme Court with Vail at the Baltimore office. With a large group of onlookers and newspaper reporters present, Morse coded the biblical passage, "What hath God wrought?" which Vail repeated back to him. Two days later, the Democratic Convention had their nomination assembly in Baltimore where James Polk made a surprising win of the nomination. The members of the convention then nominated a senator named Silas Wright to be vice president.

Wright, who was in New York at the time, heard from Morse about the nomination (and rejected it) by telegraph! The members of the committee were so flabbergasted to get a reply within minutes that they refused to believe that it was real. After postponing a day to get a paper message that Wright really did want to reject the nomination, the committee had a conversation with Wright about his decision over the wires—the first important political messages sent over the telegraph.[467] Morse tried to convince the government to buy his patent for $100,000, but they (shortsightedly it turned out) thought it was not worth the money.[468]

In May, Morse made his company public and began the process to extend the telegraph from Baltimore to Philadelphia and New York. Soon the country was blanketed with telegraph wires, and Morse was making money hand over fist. For example, between July 1851 and June 1852, the Washington to New York line alone sent over 250,000 messages and made over $100,000.[469] In 1854 the US Supreme Court upheld Morse's patent claim on the telegraph, and all US companies that used his system had to pay him royalties, leaving Morse incredibly wealthy.

Morse then spent his free time arguing (as a Northerner where slavery was illegal) for the joys of slavery, saying among other things that "slavery … [is] divinely ordained for the discipline of the human race,"[470] and that abolitionism (antislavery) is a sin. Ironically, the telegraph increased long-distance communication, which helped the abolitionists let people know about the horrors of slavery. Morse died in 1872 and is, according to the Yale website, "among the most honored Yale graduates on campus today,"[471] with little to no mention of his political and racial views.

Meanwhile Henry continued his research first at Princeton before moving on to become the first director at the newly created Smithsonian Institution. Politically, he went the other way from Morse and became a personal friend of Abraham Lincoln. His relationship with Morse had soured when Alfred Vail published a book in 1845 without recognizing Henry's contributions. Supposedly, he didn't talk about Morse and the telegraph much, but he did once say, "If I could live my life again … I might have taken out more patents."[472]

5.3 Aleck, Mabel, and the Speaking Telegraph

In 1861 when Alexander Graham Bell (who was known as Aleck) was 14 years old, his father took him and his 15-year-old brother Melly to see a "speaking automaton" machine. This was not a surprising action, considering his father was a linguist. In fact, Bell's father, uncle, and grandfather were all famous elocution instructors, and his father, Alexander Melville Bell, was considered one of the most famous in England. The children of an illustrious linguist were not easily impressed and grumbled that "the articulation was disappointingly crude."[473]

Bell's father therefore challenged his complaining sons to build a better machine, which they actually did. However, their machine ended up sounding like "a baby in great distress," shouting "mama" pathetically. As they were teenagers, Aleck and Melly promptly used their doll to prank their neighbors so that, according to Bell, several strangers came to the "baby's" aid, saying, "What is the matter with that baby?"[474] Forty-eight years later, Alexander Graham Bell said that the crying-baby project started him "along the path that led to the telephone."[475]

The next year, Bell got a job as a student teacher of music and elocution, which he stayed at for three years. In 1865 Bell's grandfather died. His father took over his grandfather's business in London, and Bell moved there to be his father's assistant. That's when he showed his father his theory that vowels contain "faint musical tones."[476] Bell's father was impressed and shared it with a professor named Alexander Ellis, where he learned that his theory had already been published by a German scientist named Hermann von Helmholtz.

However, Bell was fascinated to hear that Helmholtz had come up with this theory while experimenting with electrically vibrating tuning forks. Ellis kindly gave the paper to young Bell, but Bell could not read German and did not know that Helmholtz had only made tuning forks vibrate at a single note electrically and didn't recreate vowel sounds. Bell became convinced that "if Helmholtz could transmit and reproduce vowel sounds, you could reproduce consonant sounds as well; you could reproduce speech."[477]

Soon, he was electrifying tuning forks and trying his best to get speech out of electricity but was failing miserably. Note that although Bell referred to his idea as a telephone, his original idea was more of a long-distance electronic automaton machine, requiring the operator to input an electrical system that would cause the machine on the other end to mimic human speech. Bell also noticed that a tuning fork ringing at one note would make another tuning fork ring at the same note. Because of this, he came up with an idea of sending multiple signals over the same time at different frequencies, which he called a "musical telegraph."[478] Unfortunately, he also had no luck in producing this device.

Around this time, Bell's father created his own method of writing down forms of speech called Visible Speech, where each sound was represented by a certain drawing that represented the mouth's movements when making that sound.[479] Aleck, his brothers, and his father would give demonstrations where Bell would reproduce sounds from the visual clues without having heard them first. This inspired Bell's father to attempt to use this method to teach deaf people to speak. (They also might have been inspired by Bell's mother, Eliza, who had started going deaf some 10 years earlier.) In 1869 they used Visual Speech to teach four deaf children between the ages of seven and 12 to speak, and "it was at once evident that Visible Speech would be an instrument of great power in the hands of teachers of the deaf."[480] Pretty soon, various schools around England, Scotland, and America were working with this new system.

This was also a tragic time for the Bell family. In 1867 Aleck's 19-year-old brother Ned fell ill from tuberculosis and died. By 1870 Aleck and Melly also fell ill from the disease, and soon his older brother Melly died. Petrified that they would lose all three of their sons, the Bell family moved to the backwoods of Canada to convalesce. In Canada, Aleck recovered quickly, and his father went on a tour of New England to promote his language system. On his travels, Aleck's father was offered a job as a teacher for the deaf in Boston that he refused as he was sick of teaching. Meanwhile, Bell became bored and started going on what his parents considered to be dangerous trips to record the language of native tribes. Bell's parents then encouraged him to take the job offered to his father in Boston, as they felt it would be safer than Canada. As Bell's father wrote him in 1870, "Our earthy hopes have now their beginning, middle and end in you. Oh, be careful, and leave [no] opening for that fatal disease to enter."[481]

In 1871 Aleck Bell started a job in Boston at the Clarke School for the Deaf, using his father's visual language system. Although he was, in general, a very shy man, in the classroom he felt confident and well liked. Despite all of his future achievements, from this moment on he defined himself as first and foremost a "teacher of the deaf."[482] Although Bell was generally beloved by his students, Bell's later actions made him far from beloved among the Deaf community, as I will explain later in this chapter.

This brings us to a remarkable girl named Mabel Hubbard. Mabel was the second daughter (out of four who lived past childhood) of a wealthy lawyer named Gardiner Hubbard and his young wife, Gertrude. When Mabel was around four years old, she contracted scarlet fever, which left her completely deaf. At the time, deaf people were put in special asylums where they were kept in complete isolation from the hearing world. Gardiner Hubbard refused to place his darling child in an institution but was shocked to realize that there were no schools or tutors in 1863 to teach deaf children to speak or read lips. However, he was inspired by talking to a teacher for the blind who said that there were people in Germany who had managed to teach the deaf to communicate verbally.

Unfortunately, these scientists (in a very Victorian way) insisted that this was only possible by refusing to let deaf children use sign language or any nonverbal communication at all. Hubbard was ecstatic that there was a chance that his child could be a part of society and have a "normal" life, but poor Mabel Hubbard struggled with everyone ignoring her desperate signs and forcing her to speak in order to get a response. Her father later described how "it was a battle of wills. She howled with rage. Floods of tears and violent tantrums."[483] However, after months of pain, Mabel brilliantly learned how to communicate by reading lips and speaking. They didn't even let her write for a year, but once they did, she excelled, especially in history. One day, when Mabel was nine years old, her teacher told her father that he was "sure her knowledge of American history is equal or superior to that possessed by any hearing child of her age."[484] Pleased, in May 1867, Hubbard decided to get his daughter tested and was happy to find that, yes, Mabel was quite advanced and had no trouble reading the lips of a stranger, speaking in an understandable voice, and of course, reading and discussing history.[485]

Mabel's parents were pleased for their daughter, of course, but were also distressed about what this meant for other deaf children in the country. Gardiner Hubbard decided it was his civic duty to create a new school with the aid of his daughter. He'd actually tried three years earlier in 1864 but had been rebuffed by a member of the school board named Lewis Dudley, who had a deaf child in an institution. After Mabel Hubbard spoke to the committee in 1867, the same Lewis Dudley stood up and said:

> You know, gentlemen, how I spoke to you three years ago—how I told you of my daughter Theresa, one of the advanced pupils at the American Asylum, and how I would refuse my consent to have her taught speech if the possibility arose. I have witnessed a miracle. Mr. Hubbard's nine-year-old daughter Mabel is far more advanced and superior in every respect to my thirteen-year-old Theresa. His daughter speaks! She understands the speech of others. She is part of the world around her and mine—mine is isolated—locked out of everything. Gentlemen, I tell you, for the future of all children like our daughters, give Mr. Hubbard the charter and the funds for his school![486]

After that, the committee voted unanimously for a new school for the deaf with the idea of focusing on teaching their students to communicate with the hearing world. Unfortunately, they also caused harm to those who struggled with speaking. By discouraging signing, they made it harder for deaf students to learn.

Three years later, in March of 1870, the Hubbard family brought 12-year-old Mabel to Germany to see if she could be helped any further at one of the revolutionary German schools. At first the teachers in Germany refused to believe that she was deaf. Once they verified that she could not hear, they announced: "We can do nothing for her here. I tell you no German

Figure 6: 14-year-old Mabel Hubbard in 1872 (top); 28-year-old Bell in 1876 (bottom)

child in any oral school can match her in any way—speech, or speech-reading, or everyday knowledge. It is a true miracle."[487]

So, the Hubbard family decided to enroll Mabel in a "regular" school where everything was in German. Mabel was so gifted in languages that she soon became the family's translator. The Hubbard family lived abroad for over two years, and when they returned, Mabel learned that she was to receive tutoring from the Clarke School's new teacher: Alexander Graham Bell.

Mabel met Bell in 1873, and she wasn't impressed, writing in her diary, "I did not like [him]. I do not think him exactly a gentleman." She even added, "*I* could never marry such a man!"[488] Despite her reaction, Mabel was surprised when mere weeks after meeting him, Alexander Bell discontinued his private lessons and had his assistant take on the duties instead. Her sisters teased her that Bell must hate her, but in truth, the opposite was the case. For the first time, 26-year-old Alexander Graham Bell was starting to feel physical and emotional attachment and realized that he couldn't remain as her teacher. He continued to monitor her classes from afar and would come over to her house for long conversations about history and philosophy. Soon, he became a part of the Hubbard's family.

One night in October of 1874, after a piano recital, Alexander Graham Bell regaled Gardiner Hubbard with his crazy ideas—particularly his plan to send several telegraph signals at the same time at different frequencies. Hubbard was instantly intrigued, and Bell wrote his parents, stating: "I am tonight a happy man ... [Hubbard] now offers to provide me with <u>funds</u> for the purpose of experimenting if we go into the scheme as partners."[489]

Meanwhile, Bell's work as a teacher of the deaf was giving him telephone ideas. Specifically, at around this time, Bell started to use something called a phonautograph to change the sounds his students were making into physical symbols. The phonautograph was invented in 1857 and consisted of a cone with a thin membrane on the end. The membrane had a lever connected to it with a needle. When you talked into the cone, the needle would vibrate and mark a glass beneath it. In 1874 it occurred to Bell that the phonautograph resembled a human ear. He therefore asked a local ear doctor to make a model after the ear, and the man gruesomely asked, "Why don't you use a human ear, taken from a dead man, as a phonautograph?"

Bell thought that was a great idea but asked, "Where can I get a dead man's ear?"

"Oh," the doctor calmly replied, "I will get it for you."[490]

Bell then took this dismembered organ and created his own ghoulish phonautograph. Bell said later:

> As I was holding the human ear in my hand, it struck me that the bones of that human ear were very massive compared to the membrane. The membrane was like a little piece of tissue paper, hardly the size of a fingernail, and the bones that were moved by the little membrane were really very heavy. It suddenly occurred to me, that if such a small membrane as that would move bones so massive in comparison, why would not a larger membrane move my piece of iron [magnet]? At once the idea of a membrane speaking telephone became complete in my mind. All I had to do was to attach a steel reed, not tuned to any definite pitch, to the center of a stretched membrane, just as in the phonautograph, so that it would vibrate in front of an electromagnet, and put another at the end of a telegraph wire, and we would have ... a speaking telephone.[491]

Bell wrote to his parents a quick letter in November of 1874. "I have scarce been able to breathe to anybody for fear of being thought insane ... please keep this paper as a record of the conception of the idea in case anyone else should at a future time discover that the vibrations of a permanent magnet will induce a vibrating current of electricity."[492]

With funding from Hubbard and the father of another one of his students, named George Sanders, Bell hired a local machinist, 20-year-old Thomas Watson, to help him with his investigation into the musical telegraph. One day, early in 1875, Bell told Watson about this fantastical idea to "talk by telegraph" with vibrating magnets, which Bell called a telephone. However, after discussing it for hours, Aleck Bell decided that it was too crazy to work on, telling Watson, "Mr. Sanders and Mr. Hubbard would not welcome such a will-o'-the-wisp idea, and they are pressing me—and rightly so—to complete this telegraph matter. Until I do, I have no right to consider building a telephone."[493] In March of 1875, Bell visited our old friend Joseph

Henry and asked him for his advice on making tuning forks that electrically make sounds. Henry told Bell that he had "the germ of a good invention" for the telephone. When Aleck Bell told Henry that he worried that he didn't have the scientific expertise to finish his project, Henry's response was "GET IT!" As Bell stated years later, "I cannot tell you how much these two words have encouraged me."[494]

Still, Bell tried to remain focused on the musical telegraph idea. Bell knew that electricity creates a magnetic force, so he placed metal reeds (basically flat tuning forks) near magnets and pulsed current through them in an attempt to find the trick to only make certain notes ring while the others remained silent. While working on this experiment on June 2, 1875, Bell thought one reed was stuck on its magnet and asked Watson to free it. When Watson freed the reed, it vibrated, and to Bell's shock, a separate reed vibrated in sympathy. They experimented over and over again. According to Bell, "We did not do anything all day but pluck reeds."[495] What was happening? It turned out to be a combination of Faraday's induction experiments (moving magnets near wires to create current) and Sturgeon's electromagnet study (current in a coil acts like a bar magnet and attracts or repels another magnet).

When the first reed vibrated, it moved back and forth in front of a magnet, which created or induced an oscillating current in the reed. This current then traveled in the wire to the other reed. The second reed received current that vibrated back and forth exactly like the original reed vibrated back and forth. Because that reed was near a magnet and it had current in it, it received a force either toward the magnet or away from it depending on the direction of the current (similar to the force on a wire in a motor).

Therefore, the second reed vibrated in exactly the same rhythm as the original reed. The vibrating reeds implied to Bell that his idea of a telephone with vibrating magnets was possible. Despite the fact that his financiers were not interested, by July of 1875 Bell and Watson created a crude system with membranes attached to reeds and tried it out with one transmitter and one receiver. Bell couldn't hear a thing from the soft-spoken Watson, but when they reversed positions, Watson excitedly said, "Why, Mr. Bell, I heard your voice very distinctly, and could *almost* understand what you said."[496]

In the middle of these amazing experiments, Bell's personal life was getting complicated. In June 1875, Bell decided that he needed to tell Mabel about his feelings but was stymied by her parents (who wanted him to go slowly, considering she was just 17) and by Mabel's hesitant feelings, which came out as an outright rejection. However, in August of 1875, after she almost drowned in a swimming accident, Mabel became disturbed by the thought that if she had died, Alexander Bell would think that she hated him, which wasn't true. She decided to hurry back to Boston and tell him, "Mr. Bell, I really don't dislike you—I like you! I don't love you but I do like you. Is that enough for now?"[497] Mabel also talked to her parents and a few days later, Mabel's mother wrote Bell: "If you can win Mabel's love, I shall be happy in my darling's happiness."[498] Bell was ecstatic and steadily visited Mabel as well as worked on his telegraph idea, his telephone idea, and his teaching and tutoring.

Meanwhile, Mabel's father, Gardiner Hubbard, started to express concern that Bell was not going to be very successful and be able to support his daughter. Hubbard told Bell directly that he had a tendency "to undertake every new thing that interests [him and] accomplish nothing of any value to anyone."[499] It was time, Hubbard thought, to focus on the telegraph project and give up the distracting teaching and the improbable telephone. In November 1875, Hubbard told Bell that he had to choose the telephone and teaching or Mabel. Bell refused to give anything up, stating: "Should Mabel love me as devotedly and truly as I love her—she will not object to any work I may be engaged in. If she does not love me well enough to accept me what-ever my profession or business may be—I do not want her at all. I do not want a half-love."[500] A little ashamed of his overheated response, he tacked on, "I am sorry ... please bear with me a little longer?"[501] Mabel's father's plan backfired, as two days later on Mabel's 18th birthday, Mabel declared that she wanted to become engaged to Bell and told him that she loved him better than anyone aside from her mother. Bell wrote Mabel that night. "I am afraid to go to sleep lest I should find it all a dream, so I shall lie awake and think of you."[502]

Happy and newly focused on his research, Bell started to work on an American patent for the telephone, which Gardiner Hubbard reluctantly supported. On January 25, Alexander Graham Bell and Gardiner Hubbard met with an English scientist named George Brown, who seemed impressed with it and promised to take the plans to England and get a patent. At the time, they felt a British patent would be more important than an American patent and therefore added a postscript to the American patent, saying, "Mr. Bell will not perfect his applications in the American patent office until he hears from Mr. Brown, that he may do so without interfering with European patents."[503] However, weeks passed, and they didn't hear anything from Brown. Meanwhile, they heard that an electrical engineer working for Western Union named Elisha Gray was on the verge of patenting his own telephone, and both sides were fully convinced that the other had stolen from each other. Concerned, on the morning of February 14, 1876, Hubbard filed Alexander Graham Bell's patent for a telephone without consulting with Bell, just hours before Elisha Gray filed for his patent.[504]

Now Aleck really needed a working system. In desperation, he tried using a liquid microphone that was designed by Elisha Gray with his own speaker. On March 10, 1876, Bell accidentally spilled acid on his pants and shouted, "Mr. Watson come here! I want to see you,"[505] and was astonished when Watson ran into the room and told Bell that he heard him clearly through the telephone. This was the first instance of using a telephone to transmit understandable speech.

Now that they could transmit understandable sounds, they quickly learned how to improve their speaker by replacing the membrane with a solid

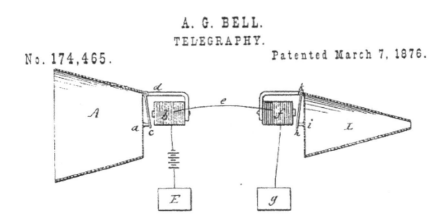

Figure 7: Diagrams from Bell's 1876 telephone patent. Part L is the speaker, which makes the magnet at part i vibrate against the electromagnet at part f. This changes the current in part b, which causes the magnet at part a (the speaker) to create sound.

metal backing. Finally, their microphone and speaker worked well enough to transmit speech. By May 5, 1876, Aleck wrote his parents: "All the experiments were great successes ... if successful [this will be] one of the great events of my life. It will be one of the milestones by which I measure time."[506]

Bell's design for the speaker was used in telephones until the 1980s (although a completely different design was used for the microphone, as I will discuss in the next chapter). Even today, many stereo speakers use basically the same idea.[507] They have a cone connected to a coil of wire with a magnet nearby. When the vibrating current goes through the wire, the magnet creates a force on the wire and the cone, which causes the cone to vibrate in the same way as the electricity vibrates.

With the pressure from Hubbard, Alexander Graham Bell was awarded the patent for his telephone less than one month after filing it, and it is considered to be one of the single most profitable patents of all time.[508] Three months after getting the patent, in June of 1876, Gardiner Hubbard wanted Bell to demonstrate his device at the Centennial Exposition in Philadelphia (Hubbard was in charge of the educational exhibits), but Bell did not want to go. He said he was busy with teaching, but he was probably scared about how it would work or be received. Mabel talked Bell into going to the train station with her and then cried until he acquiesced. "Who can bear to see a young girl weep? I just jumped on that train. I did not have baggage or anything else. So, growling like a bear, I went to Philadelphia."[509]

In Philadelphia, the judges went from exhibition to exhibition, and right when they were going to hit Bell's telephone, they decided to stop for the day. Luckily, in the crowd of judges was the emperor of Brazil, Dom Pedro II, who had met Bell before due to his work teaching the deaf. Upon recognizing Bell, Dom Pedro decided that he wanted to see Bell's demonstration, and, according to Bell, "the judges followed like a flock of sheep. My exhibit was saved."[510] Of course, none of the judges had any idea what Bell's device could do. Don Pedro put his ear to a box and sat up excitedly yelling, "It talks!" The scientist William Thomson (Lord Kelvin) was visiting from England and shouted, "It does speak. It is the most wonderful thing I have seen in America."[511] Bell recounted the events as follows: "I went to bed the night before, an unknown man, and awoke to find myself famous. I owe it to Sir William Thomson, back of him to Don Pedro, and back of him to the deaf-mutes of Boston."[512]

Soon, Mabel pushed for Bell to start a series of "telephone demonstrations" throughout New England and Canada. In addition, Mabel noted that Bell went by "A. Graham Bell" on publications to distinguish himself from his father, who was also an Alexander Bell. She told him: "Be sure that when you lecture, the gentleman who introduce you say 'Alexander Graham Bell.' No A. for me,"[513] which is why Alexander Graham Bell is almost always referred to by his full name. These talks were a huge success, but they took up much of Bell's time. When Mabel and Bell got together, however, they would stay out late, and once Mabel left a note for her mother that read, "Mamma dear, please don't scold us. We really couldn't help it. We were talking, so we had to stop under every lamppost so that I could see what Alec had to say!" (Mabel preferred to spell his name as Alec rather than Aleck.)[514]

In July of 1877, Bell and his future father-in-law, Gardiner Hubbard, founded the Bell Telephone Company (which is now AT&T).[515] He married Mabel two days later. Although his patents made Alexander Graham Bell and his father-in-law very wealthy, Bell himself was not that interested in the advances in the telephone after he had invented it. He famously even refused to have one in his house. After marrying Mabel, Bell and his new bride went on an extended honeymoon in Europe that was also a European traveling telephone show where even the queen of England got a demonstration from "Professor Bell."

While they were still in England, 10 months after the wedding, in May of 1878 Mabel Bell gave birth to a baby girl, whom Alec wanted to name Darwina in honor of Charles Darwin. Mabel insisted on the name Elsie May in honor of her mother.[516] This love of Darwin was not just an admiration of a new way of thinking about biology—it was to lead Bell's life to a dark and disturbing new field: the study of eugenics.

Almost as soon as Bell returned from England in 1879, the Massachusetts State Board of Health asked Bell to gather statistics on the inheritance of "defects" like deafness for the Massachusetts 1881 survey.[517] It took Bell until 1883 to gather enough material to publish his paper, which talked about how people with "congenital defects" could produce a "vigorous but defective variety of the race." And by that he specifically meant that "in this country *deaf-mutes marry deaf-mutes* [which] should result in the formation of a deaf variety of the human race."[518] He did not advocate for the forced sterilization of deaf people, nor for laws against their marriage (although other eugenicists did), but he did decide that the solution to the "problem" of deaf people marrying was to force all deaf people to live in worlds where they were kept completely separate from other deaf people and without the use of sign language, which he was strongly against. In this quest, he also pushed for the firing of all deaf teachers of the deaf. Bell declared that eugenics was "of transcendent importance to mankind [and] no higher or nobler subject of research can be found."[519]

Bell's position of authority and wealth, combined with his history of teaching the deaf, made him a powerful spokesman for this movement. His wife, of course, was the living embodiment of the power of forcing deaf children to live in a purely hearing world with no sign language or connection with the Deaf community. There was no acknowledgment of how traumatic it was for her or how she ended up feeling uncomfortable with other deaf people. In fact, she was a supporter of his eugenics work with the deaf. In 1880 Bell went to Milan for an international symposium for the education of the deaf, where Bell joined the majority in their resolutions to ban or strongly discourage sign language.

It took many years for the Deaf community to recover from this. The president of the National Association of the Deaf, George Veditz, wrote that Alexander Graham Bell "comes in the guise of a friend, and [is], therefore, the most to be feared enemy of the American deaf, past and present."[520] Veditz also collected money to make the first film of sign language in 1913 and signed, "It is my hope that we will all love and guard our beautiful sign language as the noblest gift God has given to deaf people." In 1980 at the 15th Congress on the Education of the Deaf, the committee formally apologized for the actions of the 1880 convention and said they were an "act of discrimination and a violation of human and constitutional rights."[521]

Despite the real harm Bell caused the Deaf community and innumerable deaf people, he was, ironically, a surprisingly gifted and dedicated teacher and was beloved by his students. One of the most famous examples was in 1887, when Bell met a family with a six-year-old blind and deaf girl named Helen Keller who was unable to communicate. Bell had an instant connection to the young child and insisted that Keller was very intelligent and should not be institutionalized. Instead, Bell suggested that Keller get a tutor from the school of the blind, which is how Helen Keller met her tutor and lifelong companion, Anne Sullivan. Keller said that interacting with Bell was "the door through which I should pass from darkness into light, from isolation to friendship, companionship, knowledge, love,"[522] and dedicated her first book, *The Story of My Life*, to him. Helen Keller revisited Bell two years later, where he was delighted to find that, due to Anne Sullivan's teachings, she was able to communicate and was completely transformed.

Bell let Keller go and play with his now two daughters, Daisy (nine) and Elsie (11), who promptly showed Hellen their favorite spot on the roof of the stable. Elsie recalled, "He was a very lenient father, but that time—Oh, we got an awful scolding for doing that—taking Helen up a ladder onto the roof ... but Helen certainly had a good time!"[523] Helen Keller and Alexander Graham Bell remained close for the remainder of his life. Hellen Keller grew up to be a college graduate, a prolific writer, and a fierce advocate for disabled rights, women's rights, labor rights, and civil rights (including being a cofounder of the American Civil Liberties Union).[524] She was one of the most famous women in her time, and her fame only increased after a movie version of her life was produced in 1962, titled *The Miracle Worker*, after Mark Twain's term for Keller's teacher. However, many biographies of Keller end in childhood, especially blurbs in school textbooks, as few people want to acknowledge her controversial fierce political opinions as an adult (especially her socialist beliefs and her civil rights work).[525]

There's also an interesting connection between Alexander Graham Bell, his father-in-law, Gardiner Hubbard, and the magazine *National Geographic*. In 1888 Gardiner Hubbard formed a group of amateur geologists called the National Geographic Society, and he was their president until he died in 1897, whereupon Bell became the new president. However, Bell quickly became frustrated that the group was small and that their pamphlet of members' ideas was not very interesting. In 1899 Bell heard from his oldest daughter, Elsie, that a young man she fancied named Edwin Grosvenor might be a good editor. Grosvenor ended up being a great son-in-law (he married Elsie in 1900) as well as a fantastic editor. Specifically, Grosvenor's interest in photography led to him revamping the *National Geographic* magazine to be the picture-based magazine it is today. He took the membership from 1,000 members under Bell in 1899 to over two million when Grosvenor retired in 1954.[526] In addition, Grosvenor's push for a National Park Service is considered a major reason for the creation of the National Parks in the United States.[527] By 1904 Bell realized that the society and its magazine were in good hands and left it to Grosvenor so that Bell could, as he put it, "devote all my time to my other interests: the deaf, eugenics, sheep-breeding and aviation."[528]

Alec and Mabel were happily married until his death from diabetes in 1922. At his deathbed, she whispered, "Don't leave me," to which he signed "no" but fell into unconsciousness and died soon after.[529] Mabel tried to hold the family together after his death, but her daughter said, "You never forget for a moment that the heart of everything had gone out of life for her forever."[530] Mabel died a year later.

During his life, Alexander Graham Bell was honored and respected as America's second most famous inventor, behind longtime rival Thomas Edison. However, Edison would have an even bigger rival, a shy man named George Westinghouse Jr. And it was *this* rivalry that started the path to the electrical world of today.

Chapter Summary

- ✧ **1831:** Joseph Henry reports on how parallel coils and series batteries make super strong electromagnets and parallel batteries to make long-distance electric communication possible, and he creates the first electric doorbell.
- ✧ **1832:** Painter Samuel Morse goes to England to recover from his wife's death, hears about electromagnets on the boat back, and becomes obsessed with creating a telegraph system with a series of dots and dashes.
- ✧ **1835:** Henry invents a telegraph with an electric relay so that parallel batteries can be used to pull a switch and series batteries can create a super strong electromagnet.
- ✧ **1836:** Morse meets Dr. Leonard Gale, who uses Henry's theories to improve Morse's telegraph.
- ✧ **May 24, 1844**: Morse sends the signal from Washington, DC, saying, "What hath God wrought?" to Vail in Baltimore.
- ✧ **1867:** Mabel Hubbard's abilities to communicate are used to convince

the Boston school board to create a new school system for deaf students without sign language, including the Clarke School.

✧ **1869:** Alexander Graham Bell and his father try his father's visual system to teach deaf children to speak.

✧ **1871:** Alexander Graham Bell is given a job at the Clarke School.

✧ **1874:** Gardiner Hubbard (Mabel's father) funds Alexander Graham Bell in his search for a "musical telegraph."

✧ **June 2, 1875**: Bell and Watson get reeds to vibrate at a distance.

✧ **March 10, 1876**: Bell transmits understandable speech.

✧ **July 1877**: Gardiner Hubbard creates Bell Telephone Company.

Chapter 6

Edison and Westinghouse
(1862–1886)

George Westinghouse is in character and achievements one of the great men of our time.

– William Thomson (Lord Kelvin) (1914)[531]

It is with the greatest pleasure that I greet in our midst ... the greatest of the giants, who have made the modern world, the genius Edison.

– Charles Steinmetz (1917)[532]

I found it very difficult to write about Thomas Edison and George Westinghouse, but for vastly different reasons. Edison was a total pack rat, keeping every letter, telegraph, laboratory notebook, lawsuit transcript, newspaper clipping, and even a short personal diary. There are literally tens of thousands of pages of original material to sift through. In addition, Edison constantly announced everything that he was thinking to the press with an exaggerated style that made it all seem much further along than it was. As a person who delights in finding one or two personal stories, it's almost oppressive how much I had to choose from, all the while being careful about whether what Edison said about himself could be cited as fact or hyperbole.

I had the exact opposite problem with George Westinghouse. Westinghouse kept nothing, hated to talk to the press, and liked to understate and overperform. Luckily, by using biographies and personal reflections of people around him, I was able to piece together his story, which turns out to be strikingly similar to Edison's despite their opposing styles. Both Westinghouse and Edison were men born at around the same time, in similar areas of the same country, with little interest in classroom learning, and who created an empire through the strengths of their own inventiveness and endless personal drive to discover. Oh, and they both changed the world.

6.1 Thomas Alva Edison

Thomas Alva Edison (Al to his friends and family) was born in 1847, the same year as Alexander Graham Bell, to a lower income family in Ohio, although he grew up in Port Huron, Michigan. Edison's formal education was limited to a total of three months, and like Faraday before him, Edison learned from reading. (He was a voracious reader.) Like Faraday, Edison also never got the hang of math.[533] The word "relentless" comes to mind when describing Edison, as he had relentless energy, curiosity, and of course, ambition.

When Edison was just 12 years old, he sold food and newspapers for 14 hours a day on a train from Detroit to Port Huron and back. Edison soon established a side hustle of purchasing fresh fruit, vegetables, pastries, and newspapers in Detroit and reselling them at a mark-up in Port Huron. Soon, he had two stands run by his young friends, making him a steady profit.[534] By the time Edison was 15 years old, he realized that the real money was in publishing the paper—not selling it. He eventually collected enough castoff items to create his own paper, the *Grand Trunk Herald*, which he made at the back of the train and sold with the other publications as if it wasn't made by an uneducated teen. Supposedly, at the newspaper's pinnacle, he sold around 200 papers a day and he had four assistants.[535]

By 1862 the telegraph arrived in Michigan, and Edison was entranced. He sold his paper to some friends and then spent all his time loitering around the telegraph office in a small town called Mount Clemens where the telegraph owner, named James MacKenzie, was friendly to him. According to Edison, one time he saved MacKenzie's three-year-old son from being hit by a train. After that, MacKenzie trained Edison to work as a telegraph operator and got him a job. For several years, young Edison was hired and fired from a litany of jobs throughout the country, mostly as a night telegraph operator. Meanwhile, he read everything he could find (including Faraday's electricity books) and experimented as much as he could in his rented room above a saloon.

By the time Edison was 22 years of age, he filed for his first patent for an electronic vote counter—the first of an astonishing 1,093 patents he would hold in the US alone. Unfortunately for Edison, this was not a success. It worked well, but no one wanted it as legislators needed time to filibuster. After this, Edison said, "Anything that won't sell, I don't want to invent."[536] Despite this setback, Edison quit his job at Western Union in Boston to "bring out his inventions."[537] He had a series of businesses, which he ran with maniacal energy, and frankly, drove everyone crazy, including himself. He said that the stress had turned his hair "damned near white. Man told me yesterday I was a walking churchyard."[538] By 1870 Edison had backing to create his own company in Newark, New Jersey, with over 50 workers. This mainly involved contract work in setting up and improving telegraph equipment for financial companies.

In the beginning of 1871, Edison created an "automated printer" that would send Morse code at 200 to 300 words a minute and, as an extra benefit, removed almost all skill required in sending Morse code. A backer of Edison's happily told him, "You captivate my whole heart when you speak of working machines which require 'No intelligence.' That's the thing for telegraphers."[539] Edison's idea was that you typed a message into a modified typewriter that converted the letters into imprinted Morse code on a chemically treated sheet. This strip could be slid across a drum sending a signal to a receiving station, where another chemical sheet would record the telegraph. In truth, it didn't shorten the time to send quick telegraphs, as the paper needed to be chemically treated. But for long news reports (especially ones that were sent to various places), it was a revelation, and a real moneymaker.

In late fall of 1871, 24-year-old Edison hired a girl named Mary Stilwell, who was just 16 years old, to work at one of his shops typing on his new automated printer. One day when she was flustered about his presence, he declared that "it doesn't matter much, unless you would like to marry me." When she laughed in response, he decided that they should definitely get married: "Tuesday, say. How will Tuesday suit you, next week Tuesday, I mean?"[540] She didn't agree on that Tuesday, or the Tuesday after, but by December of 1871, they were wed. At first, he invited her into the lab but realized that she was a terrible laboratory assistant, writing in his notebook in January that "Mrs. Mary Edison My wife Dearly Beloved Cannot invent worth a Damn!!"[541] and on Valentine's Day: "My Wife Popsy Wopsy Can't Invent."[542] After that, Mary tended to stay away. Edison often worked a minimum of 18-hour days, but despite this, they had three children in the next six years (the oldest two he nicknamed "dot" and "dash" in a bit of telegraph humor).[543]

In 1874 Edison introduced his version of an induction coil (or a coil that used induction between coils to create a shock) that was likely born of Edison's love of practical jokes. Edison's "inductorium" cost six dollars and was touted "as a specific cure for rheumatism, and as an inexhaustible fount of amusement."[544] This shocking device sold so well and so easily that, as one biographer put it, Edison felt that "marketing to the masses was not particularly difficult. Invent it, and they will come."[545]

Meanwhile, Edison's research offices in New Jersey were growing dramatically. In March of 1876, Edison had moved his company from Newark to Menlo Park, New Jersey. It was not an ordinary building but an "invention factory" churning out a promised, "minor invention every 10 days and a big thing every six months or so."[546]

Then, as described in the last chapter, in 1876, Alexander Graham Bell patented his telephone. The heads of the telegraph companies were justifiably nervous. Who would want to use a telegraph when you could use a telephone instead? After several failed attempts to steal Bell's research, the head of Western Union, William Orton, came to Edison with an earlier version of the telephone devised by a man named Philip Reis in 1861. According to Edison's sworn testimony, Orton "begged him to construct a telephone on the basis of Reis's telephone, so as to out-rival Graham Bell."[547]

Edison studied Reis's system and decided that Reis's speaker was useless, but that his microphone had the germ of a good idea. See, Bell's microphone used induction involving a moving coil near a magnet to create (or induce) current. However, induction is a very subtle effect, especially as they didn't have lightweight, powerful neodymium magnets at the time. Reis's idea, on

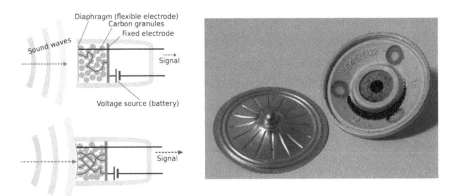

Figure 1: Diagram of how microphone works (left); photograph of microphone with visible granules (right)

the other hand, used a voltage source from a battery so that the sound caused more or less pressure on mercury contacts, which therefore changed the current in the wire. In Reis's microphone, if you wanted to increase the amplitude, you just needed to use a bigger battery. However, Edison knew that mercury contacts were not stable over long use nor were they easily portable. So, he and his team worked night and day on different systems that used this method to transform sound into varying electrical signals.

By November 11, 1877, Edison came up with a simple but powerful solution. He placed a loose amount of carbon granules between two metal plates where one side was a little flexible (see figure 1) and placed current across it.[548] When a person talked into the microphone, the pressure compressed and extended the carbon. If the speaker was connected to a battery, then when the carbon flakes were compressed, the resistance of the microphone went down and the current increased. This allowed for variable current with speech and was arguably the first practical commercial speaker and it was used commonly up until the 1980s.[549]

The president of Western Union was at first delighted and paid Edison very well for his invention.[550] However, Bell (or, technically, Bell's new father-in-law) fought Western Union and kept them from taking the telephone outright. Bell could do without Edison's microphone, but Edison's microphone could not work without Bell's speaker. After a year of legal battles, in 1879, Western Union's leaders became tired of the lawsuits and sold Edison's patents to Bell Telephone, which vastly improved the quality of the telephone.[551]

Ironically, William Orton's desire to control the telephone and retain the power of the telegraph accelerated the telegraph's demise.

While Edison and the men he called his "muckers" were working day and night on the microphone, he discovered something else. Just after midnight on July 18, 1877, Edison was playing with one of his diaphragms and feeling the vibrations (he had trouble hearing the sound due to being partially deaf) when he casually said to his assistant Charles Batchelor, "Batch, if we had a point on this, we could make a record on some material which we could afterwards pull under the point, and it would give us the speech back."[552]

Despite it being past midnight, the crew immediately jumped up to see if it would work. Within an hour, they had jury-rigged a system where a needle was soldered to a speaking tube and then placed on a wheel used with the automatic telegraph. While Edison screamed his phrase that he used for all sound experiments, "Mary Had a Little Lamb," Batchelor pulled wax paper through the machine. The crew observed with delight as the paper came out with indents on it. When the paper was reinserted in the machine, the cone made a garbled sound that had a faint relationship to the nursery rhyme, but it was close enough. They worked on it until the morning, and according to Batchelor, "before breakfast … we had reproduced almost perfect articulation."[553] Edison wrote in his notebook, "There's no doubt that I shall be able to store up and to reproduce automatically at any future time the human voice perfectly."[554]

Although Edison was immediately convinced it could work "perfectly," he and his team were completely focused on the telephone and shelved this discovery. Then, four months later on November 3, 1877, *Scientific American* published an article about some promising experiments coming out of France that involved reproducing speech with an artificial mouth. Three days later, Edison's vice president, Edward Johnson, published a letter to the editor about the "still more marvelous results achieved by Mr. Thomas A. Edison."[555] Suddenly, Edison needed to actually perfect his machine, which he hadn't touched in months. Luckily, for once it was not challenging to get a device worthy of display. In fact, it only took a few days for Edison and his crew to demonstrate what they labeled a "phonograph" with a tinfoil-covered cylinder. The world was entranced, and Edison was a superstar. Joseph Henry, the American scientist who created the first electric doorbell and inspired Samuel

Figure 2: Edison showing off his phonograph (April 1878)

Morse and Alexander Graham Bell, said that Edison was "the greatest genius not only of this age, but of any age."[556] By April of 1878, Edison was traveling to Washington, DC, to display his inventions to the president and to near-endless newspaper acclaim.

However, Edison didn't find this newfound fame to be as delightful as expected. He was getting around 75 letters a day, all demanding *something*, and he was struggling with too many ideas and too many distractions.[557] In addition, the public started to be frustrated with Edison's tinfoil pho-nograph, as it worked for a short demonstration but fell apart on repeat-ed playback and could not be removed and reinstalled. (A few years later, Alexander Graham Bell and his assistant Charles Tainer discovered that wax records were far more robust, and the record industry grew in fits and spurts from that point.)[558] To escape these pressures, in July of 1878, 31-year-old Edison agreed to go with a friend named Professor George "Barky" Barker (Edison had a nickname for absolutely everyone) from the University of Pennsylvania on a two-month tour to Wyoming and all points west to watch a solar eclipse.[559] During their "western adventures," Barky told Edison about an inventor named William Wallace who had spent nearly $1,000 dollars working on a crude electric generator.[560] Edison became so excited about this description that the whole party rerouted their trip home to include a visit to Wallace's factory in Ansonia, Connecticut, on September 8, 1878.[561]

At Wallace's laboratory, Edison and his friends were amazed to find a generator lighting eight very bright lights called arc lamps *at the same time*, which was the equivalent of 8,000 candles. According to a reporter who was on the trip with them

Edison was enraptured … He ran from the instrument to the lights, and from the lights back to the instrument. He sprawled over a table with the simplicity of a child, and made all kind of calculations. He calculated the power of the instrument and of the lights, the probable loss of power in transmission, the amount of coal the instrument would save in a day, a week, a month, a year, and the result of such saving on manufacturing.[562]

Edison immediately realized that "what had been done had never been made practically useful [because] the intense light had not been subdivided so that it could be brought into private homes."[563] Edison rushed back to Menlo Park with a germ of an idea. Instead of a few very powerful lights, he would generate electricity to power thousands of weaker lights that would light up all the houses in New York. Over two nights, Edison managed to get a thin cotton filament to glow brightly with an induction coil and a thermal regulator to keep it from lighting on fire. He declared, "I have it now!"[564] Edison immediately called his friend at *The New York Sun* to tell them of his triumph. "When 10 lights have been produced by a single electric machine, it has been thought to be a great triumph of scientific skill. With the process I have just discovered, I can produce a thousand—aye, 10,000—from one machine." Edison promised that he would display this new system "in a few weeks."[565] Instead, it would take years, consume his life, and destroy his reputation.

6.2 The Generator and Arc Lamp Grow Up

When Edison was inspired by William Wallace's arc lamp demonstration in 1878, the electric generator was 47 years old but was only just reaching the point that it was useful for large-scale industrial systems. Recall that Michael Faraday discovered that moving a magnet near a coil of wire would induce current in that wire in 1831. Mere weeks after Faraday's publication, a French instrument maker named Hippolyte Pixii (who was André-Marie Ampère's technician) tweaked Faraday's design to make his own hand-cranked generator, which was significantly more powerful, by spinning a U-shaped magnet near coils of wire with iron inside them (see figure 3).

When Pixii did this, an interesting thing occurred. As the magnet was moved toward a coil, the current would go one way and then, a half a turn later, the current would swing back the other way. By spinning the magnet faster, he could get more current, but it would also make the current swing back and forth faster. We would now call this alternating current, or AC. At the time, however, the

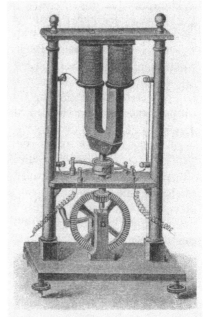

Figure 3: Pixii's Generator

sinusoidal current seemed like a negative result. Pixii went to Ampère, who suggested he could fix this problem with a device we call a "commutator."

Basically, the current went in wires through curved metal leaves called "brushes" to a disk. Another two pairs of brushes then picked up the current from the disk. The disk was composed of two pieces of metal with an insulating piece between them. It connected to the crank that rotated the magnet so that half the time the current was received from one brush and the other half from the other brush. The result of all of this is that the alternating current changed to a current that pulsed but only went in one direction, or direct current (DC). Even with the commutator, this machine was not useful for telegraphs (as they needed a constant current—and Pixii's was too uneven or bouncy) and was basically only useful for classroom demonstrations. Poor Pixii died in an accident at age 26, two years after his invention, and "there is no evidence that he ever made a dime off of his generator."[566] Although it took many years, all future electric generators originated from this device.

Over the years, more complicated generators with more and more magnets were used with the hope to power machines, conduct electro-chemical processes, and to light electric arc lamps. (The discovery of the arc lamp by Humphry Davy is discussed in chapter 2.) In Brussels, around 1850, a physics professor named Floris Nollet (who claimed to be the great-nephew of Abbé Nollet, the rival of Benjamin Franklin discussed in chapter 2) patented a behemoth machine with 40 magnets and 16 coils that he called "the Alliance."[567] Tragically, Nollet died before he could put it into fruition, and a company called the Société de l'Alliance was formed to try to profit from his ideas. However, this device was glitchy (and the company had a bit of a fraud problem).[568] Nothing much happened of any consequence until 1856, when a French professor of physics named Victor Masson became frustrated with the commutator breaking and just threw it away. To his surprise he found that the alternating current would light an arc lamp just as well without a commutator.[569]

This was the first instance of *using* the current that went back and forth (alternating, or AC) instead of forcing current to be in one direction (direct current, or DC).[570] It turns out that arc lamps work because the high voltage melts the metal rods and then makes the conductive gas between the rods glow. With alternating current, the light could flicker, but the rods would burn evenly. In 1863 this generator was used to light arc lamps in lighthouses along the French coast, and in 1906 it was called "probably the first

Figure 4: The Alliance Generator electrifying an arc lamp

important *practical* use of the electric light."[571] Despite the success of the Alliance with the arc lamp using AC, most scientists were not willing to give up on commutators and DC generators, even though commutators often sparked. There was still hope that they could be used for electroplating and telegraphs, as well as a general feeling that current should go in one direction.

Generators became far more powerful in the 1860s, when several people came up with the idea of using electromagnets instead of permanent magnets in their machines. One popular design was created by an Englishman named Henry Wilde in 1866. It had large electromagnet "legs" that were electrified by a separate magnet-based generator (or magneto) to "excite" the electromagnets (see figure 6).[572] Wilde found his results to be "most splendid" and offered ecstatic descriptions of how his compound generator could produce incredible light or melt metal bars.[573] Note that energy is conserved—you can't get something for nothing. This means that these generators produced more power but were correspondingly harder to rotate. Wilde's design became the basic design of most generators from then on, including Edison's.

Just months after Wilde published (and in one case, months before Wilde), multiple people, like Samuel Varley, Charles Wheatstone, and Werner von Siemens, declared that they not only thought of using electromagnets, they also thought of using the generator to power its own electromagnet.[574] They started by giving the electromagnets a start with electricity from a battery or by rubbing the iron with a magnet, or even using the magnetic field of the earth to make them weakly magnetic. The coils were then spun near these

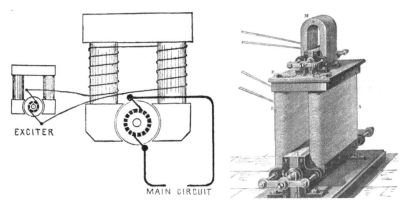

Figure 5: Drawing of an exciter (with permanent magnets) electrifying the coils of an electromagnet for a generator (left); Wilde's machine, where the exciter is on the top (right).

weak magnets, which caused current to be induced in the coil. Some of that current was then siphoned off to the electromagnet, increasing its magnetism in a process called "self-excitation." This "feedback loop" is what makes electric generators so very powerful. Currently, we use semiconductor diodes to make the current one way before feeding it back to the generator. But at the time, they could only use self-excitation with DC generators, which convinced many people that DC was the wave of the future.

The most popular DC generator in the 1870s and 1880s was called a Gramme machine, invented in 1871 by a Belgian electrical engineer living in Paris named Zénobe Gramme. Gramme was inspired by a DC generator invented by an Italian professor named Antonio Pacinotti in 1865 that was designed to "give greater regularity and consistency of action."[575] Gramme's DC generator (or dynamo, a name created by our friend Michael Faraday in 1831) was the first generator that was "on a scale large enough for industrial and commercial application."[576] By 1881 it was written that "of dynamo-electric generators none are better known, or more extensively employed, than those of M. Gramme, whose invention has excited the interest of the scientific world since its first presentation."[577]

Gramme's machine made many people aware that generators could be practical and therefore profitable. In addition, in 1873 while demonstrating his device, Gramme's assistant accidentally connected the wires of a battery and found that his system was reversible—meaning that it was also a good electric motor.[578] In other words, if you spin the wires near magnets or electromagnets, it can create DC electricity. If you add DC electricity to wires near magnets or electromagnets, the magnets (or the wires) can spin.

Soon after Gramme demonstrated his device, a 25-year-old Russian officer named Pavel Yablochkov (also written as Jablochkoff) received a medical release from being a military officer and got a job as a telegraph specialist for the Moscow–Kursk railroad. Free to experiment with electricity, Yablochkov and his friends built their own Gramme machine and used it to power an arc lamp that they demonstrated to the czar in 1874. This would mark the first time a train made use of an electric light. Flushed with success, Yablochkov and his friends started an electric workshop that failed miserably, and in 1875 Yablochkov left his wife, child, and a bunch of irritated debt collectors to escape to Paris.[579]

In 1876 Yablochkov got a French patent for his version of the arc lamp called the Jablochkoff candle, which worked better than any previous version. His first public demonstration was in London on April 15, 1876, and it took the world by storm. George Westinghouse said that Yablochkov's candles were the "starting point of the creation of a new branch of industry."[580] Suddenly, everyone was making their own version of generators or arc lamps. However, Yablochkov's candle only worked for AC, so people either reluctantly used AC generators or made special versions of the Jablochkoff candle that would work for DC current. Meanwhile, with the success of his lamp, Yablochkov could pay off his debts and return to Russia, where he found the towns and industrialists resistant to his technology. He died broke in 1894 at the age of 47.[581]

In 1876 Edison's friend Professor George "Barky" Barker was in Paris and learned about Yablochkov's new arc lamps. He told his friend William Wallace about it (the same William Wallace that Edison visited in 1878), and Wallace became one of the first to develop and display an arc lamp in the United States.[582] Wallace then gained the attention of an American inventor of a self-exciting dynamo machine named Moses Farmer. Wallace then collaborated with Farmer on a dynamo to display at the Philadelphia Centennial Exhibition of November 1876 with a corresponding DC arc

Figure 6: Yablochkov (left); Demonstration of the power of Yablochkov lamps as compared to the weaker gas lamps in London, 1878 (right)

lamp of his own device.

The Wallace-Farmer system gained quite a bit of attention and praise. Unfortunately, they lost a competition to Brush's superior generator and lamp in May of 1878 to "examine into the merits of, and to test, the various machines offered for sale … regarding the adaptability of such machines to the production of Light."[583] Brush went on to form a very successful arc lamp company, and Farmer switched to focusing on making better lights (patenting a version in 1879, which was later bought by Edison) while Wallace worked more on the dynamo. It was only four months later that Edison visited Wallace's lab and was inspired but also fully convinced that arc lamps were not the way to go. In fact, before leaving Wallace's lab, Edison supposedly turned to Wallace and thanked him for the demonstration and added cheekily, "Wallace, I believe I can beat you making electric lights. I don't think you are working in the right direction."[584]

6.3 Edison's Electric Light

In September of 1878, Edison felt good about his immediate progress with the glowing filament, but despite his happy talk to the newspapers, Edison knew that this was a major project that needed significant capital. By October 3, Edison wrote his lawyer to say, "All I want at present is to be provided with funds to push the light rapidly."[585] Edison's reputation was so impressive that America's wealthiest investors hurried to get a piece of the pie. A month later, the newly formed *Edison Electric Light Company* had collected $300,000 in investments with $50,000 earmarked for Edison to develop his lighting system.[586]

At first Edison was convinced that he could light up lower Manhattan with just 15 to 20 Wallace-Farmer dynamos. However, within months he came to believe that they were unsuitable for his grand system. In December of 1878, Edison purchased the five best generators available at the time and assigned a team led by Charles "Batch" Batchelor to take them apart and cobble together a version that was powerful enough to light thousands of lights at a time. By January 2, 1879, Batch wrote in his notebook that he had "begun to make a practical working machine after a few weeks hard study on magneto electric principles."[587]

By March, Edison's team had devised a generator that would produce strong and relatively constant DC power. It had very large electromagnets to create a large magnetic field and a small rotating coil in the center that was spun with a steam engine (see figure 7). They called their machine "Long-Legged Mary-Ann," as the two electromagnets looked like legs to the overworked male engineers. One of the biggest changes from other generators was that the coils of wires that were rotated in "Mary-Ann" were made with very low resistance, which caused the system to generate more current than the others that were previously used. By July, a member of the team wrote to his father that "we have now the best generator of electricity ever made."[588]

The generator was working well, but the light bulb was not. Edison was convinced that the arc lamp was not the way to go, as it was just too bright, and instead focused on incandescence. Incandescence is the effect where thin materials will glow when a current goes through them. This was actually discovered back in the 1740s when Benjamin Franklin described how thin pieces of gold would glow when a Leyden jar was discharged through them. However, gold is expensive and melts easily, so most people attribute the discovery of incandescence to Humphry Davy. This is because Davy wrote in 1801 how electricity would make "a thin slip of platina" (a platinum alloy) glow with "a vivid light."[589]

Despite the early start, the incandescent light bulb was slow to develop. It took until 1841, when an Irish inventor named Frederick de Moleyns patented an incandescent light with a platinum filament in a vacuum tube, although it wasn't recorded

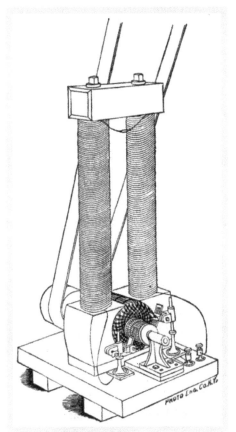

Figure 7: Edison's 5 kW DC generator "Long-Legged Mary-Ann" (which was only around five feet or 1.5 meters tall)

how long the bulb lasted. In 1845, an American named John Starr developed a "burner" that used carbonized carbon. By the time that Edison turned to it, there were at least a dozen different incandescent light bulb patents, usually made with either a carbon or a platinum filament, not to mention all of the arc lamps and early neon and fluorescent lamps.[590]

As soon as Edison left William Wallace's laboratory on September 8, 1878, he decided that the problem with incandescence was that the current must have "careful regulation" or the filament would heat up too much, causing it to either burn out or be too dim to glow. His initial solution was to create a thermal regulator, which was usually a wire wrapped around a metal with a spring that would break the circuit when too hot, and then when cooled reengage the circuit again. By September 12, Edison had devised 45 different regulators.[591]

However, Edison found that a piece of carbonized carbon would quickly reach burning temperature but took a significant time to cool down or burn out before the thermal regulator could stop the current. Therefore, Edison quickly gave up on that idea and went in search of a filament that could glow for long times without burning out.

As Edison was determined to light thousands of light bulbs with one generator, the bulbs had to be parallel instead of in a series. This would ensure that if one light was turned on, the whole system wouldn't turn off. (If you remember old Christmas lights—if one went out, the circuit would be broken, and the whole string would go out.) By November 1878, unlike most of his competitors, Edison realized that he needed a long-lasting light bulb with a high resistance—not a low-resistance filament as was needed for bulbs in series. By December of 1878, Edison and his team gave up on carbon and began to focus on very thin pieces of platinum, which would only have high resistance when they're very thin. However, he found that these thin filaments would melt at disturbingly low temperatures. By January of 1879, Edison's team concluded that the problem was because air was absorbed by the pores of the metal, which lowered the melting temperature. They tried to isolate the wire away from air by encasing it in a bowl of glass and then pumped as much air out of the bowl as possible. These bowls of glass were fitted to screw caps from kerosene cans that looked a little bit like tulip bulbs and were thus called "light bulbs."[592]

That helped a bit, but they found their vacuum pump was not efficient enough and had to develop their own. They quickly developed a vacuum that would create about one-hundred-thousandth of an atmosphere in August of 1879 and improved it to a vacuum that would produce one millionth of an atmosphere two months later in October.[593] With the improved vacuum, the platinum filament worked well, but then Edison realized that platinum was too expensive to be commercially viable. Desperate to remedy the issue, Edison sent out over 2,000 letters in May to "public men in mining regions" looking for new sources of platinum, to no avail.[594] Edison then realized that with a superior vacuum he could possibly go back to using cheap carbon. On the morning of October 22, 1879, Edison took a piece of burnt cotton sewing thread, put it in a horseshoe form, and found his lamp would last for over 13 hours.[595] Within two weeks, on November 4, 1879, Edison filed for a patent for an electric lamp with a cotton filament.[596]

By the end of December, Edison gave a giant public demonstration of his system—the third in a year and a half—declaring that he'd found the solution. The demonstration was performed for the public with several of Edison's assistants watching out for sabotage. This turned out to be needed, as at least one man (who turned out to be an employee of the Baltimore Gas Company) was caught trying to short circuit the display.[597] Edison's display was popular with visitors, but a few newspapers were getting sick of his grand statements. The *Saturday Review* sarcastically wrote, "What a happy man Mr. Edison must be! Three times within the short space of eighteen months he has had the glory of finally and triumphantly solving a problem of world-wide interest … there is no reason why he should not for the next twenty years completely solve the problem of the electric light twice a year without in any way interfering with its interest of novelty."[598] After that, the price of Edison Light Company's stock plummeted from $4,000 to $500.[599] The *Saturday Review* had a point—Edison had only proven that lights would work on a small scale and for a few hours, or at best for a few days.

Edison needed a material that would last hundreds of hours, not 15. He focused on natural materials, saying, "Now I believe that somewhere in God Almighty's workshop, there is a vegetable growth with geometrically parallel fibers suitable to our use. *Look for it*!"[600] Special envoys were sent all over the world. A particularly unfortunate employee named Mr. Ségrador survived mercury poisoning in Menlo Park only to succumb to yellow fever in Havana, all in Edison's service.[601] Day after day passed with the "Edison boys" basically trying every object they could find, including a good-natured competition between clippings from his workers' beards (which didn't work very well).[602] Even though Edison did not have a decent working light bulb, he was determined to electrify eight miles of Menlo Park with over 400 light bulbs.[603] He wanted wires placed safely underground, and on April 20, 1880, his men started digging. Luckily, in July an employee found that Mandrake bamboo from Japan made a pleasant glow that lasted for over 1,500 hours.[604] Finally, Edison was producing some results.

By March of 1881, Edison and most of his team moved from Menlo Park to New York City, and Edison transformed from an inventor into a manufacturer. He managed Menlo Park, Edison Machine Works, Edison Tube Company, and Bergman and Company and employed over a thousand workers. Although Edison was inundated with more than 3,000 applications to light individual houses and stores, he refused. Edison didn't want to create an electrical lighting business for individuals, he wanted to make power stations that would electrify whole towns and cities.[605] On September 4, 1882, almost four years to the day of his visit to the Wallace laboratory, Edison started a single generator at a station in New York City on Pearl Street. According to a witness, "It was a terrifying experience ... the engines and dynamos made a horrible racket from loud and deep groans to a hideous shriek, and the place seemed to be filled with sparks and flames of all colors. It was as if the gates of the infernal regions had been suddenly opened."[606]

In truth, Edison didn't invent the light bulb, which had been around for many years before him. Instead, Edison invented the first industrial light bulb distribution system. What's little remembered now is how much Edison had to create for this. In addition to making an affordable, long-lasting light bulb that would be able to be mass-produced easily, he also had to make all the light fixtures, a power source for the electricity, and the lines to get them to the light fixtures. Once everything was set up, he then had to determine how to transfer the electricity long distances without losing power or using too much copper or accidentally electrocuting street workers. Then there was the problem of inventing all the switches and all the safety devices. (And when he forgot about the safety devices, he had to deal with the fires.) "Everything is so new that each step is in the dark. I have to make the dynamos, the lamps, the conductors, and attend to a thousand details the world never hears of."[607] No wonder he was always looking for new wealthy investors, and his factory in Menlo Park took up two whole city blocks.

Meanwhile, everyone who could was suing Edison. This proved to be complicated, for the incandescent bulb was far older than Edison, and everyone including Edison had patented a version of the light bulb before it was commercially ready. In January 1884, Edison won one of his biggest cases against Joseph Swan, an Englishman who had patented a filament light bulb before Edison. Edison quickly sent a telegram to *The Electrical World* stating that as Swan failed to prove that *anyone* had made a commercially viable filament lamp before him, the decision in his favor "practically affirms that every other incandescent lamp is an infringement upon the Edison patent."[608] With this win, Edison's company began to aggressively sue all other electric lighting companies that used incandescent lighting for patent infringement. They hired a Black draftsman and inventor named Lewis Latimer to be an expert on the history of lighting for all of the lawsuits that Edison was embroiled in.[609]

This was an unusual event because although slavery had just ended (Latimer was the son of escaped slaves), racism was rampant in all parts of the US. Latimer was uniquely suited to the job, as he had been working on light bulbs for a rival from the beginning. Latimer's engineering career started when he was released from the Navy as a 16-year-old (he lied about his age to join) when the Civil War ended in 1864 and got a job as an office boy at a patent law firm. He taught himself to make scientific drawings and eventually became that firm's draftsman. Through drafting the patents, Latimer learned about many technological advancements, including when he drew up Alexander Graham Bell's 1876 telephone patent. However, by 1878, Latimer's boss died, and his replacement would not put up with a non-White employee, which is how Latimer ended up working for a rival of Edison's named Hiram Maxim between 1879 and 1881.

Latimer had designed a superior light bulb for Maxim and was put in charge of organizing the international lighting systems for him. In fact, it was in lawsuits *against* Edison that Edison learned that Latimer was knowledgeable of the history of light bulbs and generators and was skilled at explaining it to laymen. Latimer's fortunes changed when Maxim decided to drop electric lights and move to making machine guns, as Maxim's friend told him, "Hang your chemistry and electricity! If you want to make a pile of money, invent something that will enable these Europeans to cut each other's throats with greater facility."[610] Latimer, who had no knowledge (or interest) in guns, found himself out of a job when no one wanted to hire a Black man—even one who was an expert in lighting. As you might imagine, he was delighted to get a job with Edison in 1884. Latimer soon moved up the ladder to be a valued member of the company and wrote an influential book about the history and physics of light and generators in 1890, called *Incandescent Electrical Lighting*. Although Latimer invented a method to make a better filament in 1881, his superior light bulb was not used by Edison until at least 1892 or later, as the patents were held by his rivals.

While Edison and many others were working on the light bulb, Edison's young, neglected wife, Mary, started to complain of anxiety and paranoia. Unfortunately, her pleas for help were completely ignored by her husband. On August 5, 1878, when Edison was on his fateful western tour, Edison's secretary sent him a message that his wife, who was around six months pregnant with their third child, was so worried that their children would be killed by trains that she fainted.[611] When in 11 days Mary was doing no better, the secretary told him, "I advise your coming home at once on account of Mrs. Edison's health."[612] However, when Edison did return, he was more obsessed with developing the electric light and its distribution system than ever before.

Meanwhile, Mary Edison continued to deteriorate, and according to a newspaper account following the birth of her third child in 1878, "Mrs. Edison seldom enjoyed a day free from pain."[613] Mary was treated with morphine, which quickly became an addiction, and some of her friends became concerned as Mrs. Edison "became so accustomed to the morphine that she had to be closely watched lest she should take an overdose."[614] By January of 1882, Mary Edison's doctor wrote to Edison that "something ought to be done."[615] But nothing worked, and by August 9, 1884, Mary Edison died from what her doctor called "congestion of the brain" but what would currently be considered complications from a morphine addiction.[616] She was just 29 years old and left three children: Marion, who was twelve, Thomas Jr., who was nine, and William, who was six.

Edison's oldest child, Marion, was awakened by her father the morning

after her mother's death. "I found him shaking with grief, weeping and sob-
bing so he could hardly tell me that my mother had died in the night."[617]
Meanwhile, Edison's lighting business was considered less appealing in practice rather than in theory, as few wealthy individuals were willing to redo
their homes or offices for electricity when gas lamps seemed to work well.
The combination of Edison's issues with the phonograph and Edison's "subsequent failure to utilize the electric light in private dwellings to take the
place of gas," caused Edison's reputation to freefall. In 1884 a book on no-
table New Yorkers stated, "A year ago [Edison] was regarded as a wonder, a
miracle, a prodigy; now he is generally considered a failure."[618]

Six months after the death of his wife, in February of 1885, Thomas
Edison went to New Orleans for a world's fair. This is when a 28-year-old
Edison met another teenager, 19-year-old Mina Miller, and fell in love.
Edison wrote that he was so distracted with thoughts of Mina that he almost
got hit by a streetcar, adding, "If Mina interferes much more [I] will have
to take out an accident policy."[619] By February 1886, Thomas Edison was
married again and bought his new bride a mansion in West Orange, New
Jersey. He sold much of his stock in Edison Electric to build a state-of-the-
art laboratory there. This allowed him to focus on "making only that class of
inventions which require but small investments ... and of a highly profitable
nature," with "no cumbersome inventions like the Electric Light."[620]

Edison's electric light was cumbersome, at least financially. Back in 1878,
Edison had declared that "when the brilliancy and cheapness of the lights
are made known to be public—which will be in a few weeks ... illumina-
tion by carbureted hydrogen gas will be discarded."[621] By 1886, however,
the public knew about lights, and they were less than enthralled. For example, the Edison Electric Illuminating Company of Jackson, Mississippi,
owned $100,000 in capital stock but only made a total profit of $139 from
the first four months of 1886. Most other Edison companies were similarly
floundering.[622]

In May or June of 1886, the workers at Edison's Machine Works went on
strike for better pay. Edison, who was short on cash and wanted to move to a
different place anyway, used this as an excuse to quit New York City entirely
and start again in upstate Schenectady. He put his former secretary, Samuel
Insull, in charge. Insull had none of Edison's brilliance in discovery but instead

was an excellent sales manager. For example, Insull pushed sales so that, for example, sales of wire installation went from around $850 a month to around $8,500 a month in a single year.[623] Years later, Insull mused, "We never made a dollar until we got the factory 180 miles away from Mr. Edison."[624]

Due to the work of Samuel Insull, Edison's light slowly started to gain popularity and become more profitable. Then, in November of 1886, Edison heard something disturbing. A man named George Westinghouse from Pittsburg, Pennsylvania, had started a new illuminating company and was using alternating current, or AC, to do so. Edison had heard of AC and transformers back in 1885, and his company had actually purchased a patent but then decided that it wasn't interesting enough to retool their entire system. In September of 1886, Edison's vice president asked the advice of a former employee named Frank Sprague about AC. Sprague told Edison that "where long distances are used between the two systems … alternating current distribution unquestionably has the advantage," and that "you cannot too soon take steps to prevent someone getting in the field ahead of you."[625] Edison could have easily taken Sprague's advice and been a leader of AC. But due to a combination of a misunderstanding and stubbornness, he started an outright war against Westinghouse instead.

6.4 Enter George Westinghouse

George Westinghouse Jr. was born in 1846 in a small town in New York to Emeline and George Westinghouse Sr., who were farmers. Westinghouse grew up on the farm and worked at his father's small machine shop fixing farming equipment. Unlike Edison, Westinghouse did have a few years of education. But like Edison, he was completely disinterested in schooling and was described as "a rather inept pupil."[626] The neighbors regarded him "with an air of pity and wondered what was to become of so ill-promising a boy when he grew up."[627]

Westinghouse only went to school until he was 15, and then he ran off to join the Union army in the Civil War. After the war in 1864, Westinghouse finally went to college but quickly became bored and disenchanted. His former teacher recalled, "While the other boys were struggling with German syntax or French pronunciation, he would amuse himself making pencil drawings on his wristband. His sketches were always of locomotives, stationary engines, or something of that sort."[628] Despite his teacher's efforts, Westinghouse remained stubbornly uninterested, and the teacher flatly described Westinghouse by saying, "He was my despair."[629] Obviously, college didn't last long, and Westinghouse quit after one semester. Since he had no prospects, Westinghouse went back to working for his father.

His father was pleased when the following year George Westinghouse invented and patented a steam engine and an early steam-powered car to use on farms. He called it a Westinghouse farm engine. However, when Westinghouse had an idea for a new way for derailed trains to get back on the track (called a "frog," as it helped the train jump from track to track), his father refused to give him the money to patent it because neither of them knew anything about railroads. Undeterred, the 20-year-old Westinghouse convinced two local businessmen to give him $5,000 for part ownership of this invention.[630]

While traveling to demonstrate this device to investors, he sat next to a young woman named Marguerite Walker and immediately fell head over heels in love. That evening, after his sister teased him that he looked like he'd won the lottery, he merrily agreed that he could win the lottery if it all worked out. With the family trying to figure out what had made George Westinghouse so gleeful, he announced to his entire family that he'd met the woman he was going to marry.[631]

Westinghouse's parents were shocked, especially as he was still living at home. But George was undeterred, and Marguerite was quickly as smitten as him. By the following year on August 8, 1867, they were married. Meanwhile, Westinghouse's relationship with his business partners started to deteriorate when they tried to convince him to sell his frog patent, and he had no money of his own to leverage. Desperate, he found another steel company called Cook and Anderson that was willing to buy his old partners out and let him have a say in the company.[632] The only problem was that this new company was not in New York state, but over 450 miles away in the horrifically polluted town of Pittsburgh, Pennsylvania. Pittsburgh of the mid- and late-1800s was a successful center of unregulated steelworks, ironworks, trains, and coal—lots and lots of coal. In 1868, at around the time that Westinghouse went there, a traveling author noted that "every street appears to end in a huge black cloud," describing the town as "Hell with the lid taken off."[633] Despite this, Westinghouse left his new bride with his parents, and formed a new company in Pittsburgh. He turned into a traveling Westinghouse frog salesman.[634]

Meanwhile, Westinghouse ruminated on another train invention. Back in 1866, a train he was on was delayed due to two freight trains colliding on the track ahead of him. As the tracks were straight, it seemed inconceivable to Westinghouse that the accident couldn't have been prevented. However, when he discussed it with a brakeman, he was informed that train brakes couldn't make unexpected stops.[635] Train brakes had to be manually pulled for each car separately, and the brakemen needed to run from car to car on the roofs. This took a ridiculously long time to do and made train travel (not to mention the brakeman's job) extremely dangerous.

At first, Westinghouse thought of linking friction brakes to the engine, an idea that he modeled in his father's shop and soon found to be impractical. He then turned to the idea of brakes that used steam, but he found that the steam would condense over a long pipe. A few months later, while he was reading a report on a new method for drilling in coal mines, Westinghouse found the solution—compressed air.[636] The first system worked with the conductor adding pressurized air to compress the brakes. But after a few years, it was switched so that the air pressure was needed to keep the brakes from stopping the train. If a conductor removed the air (or if an accident happened with the air tube), the pressure would be removed, and the brakes would be applied. Westinghouse wasn't the first to think of using air brakes, but he was the first to make a practical system. This was a major safety advance in a world where train travel was so prevalent.

In the early summer of 1868, Westinghouse went to New York City to sell his frogs (the device to help trains jump back on the track). Famously, he met a man named Commodore Vanderbilt, the president of the New York Central Railroad and the patriarch of the wealthy and influential Vanderbilt family. Westinghouse was made to wait two days for an audience, but his patience was rewarded when Vanderbilt agreed to a large order of the frogs. However, when Westinghouse pushed his luck by pitching his brake system, Vanderbilt was decidedly uninterested, saying, "If I understand you, young fellow, you propose to stop a railroad train with wind. I'm too busy to listen to such nonsense."[637]

Despite that setback, the money from Vanderbilt was enough to stop

Westinghouse's wandering and bring Marguerite to Pittsburgh, where they rented a flat in a cheap part of town. Despite the gloom of the city, the young couple were delighted to be reunited and vowed to never be separated for long again. It was a vow that they kept for the rest of their lives (when George was forced to travel without her, he called or telegraphed her every day, even setting up a private phone while in England).

Soon after settling in Pittsburgh, the couple met and became close to a man named Ralph Baggaley, who ran a foundry. He offered them a few thousand dollars for the air brake investment, even though a consultant told him it was impractical. (Baggaley supposedly dramatically tore up the consultant's report.)[638] By April 1869, Baggaley and Westinghouse convinced a reluctant railroad executive to let them test a prototype if they paid for everything, including any possible damage. The demonstration turned out to be more dramatic than expected when a man was thrown onto the tracks by a spooked horse and the Westinghouse brakes managed to come to a quick stop, saving his life!

Westinghouse again turned to his father for financial support. After all, this was revolutionary, but George Westinghouse Sr. remained unimpressed, writing, "As I have repeatedly told you, one lesson in life that I have learned is to stick to things I know something about, and to leave the rest to others. I know nothing about railroads. Neither do you. I think you would be wise to avoid speculating with your future, especially as now you have a wife to support."[639] Luckily, railroad executives were more easily impressed, and by September 1869, 22-year-old Westinghouse and Baggaley and a half a dozen railroad executives formed the Westinghouse Air Brake Company with a market value of a cool half-million dollars.[640]

Despite these successes, Westinghouse insisted on fair pay for his employees. In 1877 the rail workers averaged between five and six dollars a week, while Westinghouse Air Brake employees averaged four dollars a day.[641] Considering that Westinghouse insisted on a nine-hour workday with half days on Saturdays, instead of the typical 10 to 12 hours a day, seven days a week, Westinghouse's employees made more than five times the pay per hour than the abused rail workers.* This made jobs with Westinghouse highly prized. Years later, the labor leader Samuel Gompers said, "I will say this for

---

* If a rail worker worked 72 hours a week for $5–$6, they averaged around 7.6 cents per hour, whereas Westinghouse's employee got $4 a day for a 9-hour day and therefore earned around 44 cents per hour.

George Westinghouse. If all employers of men treated their employees with the same consideration he does, the American Federation of Labor would have to go out of existence."[642]

On May 10, 1876, Westinghouse went to the Centennial Exhibition in Philadelphia to demonstrate Westinghouse air brakes. (He actually rented a few trains so that all of his employees and their families could go too.) It's unclear if he observed Alexander Graham Bell demonstrating his telephone for the first time, but he definitely saw some electricity demonstrations, because he left the exhibition with a desire to electrify train signals in his never-ending quest for improved train safety. One of the big advantages of electric train signals was that the tracks worked as large conductors, which reduced the cost of wire significantly. One of the big disadvantages of electric train signals, however, was that they didn't make much money, and the stakeholders in Westinghouse Air Brakes had absolutely no interest in such distractions. Undeterred, in 1881 Westinghouse put up his own money along with his new house as collateral to start a new company called the Union Switch and Signal Company. Years later a railroad operator said that "if the men who work the railroads ever choose a patron saint it will be St. George—in honor of George Westinghouse."[643]

George and Marguerite Westinghouse spent the winter of 1883–84 in New York watching as Edison electrified the city, which they followed with great interest both as consumers and for Westinghouse's signal company. Meanwhile, they learned that natural gas was found in Murrysville, a Pittsburgh suburb, and George Westinghouse was eager to return home to Pennsylvania and investigate. They waited a few months, however, as Marguerite gave birth to their first and only child, George Westinghouse III. As soon as mother and child were fit to travel, they hurried back home. On the way, Marguerite teased her husband that he would soon get caught up in natural gas as he did with brakes, stating that "the brakes had one advantage over gas—you could always work out your problems at home, instead of running off to Murrysville every day."[644]

George told her not to worry, saying "I can work out my problems at home just the same, that is, if you don't mind me boring a well through your flower beds."[645] And, as soon as they returned home, that is almost exactly what George Westinghouse did, except that he drilled behind the stable. Back

Figure 8: George and Marguerite Westinghouse (around 1884)

in 1871, George surprised Marguerite with a mansion, which Marguerite Westinghouse called Solitude, in the fancy suburb of Homewood for her birthday. This name became ironic when after three weeks of drilling, on May 29, 1884, Westinghouse's team found a natural gas well that blew the top off the drilling machine "with the infernal violence of a volcano."[646]

A visitor recalled that "for days you could not hear your own voice in the Homewood residence."[647] Everyone in the town was naturally up in arms about it—everyone, of course, but George and Marguerite Westinghouse. George, according to that same visitor, "had a never disappearing smile on his beaming face, [even] while the Fire Department was pumping water over the house to prevent it from catching fire from the burning gas."[648] When Marguerite came to investigate with their newborn on her hip, George asked her if she was satisfied with the experiment. She replied that she was quite happy, especially as "the house still has a roof on it and the kitchen isn't wrecked."[649]

George Westinghouse was delighted with this new way to provide heat and light to Pittsburgh, as it was also so much cleaner than coal. However, there was one major drawback—it was terribly flammable. Westinghouse turned his interest, once again, to safety. Within a few years, he filed 38 patents on natural gas safety and transfer, which were helped with his background in air pressure valves for his brake systems. The other problem was that the best way transport gas long distances is with high-pressure gas, but high-pressure pipes tended to leak. His ingenious solution was to place a high-pressure pipe *inside* another pipe with low-pressure gas. That way any leakage in the high-pressure pipe would just seep into the low-pressure area and not into the ground or worse, into the air. Luckily, the consumer needed low-pressure gas, so none of the gas was wasted, as the customers received the gas from the low-pressure area.

Meanwhile, the ever-busy Westinghouse was still interested in electric lighting for his train signal corporations. A few years earlier, George's younger brother Herman met a promising young engineer named William Stanley on a train, naturally. In the summer of 1884, the Westinghouse brothers convinced Stanley to move to Pittsburgh to advise both Herman's company, Westinghouse Machine, and George Westinghouse's company, Union Switch and Signal.[650]

Part of the reason that the Westinghouse brothers were so invested in Stanley was that Stanley had just invented and patented his own DC generator and light bulb. Amusingly, Stanley's first light bulb had carbonized human hair for the filament, although by the time he worked for the Westinghouse brothers, he used carbonized silk. These worked well enough but not nearly as well as Edison's bamboo.[651] (It is amusing to think that Edison's employees' joke testing of their beards would have actually worked better if they had burned their hair first.) None of Stanley's inventions were particularly different from what Edison had already patented, but they were different enough so that Westinghouse felt he could use them for railroad switches without too much fuss from Edison.

Just after Stanley joined their group, Westinghouse learned of an International Inventions Exhibition to be held in England in May of 1885. Westinghouse eagerly sent some of Stanley's inventions to the exhibition. This was why Westinghouse happened to read the report of the exhibition, and after skimming the parts about Stanley's discoveries, he found an article by Lucien Gaulard and John Gibbs, who had found a way to use a couple of coils to "render it possible to carry a large amount of electrical energy on a small conductor, and to draw it off at various points in such quantities and under such conditions as are required."[652] This, of course, reminded Westinghouse of how he distributed gas, and he became instantly intrigued, which started a whole new adventure in discovery and, inadvertently, a war with Edison that would harm both their lives.

Chapter Summary

✧ **1809:** Humphry Davy discovers the arc lamp and incandescence with his stinky battery.

✧ **1831:** Michael Faraday discovers inductance, which inspires Hippolyte Pixii to make the first AC generator, using brushes to make pulsed DC.

✧ **1863:** The first practical outdoor electric light system with arc lamps and AC is built.

✧ **1865:** Antonio Pacinotti creates an electromagnetic generator that makes smooth DC current, which inspires Zénobe Gramme to make the first large scale generator in **1871**. In **1873** Gramme's generator was found to be reversible as a motor. The motor only works with DC current.

✧ **1866:** Henry Wilde publishes an announcement of his electromagnet generator, which was in the form that was used for future generators with large bar magnets around a spinning coil. Many people adapt it to be "self-exciting" so that the generator electrifies its own electromagnets; it only works with DC current.

✧ **1868:** Westinghouse forms his first company in Pittsburg to sell his railroad "frogs," then forms his second company for air brakes the following year.

✧ **1876:** Pavel Yablochkov demonstrates his AC arc lamp, which inspires many people to investigate electric lighting.

✧ **1878:** Thomas Edison visits inventor William Wallace and decides to make lighting for homes that will light thousands of soft bulbs instead of dozens of brilliant arc lamps.

✧ **1879:** Edison files for a light bulb patent.

✧ **1882:** Edison electrifies part of New York with DC.

✧ **1884:** Edison wins a big lawsuit against Swan and starts suing many other lighting companies. Westinghouse starts a company called Union Switch and Signal, which creates electric signals for trains.

✧ **1885:** Westinghouse reads about the Gaulard-Gibbs transformer and becomes interested in developing AC for indoor lighting distribution.

Chapter 7
War of the Currents
(1880–1893)

Just as certain as death, Westinghouse will kill a customer within six months after he puts in an [alternating current] system of any size ... Holy Moses!

– Thomas Edison (1886)[653]

The alternating current will kill people, of course. So will gunpowder, and dynamite, and whisky, and lots of other things; but we have a system whereby the deadly electricity of the alternating current can do no harm unless a man is fool enough to swallow a whole dynamo.

– George Westinghouse (1888)[654]

The war of the currents, or the debate between what type of current was safe (alternating AC versus direct DC), was one of the historical stories that I *thought* I understood pretty well before I started researching this book. What I found was that the bare bones of what I knew beforehand was true. Thomas Edison did think AC was dangerous, and newspapers under his influence did publish gruesome stories of the dangers of AC. There was even a man who, with Edison's secret backing, conducted public demonstrations murdering animals to prove the deadliness of AC, which culminated in the invention of the electric chair. However, most of the details that I thought were true were either completely false or were greatly skewed from the real story. I am delighted to be able to tell what really happened, which is a more complex but just as fascinating story as the fabricated ones that are popularly told.

7.1 The Transforming Transformer

In 1880 a French engineer named Lucien Gaulard had an ingenious idea about using part of a high-voltage device called the induction coil (or a Ruhmkorff coil) in an unusual way. The induction coil, like the electric generator, dates way back to 1831 when Michael Faraday discovered induction by inducing current in one coil by changing the current in another coil. At the time, Faraday disappointedly noted that his induced current could move a compass but was unable to induce enough current in the secondary coil to be noticed "by the tongue, by spark, or by heating fine wire or charcoal."[655]

This "problem" was solved by an Irish priest and amateur scientist named Nicholas Callan. In around 1835, Callan found that if he wound both coils around the *same* iron bar, he could faintly feel the shocks from wires that were not electrically connected to a battery. He then found it was even more impressive when the primary wire (the one connected to the battery) was thick and the secondary coil was really thin and wound around as many times as possible. As he only received shocks every time the battery was connected or disconnected, Callan designed a special system with a wheel to repeatedly connect and disconnect the battery. He excitedly reported that if his assistant turned the handle once per second, he could receive 3,600 shocks in one minute.[656] Although that sounds torturous, Callan was delighted and declared the results to be "the best magneto-electrical machine ever constructed."[657] Soon many people made money selling and demonstrating these shocking devices. They were especially popular for producing "medical" cures for ailments like diabetes, rheumatism, gout, neurasthenia, anemia, and "hysteria"—all of which supposedly could be solved with electric shocks from these devices.[658]

Callan didn't know it, but he had just invented what's now called a step-up transformer, or a device that increases the voltage (and decreases the current) of a changing current. Recall that voltage is the electrical pressure, so when Callen created a new circuit by holding onto the paddles, a higher

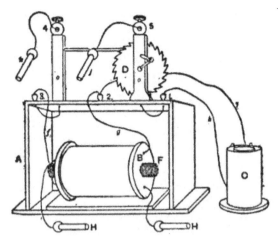

Figure 1: William Sturgeon's induction coil inspired by Callan: F is an iron core where a thin wire and a thick wire are separately wrapped. The thin wire is connected to paddles H to get shocks. The thick wire goes through wheel D to battery O so that the current is constantly interrupted (called an "interrupter").

voltage resulted in bigger shocks, but the smaller current in the wire would not have made a compass needle move. If the secondary coil has fewer loops than the primary, then you get less voltage (but more current). This is why Faraday could see the magnet moving from the current but could not feel a shock. As a side note, sometimes people get confused by this because of Ohm's law—they think that if the voltage increases, the current should also increase. However, that is not the case for a transformer because the secondary coil has a different resistance than the primary coil, meaning it can have more voltage and less current and still obey Ohm's law.

Now the race was on to produce a bigger and more constant shock or spark. The most famous device was created in 1858 by a German instrument maker named Heinrich Ruhmkorff. He patented a device that produced 30-centimeter-long sparks using a combination of electromagnetic switches and Leyden jars with the coils to produce bursts of high-voltage alternating current.[659] By 1880 the Ruhmkorff coil was so popular that almost every scientist and tinkerer knew what one was. That brings us back to Gaulard. Gaulard was troubled by the limitations of having electricity travel long distances as well as the difficulty of using different lamps that all seemed to have different voltage requirements. He then realized that since the coil took alternating current and increased the voltage, he could use those coils backward to reduce the voltage instead. This could be accomplished by attaching the high voltage from the generator to the thin wires with more loops and then connecting his lamp to the thick wires with fewer loops.

In other words, he knew that, like gas, electricity was better to transfer long distances with high voltage but that high voltage was dangerous in the home. Therefore, Gaulard's brilliant leap was to produce AC at very high voltage and very low current so that the power loss in the wires, which depends on the current squared, would be minimized.[660] Then, near the lamps, he used his device to transform the voltage to a safe level to be used with lamps. Gaulard called his device a "secondary generator," but it was quickly called a step-down transformer as it lowered the voltage in one step.

In 1881 Gaulard convinced a British engineer named John Gibbs to finance the project, and they filed for a patent on September 13 of 1882.[661] By 1884 Gaulard and Gibbs displayed their system at an electrical exposition in Turin, Italy, where they won first prize. Gaulard and Gibbs continued to push Gaulard's system at the International Exhibition in London the following year. It was the report of this exhibition where Westinghouse read Gaulard describe the device as being like "the Ruhmkorff coil, consisting as it does

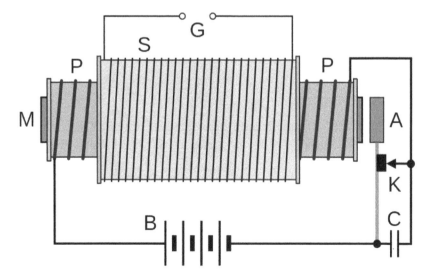

Figure 2: Schematic of Ruhmkorff coil. Notice the primary coil labeled P, which has fewer wires, and the secondary coil labeled S with many wires. This is a step-up transformer.

of two distinct coils and an iron core," being able to convert energy from high voltage to low voltage automatically. Gaulard also stated that "there is no mechanical movement whatever, the motion being entirely molecular."[662]

Excited, Westinghouse immediately cabled a junior engineer named Guido Pantaleoni who was in Italy for his father's funeral and asked him to find the two scientists and check it out. Pantaleoni didn't have to travel far, as he reported that the system was already being used in Turin, Italy, (they started from the time that Gaulard and Gibbs won the Turin Prize the previous year) and was already successfully lighting buildings some 50 miles away from a waterfall-powered generator.[663] However, Pantaleoni remained deeply skeptical. The recently developed self-excited generators couldn't be used with AC generators, and there were no AC motors. It also seemed to most scientists and inventors at the time like a step back to use alternating current with anything besides arc lamps (where the alternating current made the lamps burn evenly). Years later, Pantaleoni recalled, "Werner von Siemens [creator of the Siemens company] whom I had known, assured me there was nothing whatsoever in alternating current, that it was pure humbug."[664] Despite this, Westinghouse was sold and immediately purchased an AC Siemens generator (for arc lamps), two Gaulard-Gibbs transformers, and the services of an English employee of Gaulard and Gibbs named Reginald Belfield.

Belfield arrived in the United States at the end of November in 1885 and immediately went with his precious cargo to Pittsburgh. He found Pittsburgh to be dystopian, agreeing with an author who described the city as looking "like a huge volcano, continually belching forth smoke and flames. By day a great pall rests over the city, obscuring the sun, and by night the glow and flash of the almost numberless iron-mills which fill the valley and cover the hillsides, light the sky with a fiery glare."[665] However, Belfield admired Westinghouse, and the feeling was mutual. Soon Westinghouse hired Belfield to stay in Pittsburgh.

Westinghouse was surprised to find that, despite the fact that Gaulard described the coils in his device as being similar to those of a Ruhmkorff coil, they were actually composed of soldered disks stacked on top of each other (see figure 3). Westinghouse and his engineers ended up tearing it apart and attempting to put it back together again. According to Belfield, "Mr. Westinghouse applied himself toward the production of a piece of apparatus

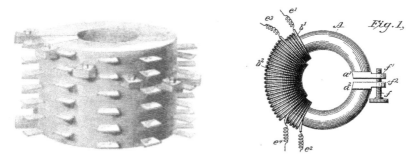

Figure 3: Gaulard's transformer (left); the "Stanley" transformer designed by Westinghouse (right)

which could be wound on the lathe, utterly discarding the unpractical sol-dered joints and stamped copper disks [of the Gaulard-Gibbs transformer] for the more commercial form of ordinary insulated copper wire. It took Mr. Westinghouse only a few days to design an apparatus which has been the standard ever since."[666]

Despite their successes, everyone in the laboratory, with the possible ex-emptions of Belfield (the engineer who worked with Gaulard and Gibbs) and Stanley (the engineer they hired for his light bulb), still believed that Westinghouse was on a fool's errand. Pantaleoni recalled, "The opposition by ALL the electric part of the Westinghouse organization was such that it was only Mr. George Westinghouse's personal will that put it through."[667] Meanwhile, by December 1885, William Stanley declared that the Pittsburgh air was just too toxic and that he wished to return to the restful town of Great Barrington, Massachusetts, where he used to vacation as a child. Westinghouse therefore agreed to give him some money to test run an AC system in peace and quiet and sent the grateful Belfield along with him to the cold but clean air.

On January 8, 1886, 38-year-old Westinghouse started the Westinghouse Electric Company. It was his fifth company with stock worth one million dollars. He sent Pantaleoni back to Italy with instructions to purchase the Gaulard-Gibbs patent, come hell or high water. When Pantaleoni asked for the price range, Westinghouse scoffed. "They'll tell you their price. Whatever it is, close the bargain, and I'll send the money by cable to you."[668] As it turns out, Gaulard and Gibbs asked for a shocking $50,000, which is around $1.4 million today.

Meanwhile, in Great Barrington, Stanley and Belfield spent three months working on their AC system, and on March 10, 1886, they were almost ready to light up a local department store when the Edison people beat them to it and electrified a local mansion. Undeterred, a week later Stanley powered a 25-horsepower steam engine in a barn, used a transformer to increase the voltage to 500 volts, ran the electricity into the town, used another transformer to decrease the voltage to 100 volts, and electrified a store with 150 bulbs.[669] Stanley and Belfield kept the details of their device secret (they even went as far as hiding their transformers in basements) but let it be known that they could electrify any building in town. Soon, the Westinghouse company had four or five more contracts than Edison's people did. Still, Westinghouse didn't like newspapers and made no announcements, so Edison had no idea what was happening for several months.

Meanwhile, in September of 1886, Stanley patented "his" transformer without mentioning Westinghouse's involvement. Westinghouse didn't object. Stanley's contract covered any of his inventions, and it seems likely that Westinghouse didn't feel any need for extra name recognition. However, this action ended up hurting Westinghouse four years later when Stanley tried to form his own AC company and asserted that he had invented all parts of the transformer. (Westinghouse knew by this time how to write a contract, and this effort failed in the courts, but history has usually given full credit to Stanley because of this duplicitous behavior.)[670]

In fact, in 1974, the Rotary Club of Great Barrington erected a plaque for Stanley with the words "William Stanley: his genius made Great Barrington the first community to be lighted by alternating current."[671] This inspired the Institution of Electrical Engineers to make a similar claim in 2004.[672] However, both plaques are wrong as Gaulard was the first to patent the idea in 1882 and was the first to implement it on a large scale at the Turin Exhibition in 1884. It was also at that exhibition that a team of Hungarian engineers named Károly Zipernowsky, Ottó Bláthy, and Miksa Déri (often referred to as ZBD for the initials in their names), were the first to demonstrate high efficiency AC transformers, along with the idea of using step-up transformers *and* multiple step-down transformers in parallel. Although modern historians often ignore Gaulard's contributions, even the ZBD group freely admitted in October of 1885 that "Gaulard and Gibbs are undoubtable to be credited with first having proved the practical applicability of secondary generators."[673]

Poor Gaulard lost his patent for dubious reasons and ended up in an insane asylum, declaring himself God.[674] He therefore wasn't in a position to push back against either Stanley or the ZBD group, and Gibbs, who was mostly a financial backer, felt powerless to promote it on its own. Gaulard then died from unknown causes (possibly from mistreatment at the asylum) in November of 1888 at the age of 38.[675] Although Gaulard's influence has been mostly lost to time, the transformer inspired almost every arc lamp provider in the world to use AC with transformers because it was cheaper, customers rarely interacted directly with the plugs of streetlights and arc lamps, and the arc lamps burned out evenly.

Thomas Edison heard about the AC transformer a few weeks after Westinghouse in mid-1885 and immediately bought a patent for the ZBD transformer. However, within a few months, Edison decided incandescent lights wouldn't be practical and didn't give it much more thought. Then, in November of 1886, possibly because Stanley filed the transformer patent on September 21, 1886, Edison learned that Westinghouse was using alternating current to power incandescent lights.[676] Amazingly, his thought process can be seen in his monthly notebook where he shared his ideas and thoughts with the vice president of the Edison Electric Company, Edward Johnson (see figure 4).

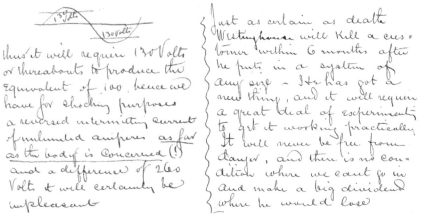

Figure 4: Edison's notes to Edward Johnson, page 7 (left) and page 15 (right) from November 1886

At first, Edison immediately and correctly understood that for an alternating current to power a 100-volt lamp it would need around 130 volts maximum. However, he incorrectly thought that the danger "as far as the body is concerned" was the difference between the maximum and minimum, or 260 volts. (It turns out that the danger to humans is also 100 volts.) Initially, Edison thought that 260 volts would "certainly be unpleasant" if a customer was accidentally electrified, but after a week or so, he became more disturbed by the idea, writing, "Just as certain as death Westinghouse will kill a customer within six months after he puts in a system of any size." It was this misunderstanding that caused Edison, in the same notebook, to declare that "1,200 volts continuous current will never do greater harm than blister the flesh, and I'll bet any amount that 1,000 volts alternate current will kill certain."[677]

Edison was also concerned about the high voltage of the wires transmitting electricity long distances. As he knew some of the details of AC transmission from Károly Zipernowsky (one of the inventors of the ZBD transformer), Edison mused: "Why Zip uses 2,000 volts alternate—this gives a difference of 4,000 volts(!) (holy Moses)."[678] Edison's second big misunderstanding was that he assumed that Westinghouse was like every other get-rich schemer that he knew. Edison expected that Westinghouse would push this dangerous new method, harm countless people, and then turn everyone off electricity forever—all for something that Edison thought was just a dangerous gimmick to get around Edison's patents. No wonder Edison was so vehemently against AC.

One note about safety—we now think that Edison was wrong about the dangers of AC current versus DC at the same voltage. However, Edison *was* correct that the higher voltage in the transmission lines used by AC was and is more dangerous, although he misunderstood how often people would interact with high-voltage lines. In addition, there are drawbacks to DC power at the time that Edison didn't understand. For one, there's a danger in having a generator plant in the middle of a busy city. Not only were they producing a lot of air and noise pollution, but fire danger was much higher in those crowded conditions. Also, low-voltage DC transmission limits the power available from electric dams since it couldn't travel long distances. Finally, it would be prohibitively expensive to provide remote places with electric power, which, as we became more and more dependent on electric safety, would endanger lives for millions of rural people.

7.2 The AC–Motor Problem

Westinghouse, meanwhile, had trouble with his system that had nothing to do with Edison's ire. He didn't have a way to convert electricity that went back and forth to motion that went in a circle for meters and electric motors. Westinghouse was first primarily concerned with a meter, as he knew from gas distribution that if he didn't have a meter to measure how much power he was distributing, he would have to charge a flat rate—incentivizing customers to use as much light as possible. Luckily, in April of 1888, an employee named Shallenberger dropped a spring near two pieces of equipment and found that the dropped spring started to spin. Within a month, Shallenberger had a working meter, and by August they had a system on the market.[679] The meter, which operated at 133 Hz, was very popular and sold 120,000 units in just 10 years.[680] Now Westinghouse had a meter but was still looking for a motor, or something that could do work that was powered by alternating current.

This was an interesting time for the development of motors. In 1886, an ex-Edison employee named Frank Sprague* had invented a constant speed DC motor with regenerative braking. By February 2, 1888—just two months before Shallenberger dropped that spring—Sprague and his company installed the first large electric street rail system in Richmond, Virginia.[681] This started a wave of interest in electric motors, as, at the time, only the very wealthy could afford indoor electricity, but almost everyone rode the public bus. Westinghouse wanted in, but was stymied by the lack of a powerful AC motor.

However, Westinghouse and his team weren't the only ones "playing" with alternating current and looking for an AC motor. In Turin, Italy, a professor named Galileo Ferraris had been advising and testing transformers ever since Gaulard and Gibbs displayed their system in 1884.[682] It was only a few months after Ferraris started studying transformers that he conceived a new way to make AC current that would create an AC motor. Ferraris's idea was to generate electricity with two separate sets of coils (A and B) at 90 degrees from each other (see figure 5).[683] These coils are identical and electrified by

---

* The same man who had recommended that Edison convert to AC

the same electromagnet, so they have identical current induced in them with the same frequency. In fact, the only difference is the timing of their maximum value, or their phase. Because the two sets of coils have two different phases, this kind of generator is now called a two-phase generator. The different currents were then attached at 90 degrees around an object that he was attempting to rotate, called the rotor. The idea is that when the coils are electrified in turn, a current is induced in the rotor and the force between that alternating current from the sets of wires and the induced current in the rotor is what causes the rotor to spin.

Let me clarify a bit how Ferraris came to his idea. Ferraris knew from the equations of James Clerk Maxwell that light was an electromagnetic wave and that the direction that the electric field is vibrating in is called the polarization of the light. If the electric field vibrates horizontally, it's horizontally polarized, and if it vibrates vertically, it's vertically polarized. Ferraris also knew that if one combines horizontally polarized light and vertically polarized light that's in phase (gets bigger and smaller at the same time), then one produces diagonally polarized light. However, if one combines light 90 degrees (or a quarter wave) out of phase, then the result is a wave where the electric field moves in a circle. In other words, through optics, Ferraris understood that if you combined two waves, one horizontal and one vertical, that are 90 degrees

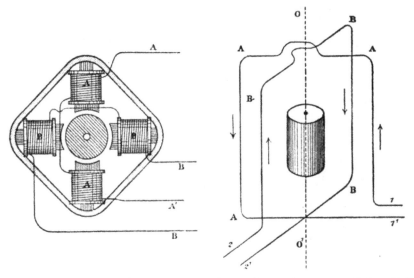

Figure 5: Ferraris's two-phase generator with A and B 90 degrees out of phase (left) and his motor (right)

apart, then you get a circular wave, and *that* inspired him to see if he could mimic this effect with electric motors.

Ferraris said that in August or September of 1885 he built a hand-cranked two-phase generator and a motor. Although this was arguably the first true brushless polyphase generator and motor ever built, Ferraris didn't think it would make a powerful motor and didn't patent it nor publish his results until March of 1888, and he mostly just demonstrated it to his students.[684] Meanwhile, a few weeks after Shallenberger dropped that spring, Westinghouse heard about Ferraris's experiments (possibly from Pantaleoni, who was a former student of his) and Westinghouse sent Pantaleoni back to Italy to get the rights to patent it.[685] In May of 1888, Ferraris was pleased with the interest and offered the rights for free. But Westinghouse generously offered $1,000 instead, which Ferraris accepted.[686]

At almost the same time, in May of 1888, Westinghouse heard that a 32-year-old inventor named Nikola Tesla was demonstrating to the American Institute of Electrical Engineers a two-phase AC motor and generator that was powerful and could be used in industry. The idea behind this generator and motor was exactly the same as Ferraris's two-phase concept. In 1889 Tesla himself admitted that "Professor Ferraris not only came independently to the same theoretical results, but in a manner identical almost to the smallest detail."[687] However, Tesla failed to mention what his independent inspiration was, as he liked to say that his inspirations came fully formed in his head and that he never needed to experiment because "there has not been a single, solitary experiment which did not come out exactly as I thought it would."[688]

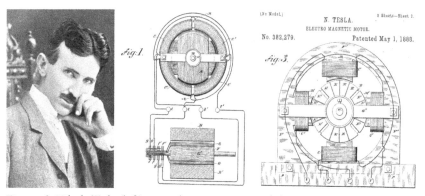

Figure 6: Nikola Tesla (left); two-phase generator with lower exciter (center); two-phase motor (right)

In lawsuits, Tesla's lawyers implied that he was inspired by Arago's wheel.[689] So let's discuss how Arago's wheel could have led to a two-phase motor and generator.

As described in chapter 4, Ampère's friend François Arago discovered that a spinning copper wheel could spin a nearby magnet with no battery involved. The following year in 1825, English scientists named Charles Babbage and John Herschel made a "reverse Arago's wheel" by spinning a permanent magnet under a copper wheel, which caused the copper wheel to spin in sympathy.[690] Fast-forward to June of 1879 when an English scientist named Walter Baily was inspired by the reverse Arago's wheel to make a copper wheel spin with four *stationary* electromagnets. Baily did this by using a homemade commutator so that the current alternated between the electromagnets (see figure 7).[691] Although this was arguably the first two-phase motor, it required a commutator and wasn't a motor as much as a tiny classroom demonstration device, measuring only a little over two inches (six centimeters) wide and four inches high (10 centimeters).[692]

The next year, in 1880, a French scientist named Marcel Deprez was inspired by Baily to make a more robust motor that used a similar commutator to Baily's to electrify a rotor (the part of motor that spins).[693] This was a form of a two-phase motor but also contained commutators (see figure 7). Tesla never admitted that he had read about any of these discoveries, but

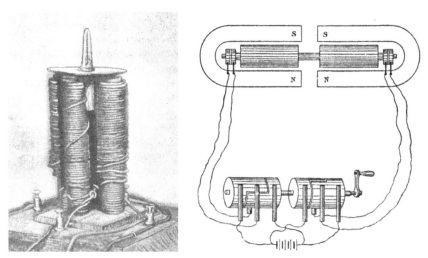

Figure 7: Baily's "2-phase" motor from 1879 (left); Deprez's Motor from 1880 with the commutator visible (right)

n his 1887 patent, he did add: "I am aware that it is not new to produce the rotations of a motor by intermittently shifting the poles of one of its elements."[694] However, Tesla correctly stated that the previous systems (aside from Ferraris's, which he seemed unaware of) "used mechanical appliances," where only the direction, not the strength, of the current changed, not the naturally rotating field from a two-phase generator.[695] In 1900 a judge in Connecticut declared in favor of Tesla's patent, stating "Baily and others did not discover the Tesla invention. … It remained to the genius of Tesla to … transform the toy of Arago into an engine of power."[696]

Westinghouse had no clue about Arago's wheel or ideas emerging fully formed, but he did hear that Tesla's motor was effective. Westinghouse therefore sent two associates to New York in late May 1888 to check it out. Although they reported that the motors were a success, they found Tesla's description incomprehensible.[697] Nevertheless, Tesla had a patent, and Ferraris didn't, so Westinghouse's lawyer recommended purchasing the patent even though he thought the asking price of $200,000 in cash and $2.50 per horsepower was "monstrous."[698] Westinghouse, as usual, wasn't bothered by paying a premium for patents and reminded his lawyer that "the Westinghouse Electric Company cannot afford to have others own the patents that are necessary to enable it to make motors to work on the alternating current system."[699] By July of 1888, Westinghouse bought the patent for far less than $200,000, but for $70,000 in stocks and cash with a further $2.50 per horsepower of motors sold with minimum royalties of $15,000 every year for the length of the patent.[700] This was still an astonishing amount of money, and in 1900 Tesla recalled that Westinghouse was "one of those few men who conscientiously respect intellectual property, and who acquire their right to use inventions by fair and equitable means."[701]

However, despite the money and Tesla's happy talk, Tesla's motor didn't work as well as was hoped. Tesla wanted 60 Hz, and Westinghouse had been using 133 Hz from the beginning and didn't want to have to change all of their equipment, especially Shallenberger's meter, for this motor. In addition, even at the lower frequency, Tesla's motor didn't work well for industry. Tesla, Westinghouse, and his team tried their best to increase the frequency of Tesla's motor, but nothing worked. According to William Stanley in 1890, they still had no viable Tesla motors after spending "$300,000 in experimental work in the endeavor." Stanley had been offered a further $100,000 in cash if he could provide one, as "they had taken a great many orders for the delivery of motors which they were unable to fill."[702] Tesla gave up on working on motors and went back to New York in less than a year while Westinghouse continued to prosper even without a strong motor.[703]

7.3 Death on the Wire

Thomas Edison watched in horror as Westinghouse's AC company became more and more successful. Yet, despite the lack of mass deaths, Edison remained convinced that it was unbelievably dangerous. In addition, Edison and Westinghouse ran far different companies. Edison had hundreds of employees, but everything had to go through "the old man." Since he'd not thought of AC, Edison was uninterested in playing catch-up with someone else's idea. Westinghouse, on the other hand, was perfectly comfortable gathering a group of brilliant and temperamental inventors and letting them create in their own way. A biographer called Westinghouse's Electric Company "one of the earliest examples of a think tank."[704]

In December of 1886, after a month of complaining about the dangers of the AC system, Edison began his attack against Westinghouse in the time-honored way: he sued. Westinghouse wasn't surprised nor was he particularly worried. He had a lot of money and knew that his AC system was actually superior. A newspaper account proclaimed that "Mr. Westinghouse … treated the matter lightly, as one of indifference."[705] Edison had rarely gone against someone with so much money and technical background, and although he sued and sued, all his efforts failed. The court cases were dragging on when, in November of 1887, Edison received a letter from a Buffalo dentist named Alfred Southwick who had a deadly idea about electricity.[706]

Southwick was just an ordinary dentist, but he, like many people, had read stories about botched hangings and was disturbed. Then he read a story about a drunk man who immediately died after touching a live electrical wire. This unnerving story gave Southwick an idea, and he decided that electricity could be used to humanely kill animals and make the death penalty less barbaric. So, he asked Edison for help. However, Edison was revolted and responded that he was morally against the death penalty. Unwilling to give up, Southwick asked again in December.[707] This time,

Edison had a different view.

What seemed to have changed Edison's mind was not Southwick's oratory but, instead, a sudden rise in the price of copper. It jumped from 10 cents a pound to 16 cents with no end in sight, which caused Westinghouse's AC (which used less copper) to go from slightly cheaper to significantly cheaper.[708] With this copper war, Edison worried that people would turn to Westinghouse's AC, and the resulting deaths would turn everyone off electricity of all kinds. For that reason, in December of 1887 Edison wrote to Southwick that the "most effective [killing machines] are known as 'Alternating Machines,' manufactured principally in this country by Mr. George Westinghouse, Pittsburg."[709]

It might have been while Edison was thinking about how damaging it would be to Westinghouse's brand to use AC to kill criminals that Edison realized that he had another tool against Westinghouse's AC: propaganda. In February 1888, Edison published a 75-page diatribe against Westinghouse titled "A Warning from the Edison Electric Light Co." and listed the physical and financial dangers of the alternating current system.[710] Interestingly, Edison and his company attempted a similar campaign against gas lighting in 1882 but had previously refrained from attacking any rival electric company for fear of confused customers being afraid of Edison's light.[711]

It seems clear that with all the dangerous new technologies and lack of any oversight, people had been killed by electricity prior to 1888, but it wasn't considered important enough to get in the paper. As several newspaper owners had significant stock in Edison's company, there seemed to be no point to publishing any mishaps, even from rivals. However, with Edison's "Warning," the newspapers had permission to publish every gruesome death, and as Edison "the Wizard" had predicted, they could bring a lot more attention to the articles. As Westinghouse's biographer wrote in 1919, high-voltage wires for arc lamps, telephones, and telegraphs blanketed the sky In New York for years without public comment. But "with the advent of the Westinghouse enterprise, all overhead cables suddenly leaped into prominence not only as eyesores but as a public peril."[712] Despite the fact that Westinghouse reported that 46 times more people died from gas accidents than from electrical current in New York City in 1888, the newspapers remained unrelenting.[713]

Then on June 5, 1888, the war heated up even more when a young engineer named Harold Brown published an anti-AC article in the *Evening Post* (owned by an investor in Edison's company) after hearing of all the deaths due to AC. In that article, Brown stated that AC current above 300 volts should be outlawed, or the "public must submit to *constant danger from sudden death*" from the "damnable ... fatal 'alternating' current."[714] Westinghouse wrote to Edison and invited him to meet one-on-one to clear this all up, saying, "I believe there has been a systematic attempt on the part of some people to do a great deal of mischief ... between the Edison Company and the Westinghouse Electric Company."[715] But Edison wasn't interested.

Instead, according to Harold Brown, Edison invited Brown "to make the experiments at his private laboratory ... [to prove] beyond question that the alternating current would PRODUCE INSTANT DEATH."[716] On July 13, Edison went as far as to write to the Society for the Prevention of Cruelty to Animals (SPCA), requesting some "good-sized animals" so that he could experiment upon them to "safeguard the lives of men engaged in electric lighting business."[717] The president of the SPCA, Henry Bergh, categorically rejected Edison's request as being "antagonistic to the principles which govern this Institution" and said he had no interest in having anything to do with an experiment that "calculated to inflict great suffering upon the animal."[718]

Edison was surprised, as he assumed that the SPCA had a lot of animals that they were going to put down anyway and thought that the SPCA would be interested in finding new, more humane methods of animal euthanasia. Bergh was mollified by Edison's second letter but remained uninterested in electrically killing animals, causing Edison and Brown to turn to other resources. By July 30, Brown gave a ghastly demonstration to scientists and reporters, causing many people to walk out as they were "unable to endure the revolting exhibition."[719] Soon, Brown was hired by the electric chair committee in New York as a consultant, which, to no one's surprise, concluded that Westinghouse's generator would be the best to kill criminals. By December 6, 1888, the *New York Times* declared that "after January 1st the alternating current will undoubtedly drive the hangman out of business in this State."[720]

Not surprisingly, Westinghouse was displeased to be thought of as a death peddler, especially considering his lifelong dedication to public safety. In fact, in 1889, Edison's lawyer bumped into Westinghouse at lunch, and Westinghouse told him that he felt "very hurt" by Edison's insults in the paper. According to the lawyer, "[Westinghouse] was really cut up about it."[721]

Then on May 13, 1889, a man named William Kemmler was convicted of chopping up his girlfriend with an ax and sentenced to be the first person to be purposefully killed with electricity. Kemmler had no concern with this method of execution, but Westinghouse did. Soon one of the best lawyers in the country, W. Bourke Cockran, agreed to argue against the electric chair as being cruel and unusual. Although Cockran tried to pretend that he took the job out of a "love for humanity," the *New-York Tribune* reported that "it leaked out that he was in the pay of the Westinghouse."[722] Edison and Brown were called as experts for using AC in the electric chair, and despite Cockran's quality lawyering, Edison's reputation as a wizard was just too much to ignore.

By October, the judge ruled against Cockran (and Westinghouse). Cockran appealed to the Supreme Court, but this failed too. Finally, on August 6, 1890, William Kemmler became the first man sentenced to death by electrocution.[723] However, Brown turned out to have little expertise, and the *New York Times* exclaimed in its headline, "Far Worse Than Hanging: Kemmler's Death Proves an Awful Spectacle."[724] The electrician immediately sent a telegram to Westinghouse (as they were using his generators): "Execution was an awful botch. Kemmler was literally roasted to death."[725] Edison was furious, both with Brown and with Westinghouse. Edison had tried to make everyone afraid of AC to save them from something he felt was very dangerous. Instead, he looked like a murderer and torturer. The only silver lining was that, without Edison's secret support, Harold Brown "disappeared from public sight, never to be heard from again."[726]

All of this fear mongering (and the lack of a working industrial motor) did very little to hurt Westinghouse's electric business, and between 1886 and 1890, Westinghouse's company sales went from $150,000 a year to more than $4 million.[727] Then, on November 15, 1890, a bank in England collapsed, causing bank failures all over the world.[728] Westinghouse had borrowed heavily to fulfill all his new orders, and his business was now on the verge of collapse. The bankers agreed to fund him but wanted another person as manager, stating, "Mr. Westinghouse wastes so much on experimentation, and pays so liberally for whatever he wishes in the way of service and patent rights."[729] Westinghouse found funding elsewhere but tried to be a bit more economical. He stopped all research on Tesla's motor (although he still had to pay $15,000 to Tesla every year as a minimum payment). Then, a few months after giving up on Tesla's two-phase motor, Westinghouse was convinced to try to make it work one more time. The invention was something that was to have profound influence on our modern electrical systems: three-phase–AC electricity.

7.4 The Hidden War: Three-Phase vs. Two-Phase

Three-phase alternating current is the type we use today in our modern electrical systems. It was invented and implemented by a man who is possibly the most underappreciated electrical engineer of all time, a Russian-Polish engineer named Mikhail Dolivo-Dobrovolsky. Dolivo-Dobrovolsky was born to a Russian mother and a Polish father in St. Petersburg, Russia, in 1862 (though he grew up in Odessa). His family was upper-middle class (his father was a landowner and civil servant), but there are no other known details about his childhood up until he went to college, where he studied mechanical engineering and became interested in politics.[730]

At the time, the czar of Russia, Alexander II, was implementing some well-needed reforms in Russia, like freeing 23 million serfs and improving the justice system.[731] Dolivo-Dobrovolsky and his college friends wanted him to do more. However, in March 1881, an anarchist group assassinated the czar and Alexander II's son, Alexander III, declaring that they would "put an end to the lousy liberals."[732] The new czar implemented a total shutdown of civil liberties, including a purge from colleges of any and all liberals. Nineteen-year-old Dolivo-Dobrovolsky was in this college purge and was thus prohibited from getting an education anywhere in Russia.[733]

Frustrated, Dolivo-Dobrovolsky decided to go to school in Germany, where he ended up switching to the exciting new field of electrical engineering. At the time, almost all electrical engineering programs used direct current (DC). Note that this was at the same time that Gaulard invented his transformer, but few people knew of it, and only a small group of people anywhere in the world were invested in AC—especially as an AC motor had not been invented yet.

After graduating in 1884, Dolivo-Dobrovolsky got a job as an engineer at a company called the German Edison Corporation for Applied Electricity, which was shortened to the General Electric Company or Allgemeine

Elektricitäts Gesellschaft (AEG) in 1887. Dolivo-Dobrovolsky continued to work on DC electricity until 1888 when he read about Tesla's and Ferraris's two-phase motor. Dolivo-Dobrovolsky, along with many others, suddenly became engrossed in multiphase alternating electricity and AC motors.

Dolivo-Dobrovolsky quickly decided that "Tesla's arrangement, with two entirely independent currents differing by 90 degrees in their phases, was not particularly advantageous" since the field in the coil would fluctuate by 40%, and "consequently the field of Tesla's motor is not only rotating, but also strongly pulsating."[734] Dolivo-Dobrovolsky then mathematically determined that three phases lowered the fluctuations to 15%. He started to work on three-phase motors. (He wasn't alone in this; several scientists were inspired by Tesla and Ferraris to make a three-phase motor.)[735]

This was when Dolivo-Dobrovolsky came to a remarkable conclusion that three-phase wasn't just better for motors—it was a new way of transferring electricity with only three wires instead of needing six.[736] This trick is only possible because if you connect three waves that are all 120 degrees apart at any point, the total will add up to zero. In this way, you can basically ground three of the six wires and only need three live wires for transmitting electricity. When you reach the end of the line, you can combine the three live wires to the ground and do not need a return. This is very important because the problem with transmitting electricity, especially over long distances, is always how to lower costs, which usually means lowering the amount of copper wire needed. With three-phase power, you can reduce the amount of wire needed for transmission by 50% *and* still use all three phases to power high-voltage three-phase motors.

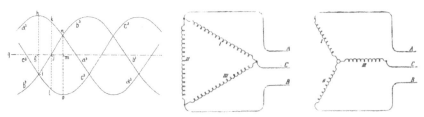

Figure 8: Dolivo-Dobrovolsky's drawing of how if you add the three waves at hi, kl, or no, the sum is always zero (left); Dolivo-Dobrovolsky's delta transformer in 1891 (center); Dolivo-Dobrovolsky's star or wye transformer (right)

In addition, in August of 1899, Dolivo-Dobrovolsky patented two ways of combining the three transformers into a single three-phase transformer, either by connecting them in a triangle, called delta transformer, or in a point, called a star or wye transformer (figure 8).[737] With these transformers, the three phases can be safely transformed to high voltages and low current for long-distance transmission without much loss and then transformed back to lower voltages to be safely used. You might be wondering how Dolivo-Dobrovolsky managed to light a light bulb with a single live wire, and the answer is he didn't. Instead, he ran a single live wire to the bulbs with a "return" of a neutral wire, which is a wire created so that, if the three phases are in balance, there's no current in them, but they can still complete the circuit.

Dolivo-Dobrovolsky also realized at this time that his three-phase motor was not very efficient because it induced circular currents called eddy currents in the rotor (the part that spun), which worked against the motion of the rotor. To reduce the amount of eddy currents, Dolivo-Dobrovolsky started to put a series of parallel slits in the rotor, which he patented in 1889.[738] These rotors started to look like large cages, and in 1894, the English scientist Silvanus Thompson called it a "sort of squirrel cage,"[739] probably since it looked large enough to hold a squirrel, and the name stuck. Squirrel-cage motors are a mainstay in engineering, and in 2017, an engineering textbook stated that Dolivo-Dobrovolsky's design from that time remains "virtually unchanged for more than 100 years of their existence."[740]

In 1890 Dolivo-Dobrovolsky's transmission system and motor impressed a man named Oskar von Miller, who was the technical director of an upcoming Frankfurt electrical exposition. Miller had initially hoped to use high-voltage DC powered from a waterfall, but the closest waterfall with a nice cement factory next to it and a turbine was in Lauffen, Germany—a full 175 kilometers (110 miles) away. At first, Miller went to a Swiss engineer named Charles Brown whose company had been experimenting with long-distance DC from hydroelectric plants. After some deliberations, Miller decided to work with the exciting new three-phase transmission,[741] and so Miller brokered an unusual cooperation between Brown's company, Dolivo-Dobrovolsky's company, the German government, and the cement factory to make this technological advance.[742]

Dolivo-Dobrovolsky and Brown then created three-phase electricity with the generator powered by a waterfall in Lauffen. A star (or wye) transformer was used to step up the voltage from 55 volts to the startlingly high (at the time) 8,500 volts with only three live wires at that high voltage running to the town of Frankfurt. This high voltage was needed because they wanted to use the thinnest wire possible. They ended up with tiny five-millimeter-thin wires. Still, even with their extra-thin wires, this system required over 60 tons of copper![743] Once in Frankfurt, Dolivo-Dobrovolsky and Brown used another star (wye) transformer to step down the voltage to around 65 volts. This was used to electrify sets of lights as well as a three-phase motor that powered an artificial waterfall (see figure 9). [744] *

This system, which many scientists and engineers had previously assumed would not work over long distances, made that impressive distance with 74% of its power intact.[745] It was heralded as "nothing short of magnificent."[746] *The Electrical Engineer* beamed, "I do not think that I am guilty of exaggeration in expressing an opinion that the Lauffen–Frankfort transmission is the most difficult and most momentous experiment made in technical electricity since that mysterious natural force … has been made serviceable to mankind."[747] This was the first electrical system that in any way resembles modern electrical distribution, and we continue to use three-phase delta transformers, and star (wye) transformers to this very day.

However, Dolivo-Dobrovolsky wasn't particularly adept at explaining the advantages of his system, and many people became confused about the difference between two-phase and three-phase, which all started to be called "polyphase": a name coined by Sylvanus Thompson (same guy who named the squirrel cage) in September of 1891 to describe the electricity at the Frankford-Lauffen Exhibition.[748] (Dolivo-Dobrovolsky preferred the terms "rotary field" or "Ferraris Field" after Galileo Ferraris).[749] In addition, unknown to Dolivo-Dobrovolsky, his collaborator on the project, Charles Brown, became jealous of the attention that Dolivo-Dobrovolsky was gaining for three-phase. In October of 1891, Brown wrote a letter to the editor of *The Electrical World* magazine stating that "the adoption of the three-phase current only increased the difficulties to be met" and that all of the real "constructive improvements" demonstrated at the Frankford exhibition were

---

* I love the idea that Dolivo-Dobrovolsky used the water from a natural waterfall to power a generator, which created three-phase electricity that was transmitted 110 miles away to power a motor that made … an artificial waterfall.

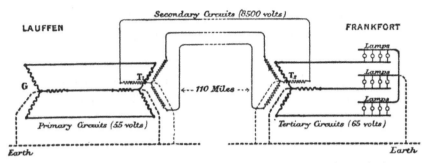

Figure 9: Simplified diagram of Lauffen–Frankfurt system. Note that only three wires are needed for the 175 km between the town of Lauffen and Frankfurt (motor for waterfall not shown).

"almost without exemption" due to him. In addition, Brown claimed that "the three-phase current as applied at Frankfort is due to the labors of Mr. Tesla, and will be found clearly specified in his patents."[750]

What Brown knew, and Dolivo-Dobrovolsky did not, was that, back in 1888, Tesla had not only patented a two-phase generator and motor but also a three-phase and a four-phase generator and motor.[751] If Dolivo-Dobrovolsky had known about Tesla's three-phase motor, he might have emphasized that Tesla's had six wires, not three, along with the advantages of the three-wire, three-phase transmission system. But he didn't, and instead focused on the advantages of three phases for the motor, so many people assumed that Tesla had invented all of it.

Still, Tesla's backers must've been worried. It wasn't enough to conflate

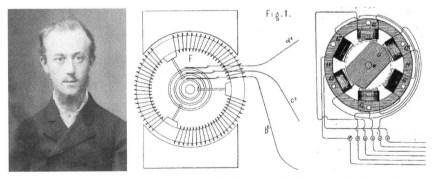

Figure 10: Mikhail Dolivo-Dobrovolsky (left); Dolivo-Dobrovolsky's three-phase generator with three wires from 1889 (center); Tesla's three-phase generator with six wires from 1887 (right)

Tesla's two-phase motor with Dolivo-Dobrovolsky's three-phase motor if Tesla's motor wasn't working and being sold—especially as three-phase electricity was breaking transmission records. In fact, Dolivo-Dobrovolsky wrote a long article about the three-phase system on April 3 before his successful demonstration at Lauffen-Frankfurt. He quipped, "Tesla's motor, which on its appearance was written up and discussed so much, seems, however, to not have fulfilled the expectations excited; in spite of the years since elapsed, there has come no notice of any serious application of it."[752]

However, luckily for Tesla, the success of Dolivo-Dobrovolsky at the fair caused Westinghouse to reexamine Tesla's motor especially after an engineer convinced him that 60 Hz would travel longer distances with less loss than 133 Hz, and another engineer named Benjamin Lamme claimed he could make Tesla's motors work for industry.[753] Lamme was one of the new forms of engineers who was college educated with a firm understanding of mathematics. He realized from mathematical modeling that the way that Tesla arranged his coils made weaker magnetic fields. Lamme recalled later, "My rough figures indicated that … coils covering the full pole pitch would give about twice as effective field as the old Tesla type [and] the secondary windings, distributed in more slots, would give further improvement."[754]

Westinghouse was thus convinced to switch to 60 Hz in his generators and motors and to spend more money and manpower to let Lamme attempt to make Tesla's motor work on an industrial scale. In late 1891, Benjamin Lamme was finally allowed to build his two-phase AC motor and succeeded in creating a two-phase motor that was industry ready by the beginning of 1892. According to Lamme, this was the first induction motor made at the Westinghouse Company, "which bears any close resemblance to the modern type."[755]

Meanwhile, Edison's company also had financial issues due to the economic crash of 1890. This brings us to the financier J. P. Morgan. Morgan, like everyone involved in electricity, had been watching the success of the AC systems, which Edison stubbornly refused to use or accept. On April 15, 1892, Morgan orchestrated a coup by merging Edison's company with another.[756]

He fired Edison and even removed Edison's name from his own company. From that time on, it was plain General Electric, or GE, instead of

Edison's General Electric. Edison pretended that he had moved on, saying, "I cannot waste my time over electric-lighting matters, for they are old."[757] But truthfully, he was heartbroken. Edison's personal secretary recalled, "I knew something had died in Edison's heart ... he had a deep-seated, enduring pride in his name. And that name had been violated, torn from the title of the great industry created by his genius through years of intense planning and unremitting toil."[758] From then on even GE used alternating current, and the lawsuits abated. The war of the currents was over. However, J. P. Morgan wanted a monopoly and began to eye Westinghouse's company (and every other electrical company) to absorb. It was the age of the monopoly, with Westinghouse as the only fly in the ointment.

Westinghouse wanted nothing to do with folding his company into a mega company run by bankers. In a bit of business trickery, Westinghouse pretended to have no interest in lighting the upcoming World's Columbian Exposition in Chicago, and the people at GE thought they had a monopoly and decided to price gouge, bidding between $13.98 and $18.51 per lamp. (The difference in prices was from pretending there were multiple bids from multiple independent firms.)[759] Westinghouse waited for the Chicago papers to complain about this obscenity and then had a cover company offer $5.49 per lamp.[760] Shocked, GE tried to rebid $6, but the committee was moved by Westinghouse's personal charm and the pressure from the newspapers to go with him. Westinghouse electrified the fair at a loss, but he decided it was worth it, as he hoped that the success of the fair would lead to his company being in charge of the electricity from the dam at Niagara, which is basically what happened.

As the fair's opening approached, Westinghouse held a meeting on the promotion of their new "Tesla" motor. Benjamin Lamme suggested that they should make what he called a "fad" out of polyphase generators "so that everybody would buy them, [and] the motor question would soon settle itself." Years later, Lamme recalled that "instructions were given immediately to get out a standard line of polyphase generators and push them on any and every occasion."[761] However, Westinghouse realized that it would be difficult to promote polyphase generators at the fair, as they didn't have enough industrial two-phase generators and transformers in stock or have enough time to build them.

According to Lamme, Westinghouse suggested using two separate single-phase generators that were staggered 90 degrees apart as "a step towards a coming polyphase supply system."[762] By this time, Westinghouse could clearly see how promoting the connection between his name and Tesla's would only help his business, as Tesla was making the rounds with his Tesla coil and everyone was amazed. For that reason, Westinghouse created the entrance to the electrical pavilion at the world's fair with the words "Westinghouse Electric & Manufacturing Co. [with] Tesla Polyphase System."[763] For the next 10 years, Westinghouse pushed his connection to Tesla at every turn.[764] According to Lamme, these actions were successful and "it was remarkable how quickly the public actually took to the polyphase generator."[765]

Although Westinghouse promoted "polyphase" generators and motors, he really meant two-phase, not three-phase, and according to Lamme, who became the chief engineer at Westinghouse Electric, "There were two polyphase schools, so to speak, namely the two-phase and the three-phase. The Westinghouse Company was known as the advocate of the two-phase polyphase systems, although it built both; whereas the General Electric Company was considered as favoring three-phase, although it also built both."[766]

It is ironic that Westinghouse was at the forefront of electricity technology by leading his company to produce indoor AC lighting, then found his company behind GE in the implementation of three-phase power. However, after losing out on some electrical bids, Westinghouse and his company ultimately gave up on two-phase electricity and, according to Lamme, "the three-phase system eventually dominated the market,"[767] as it has done ever since.

Chapter Summary

✧ **1884:** Lucien Gaulard and his backer John Gibbs demonstrate step-down transformers in Turin, Italy.

✧ **1885:** Westinghouse reads about Gaulard-Gibbs's transformer and creates a modern-style transformer. Ferraris creates a two-phase motor and generator but doesn't patent it.

✧ **1886:** Westinghouse Electric Company is formed. Stanley electrifies a town using AC. Edison hears about Westinghouse and becomes convinced that AC is deadly.

✧ **1887:** Tesla patents his two-phase generator; copper price goes up; Edison decides that Westinghouse's AC current would be best to kill criminals.

✧ **1888:** Edison writes "A Warning," and newspapers attack AC. Harold Brown writes about the dangers of AC and kills dogs and horses in demonstrations. Westinghouse buys Ferraris's motor and then Tesla's.

✧ **1890:** In August, William Kemmler is executed with AC. It does not go well. Bank failures put Westinghouse and Edison on shaky ground.

✧ **1891:** Dolivo-Dobrovolsky demonstrates three-phase, three-wire electrical long-distance distribution. Westinghouse switches to 60 Hz. Tesla demonstrates Tesla Coil.

✧ **1892:** Edison is removed from his own company. Westinghouse gets the contract for 1893 world's fair in Chicago (World's Columbian Exhibition) and promotes his connection to Tesla. Lamme makes the "Tesla motor" work on an industrial scale and pushes two-phase generators.

✧ **1893:** Westinghouse lights the World's Columbian Exhibition with AC current from two single-phase generators that are 90 degrees apart to mimic two-phase generation and calls it "Tesla Polyphase Current" to use Tesla's name as free advertising.

Chapter 8

Our Electric World

(1890–Present)

*It was chiefly due to Mr. Westinghouse that we owe
the extensive introduction of alternating currents, for
it was he who first understood its value, and aided the
efforts of pioneers, of whom I may count myself one.*

– Nikola Tesla (1900)[768]

*The quirky inventor Nikola Tesla discovered
electricity as we know it today—alternating current, or
AC—and yet he is virtually forgotten. What happened?*

– Q & A with Jill Jonnes,
author of *Empires of Light* (2003)[769]

Ever since I first saw a picture of a Tesla coil, I've been fascinated with them. Just look at that iconic picture of Nikola Tesla sitting nonchalantly while lightning bolts fall all around him. Although the picture was done with double exposure, the lightning effects were real and are still impressive over 120 years later. If I can say that Matthias Bose's electric kisses and other electric party tricks inspired the electricity developments in the mid-1700s, I can certainly say that Tesla's coil inspired the development of electronics in the 1900s.

Although Bose is rarely mentioned in modern books, Tesla has become a household name and an inspiration to millions of scientists and engineers worldwide. However, there's a dark side to the Tesla adoration. There are many who believe in a kind of pseudoscience that involves conspiracy theories that say Tesla invented *all* of electrical science, including AC, and how he was on the cusp of giving everyone free electricity by vibrating the earth, only to be held back by evil bankers and scientists who hid the real science for their own nefarious reasons. I've also been told several times in real life that Tesla was following the wisdom of the ancient Mayans and Egyptians who built their pyramids to create unlimited electricity by vibrating the earth with the right frequency. Due to conversations like this, in this chapter I will discuss not only how we got our modern electric world, but also how these myths and fallacies took over our popular culture.

8.1 The Rise and Fall of Nikola Tesla

Despite the rise of polyphase motors and generators and Tesla's name being put on almost everything by Westinghouse, Nikola Tesla himself had very little to do with the actual design or implementation of any two-phase or three-phase system. Instead, he was focused on goals even more important and revolutionary—free energy and super robots. In other words, Nikola Tesla basically lost touch with reality, but his demonstrations were so beautiful that for a few years no one cared.

It all started on a trip to Paris to see a world's fair in 1889 when Tesla heard about how Heinrich Hertz had attached an antenna to a Ruhmkorff

Figure 1: Tesla in a promotional photo for his 1900 article in *The Century Magazine*

coil and "caught" the spark in a receiver a few feet away. Tesla said that when he learned of it, he immediately repeated it in his laboratory as he had "caught the fire of enthusiasm and fairly burned with desire to behold the miracle with my own eyes."[770] Tesla then decided that Hertz had just found that high frequency/high-voltage waves would resonate with the air and transmit electrical signals wirelessly. Tesla also believed and stated in 1891 that the universe had "infinite energy [where] the eternal recipient and transmitter of this infinite energy is the ether."[771] Tesla stated that as long as he could tap into that "infinite" energy with the right frequency, you could power everything with a small triggering source.

This was not only against the first law of thermodynamics, which states that energy is conserved (which had been widely accepted as a law of physics for 30 years by this point), but it's also a gross misunderstanding of something called resonance. Resonance occurs when waves oscillate in an object in a constructive way to produce a bigger wave. When we speak, the vibrations resonate in our vocal cords and then resonate again in our vocal tract. If you've ever seen the demonstration of someone singing a high note and breaking a glass, that's an example of resonance. Cooking food with microwaves is also resonance. In all of these cases, and millions more, the energy isn't created by the vibrating object. It's just that the object is the right shape or size for that particular frequency to vibrate well and not die out very quickly. Imagine you're in a small pool and you splash at the right rate so that the pool starts to have very large waves. This kiddie-pool tsunami would get its energy from you making all those small waves, not because there's some magical, infinite energy of the pool water that you can activate with a particular frequency.

Despite the iffy science, Tesla's modified Ruhmkorff coil, which was quickly renamed a Tesla coil, was amazing. Tesla had removed the Ruhmkorff coil's complicated battery-based voltage source and replaced it with an AC source. He then used transformers to create an even higher voltage and used what's called a tank circuit to create an extremely high frequency vibrating signal. Tesla then added plate antennae and found that the plates could ionize the air *near* the coils, which allowed him to electrify light bulbs with a single wire or electrify early fluorescent light bulbs without any wire at all (if they were between electrified plates). He also conducted experiments where the electricity would flow through a person's body, which he assumed would be harmless as you don't feel the shock.

On May 20, 1891, around one week after Dolivo-Dobrovolsky displayed his three-phase system at the Lauffen-Frankfurt electrical fair, Tesla gave his first demonstration of wireless electricity to tremendous acclaim. The *Electrical Engineer* crowed, "No man in our age has achieved such a universal scientific reputation in a single stride as this gifted young electrical engineer."[772] In 1903 a critic of Tesla's admitted that "Tesla ... burst upon the electrical world with the first of a series of the most remarkable lectures ever delivered before a scientific audience."[773] It is worth a moment to imagine how this demonstration must have felt to people in 1891. These coils still inspire awe in the present day, and in 1891, the sight of electric lights was enough to draw a crowd. No wonder Tesla was heralded as a genius, where every statement he made, no matter how ridiculous or problematic, was taken as profound. For example, in 1894, Tesla was asked why he wasn't as dark as a typical Serbian. He responded that his eyes used to be much darker "but that using his mind a great deal had made them many shades lighter," to which the reporter added that lightening one's eyes through mind control was a commonly known process.[774]

At the time, Tesla often voiced his admiration of Edison and emphasized his short time working for Edison at a small arc lamp subsidiary in 1884 at every opportunity, while rarely mentioning Westinghouse. For example, in 1894, Tesla's friend Thomas Martin wrote (in a book sanctioned by Tesla) that Tesla working at Edison's company "had been a goal of his ambition, and one can readily imagine the benefit and stimulus derived from association with Mr. Edison, for whom Mr. Tesla has always had the strongest admiration."[775]

Also, despite how it's often portrayed in the media, Edison held no ill will toward Tesla at this time. In fact, he made no connection between Tesla and the battle of the currents. Between February 1888 (when Edison wrote his "Warning" about the dangers of AC), and April 15, 1892 (when Edison was removed from his electric company), Edison never mentioned Tesla even once in public or in private letters. In addition, the only comments made *to* Edison about Tesla were two letters discussing the viability of arc lamp patents that they'd previously bought from Tesla[776] and a letter from a spy in Westinghouse's company in 1890 gleefully reporting that "Mr. Westinghouse has not in Pittsburgh a single continuous motor under construction.

They have one alternating current experiment, which is a failure, and Mr. Westinghouse has quarreled with Mr. Tesla [misspelled Mr. Tessler] who invented the alternate current motor."[777]

In truth, the closest that Edison and Tesla came to a rivalry was in the mid-1890s over X-rays. X-rays were first discovered on November 8, 1895, when a shy German scientist named Wilhelm Röntgen noticed that a florescent screen glimmered outside the side of a thickly covered cathode-ray tube. As Röntgen knew the covering that he placed around the tube would block even the strongest light from an arc lamp, he immediately realized that it was "a new kind of invisible light. It was clearly something new, something unrecorded."[778] Röntgen then started to hold up various items in front of the screen. Some of these items were a 1,000-page book, a pack of cards, tin foil, pieces of rubber, and metal plates, and he found that these new rays, which he dubbed X-rays, have "a penetrative power to a degree hitherto unknown."[779] Things got crazier when Röntgen began to experiment with how powerful X-rays are by holding up a small lead disk between his machine and the florescent screen. He noticed not only the shadow from the disk but also the bones in his own hand. Röntgen then took X-ray photographs to validate his experiment, as without them he worried that people would say, "Roentgen has surely gone crazy."[780] Röntgen published in December of 1895, and the first newspaper report was written about it in January of 1896. After that, as Röntgen put it, "all hell broke loose."[781] Within days, Edison, Tesla, and basically every scientist or tinkerer with access to a cathode-ray tube and a Ruhmkorff power source dropped everything and started playing with X-rays.

At first, Tesla clearly felt that he had a close connection to Edison. In February 1896, when Tesla was delayed in making a cathode-ray tube for a doctor to experiment with medical X-rays, Tesla told the man to go ask Edison. Tesla assured the doctor that Edison would be delighted to give the doctor a tube as a favor to Tesla. (Note that every doctor in the world was clamoring for a cathode-ray tube at this time and many doctors were going to physics departments at universities in desperation.)[782] Then, after Edison, in an uncharacteristic altruistic act, actually complied, Tesla sent a letter to Edison that is tragically lost, but it seems apparent that Tesla suggested some sort of X-ray collaboration. Edison politely refused, writing, "My Dear Tesla,

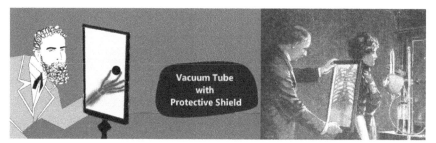

Figure 2: Röntgen discovering the medical X-ray by holding up a small lead disk in front of a fluorescent screen December 1885 (left); Doctor using an Edison screen to see a live X-ray of a patient circa 1906 (right)

Many thanks for your letter. I hope you are forgiving and will give us something that will beat Roentgen."[783]

Meanwhile, Edison came up with the disturbing idea of using X-rays to make a more efficient light bulb. The theory is that since X-rays caused a florescent screen to glow, maybe they could just coat a cathode ray with a good florescent, and then the cathode ray would produce X-rays, which would cause the florescent coating to glow with a visible light. Of course, X-ray fluorescent bulbs would let some X-rays leak into the room that could potentially be fatal, but no one knew that yet. Edison quickly found that the material that Röntgen used for his screen glowed when hit by X-rays but wasn't particularly efficient, as it took close to an hour to create a discernible shadow image of bones.

Thomas Edison and his team then tediously examined over 1,800 chemicals and minerals under X-rays. By March 25, 1896, Edison found that a screen of calcium tungstate would glow the best under X-rays. Soon, Edison began selling what he dubbed a "fluoroscope" for doctors to use.[784] Although Edison saw the profit in medical X-ray screens and even X-ray machines to be used in arcades for amusement, he still focused on X-ray fluorescent lamps. By May 19, 1896, Edison filed for a patent for an X-ray fluorescent bulb.[785] Edison never ended up marketing them as his eye was injured by looking at X-ray machines in 1901. Then, one of his employees, named Clarence Daly became deathly ill from the machines, and Edison gave up on X-rays entirely. In 1903 Edison and Daly tried to warn the public about the dangers of X-rays, and Edison told a reporter, "No, I do not want to know anything more about X-rays. In the hands of experienced operators, they are a valuable adjunct to surgery ... but they are dangerous [and] deadly."[786] *

However, back in 1896, a few days after Edison filed his patent, Tesla also pronounced that he had developed his own X-ray-based fluorescent bulb but refused to give any details aside from proclaiming that the light was "as steady as the sun and more brilliant than any artificial light now in use."[787] Irritated, Edison complained, "Let Tesla come along and show [his X-ray light]. What counts in the world is the man who produces, not the man who talks." The newspapers breathlessly pronounced, "Edison and Tesla Rivals: Each Has Invented a Vacuum Electric Light of Wonderful Softness and Illuminating Power."[788] However, this rivalry was short lived and minor. A few days later, a rival of Edison's and Tesla's named Moore tried to use that article to insult Tesla, and Edison wrote the editor that it was "foolish."[789] First, according to Edison, one shouldn't insult Tesla because "Tesla is of a nervous temperament and it will greatly grieve him and interfere with his work." And second, although Edison admitted that Tesla often stated results optimistically, "it must not be forgotten by Mr. Moore that Mr. Tesla is an experimenter of the highest type and may produce in time all that he says he can."[790]

However, Tesla didn't produce all that he said he could and quickly stopped talking about X-rays. In April 1896, Westinghouse made terms with GE for the exchange of licenses, and they decided it was cheaper to "purchase outright for $216,600 the Tesla patents for multiphase current motors, in order that both companies might manufacture apparatus covered by those patents without the payment of royalties."[791] This gave Tesla the money to make his Tesla coil even more dramatic and allowed him to conduct more experiments on remote control devices.

Flush with cash and fame, Tesla's claims of discovery became, well, ... bizarre. In 1898 Tesla announced that he'd made a remote-controlled torpedo that would revolutionize warfare by destroying entire navies in one strike. If that wasn't enough, he said this device would soon be controlled with his mind. In response, a physics professor at Tufts University wrote, "During the last six years he has made so many startling announcements and has performed so few of his promises that he is getting to be like the man who called

---

* Edison is often blamed for the death of Daly from X-rays, but this was a rare event where, in my opinion, Edison acted honorably. No one initially knew the dangers of X-rays, but once it was clear, Edison publicized the perils of X-rays even though it made his X-ray light bulb useless and reduced interest in his fluoroscope.

'Wolf! Wolf!' until no one listened to him. Mr. Tesla has failed so often before that there is no call to believe these things until he really does them."[792] Another professor added, "The shortest, most correct and complete criticism which I can make in reference to this bold boast is that what is new about it is useless, while that which is useful had all been discovered by other scientists long before Tesla."[793]

Meanwhile, Tesla wasn't the only one who had been inspired by Hertz's discovery of radio waves, and it all had to do with a speech after Hertz's death. After Hertz's early demise in January of 1894, an English scientist named Oliver Lodge wanted to give a talk about Hertz's work. However, Hertz's experiment had a receiver that was incredibly hard to see, which wouldn't work well for a public talk. Luckily, Lodge read that a tube of metal filings would stick together, or cohere, if a radio wave (or Hertzian wave as it was then known) went through it. So, on June 4, 1894, Lodge put on a demonstration. He created a spark from a Ruhmkorff coil on one side of a room that would cause a coherer to conduct electricity and cause a mirror to turn. It was instantly apparent to everyone who watched or read about this experiment that these waves could send a signal wirelessly. After the talk, the scientist Lord Rayleigh told Lodge, "There's your life work!"[794] Lodge, however, wasn't interested in profiting from experiments and preferred to be at the Royal Institute where, according to him, "pure science was enthroned to be worshipped for its own sake."[795]

After Lodge, it seemed like every tinkerer and scientist who wasn't playing with X-rays was trying their hand at wireless telegraphy. In July of 1897, an Italian Scottish man named Guglielmo Marconi filed his first patent for a system to transmit electrical signals that was based on Lodge's demonstration from three years earlier.[796] Two months later, Tesla filed for a patent for the "Transmission of Electrical Energy," which was supposed to use his Tesla coil to light lamps and power motors a distance away. Tesla felt the very high frequencies involved would "render the air strata at or near the elevated terming conducting, causing thereby a propagation of electrical energy by conduction."[797]

It turns out that the high frequency waves were not making the air conductive very far from the coil, which is why this effect is called the near-field effect. Unfortunately, Tesla did not know this fact. In theory, Tesla's device *could* have been used for sending electromagnetic signals, although it wasn't particularly effective. Tesla did say that "while the description here given contemplates chiefly a method and system of energy transmission … the apparatus which I've shown will obviously have many other valuable uses, for instance when it is desired to transmit intelligible messages to great distances." Tesla then added that another use of his device would be to illuminate the atmosphere of Earth at night, and thereby remove the need for streetlamps, or "any useful changes in the condition of the atmosphere," or the manufacture of fertilizer, or whatever else anyone could think of, as he did "not wish to limit myself in this respect."[798]

After pouring most of his money from his polyphase patents into it, Tesla realized that he couldn't get his system to electrify light bulbs at any significant distance from his generator, no matter what frequency he used to tap into the "infinite" electricity of the universe. Frustrated, he decided that the energy wasn't in the ether but in the earth. In January 1900, Tesla came to Pittsburgh to ask for money for his system of hitting the earth with the right frequency and electrifying the entire globe. Westinghouse, who was as usual overextended in his financial planning (especially with fights over the priority of Tesla's polyphase patents), gave Tesla $6,000 as a personal check. When Tesla complained that it was nowhere near enough money, he suggested that Tesla try to get money from New York bankers instead.[799]

Then, in February of 1900, a Bell laboratory engineer with the unusually repetitive name of John Stone Stone filed a patent that used a Tesla circuit to send wireless signals, with no objections from Tesla.[800] Nine months later, Guglielmo Marconi also filed a new patent that used a Tesla circuit to send wireless signals that was startlingly similar to Stone's. Marconi then started his work trying to send wireless signals across the Atlantic while the patent office rejected his patent time and time again.

Meanwhile, Tesla's hold on reality was slipping further and further away. In June of 1900, a friend of Tesla's invited him to write an article for a popular magazine called *The Century Magazine*, and Tesla wrote 36 pages on "The Problem of Increasing Human Energy." In his article, "human energy" is represented by the equation $\frac{1}{2} mv^2$ where "V is a certain hypothetical velocity which in the present state of science, we are unable exactly to define and determine," but one could increase the "mass" of humanity "by the promotion of marriage, by conscientious attention to the children, and generally stated, by the observance of all the many precepts and laws of religion and hygiene."[801] This article was so incoherent that the magazine that published it was criticized: "They evidently do not know science from rubbish, and apparently seldom make any effort to find out the difference. They should at least submit their scientific literature to competent men for criticism and revision."[802]

At the same time, Guglielmo Marconi was having some successes in transmitting wireless signals long distances, and in December 1899, articles were filed for the "Marconi Wireless Telegraph Company of America" with capital of 10 million dollars.[803] Soon, the papers were filled with Marconi's accomplishments and struggles. In January of 1901, a London paper called *The Daily Mail* had a full-page article about Marconi where Marconi stated that he had sent a signal over 100 miles and was about to double and quadruple that feat.[804] Mere weeks later, in February 1901, Tesla wrote an article where he claimed that he could send electric power wirelessly at "rates of one hundred [*sic*] and ten thousand horsepower" and that he was moments away from sending "messages without wires … from one point to any other point of the globe, no matter how remote."[805] Moreover, he claimed that had already developed a system that could determine the position and speed of storms that were hundreds of miles away. Not satisfied with those claims, Tesla added that he had observed an electrical disturbance that made him convinced that "[he] had been the first to hear the greeting of one planet to another" and then talked about creating a machine for "communicating with the Martians" by sending them messages of "1, 2, 3." He was sure that they would respond with "4," and then, he was sure, "the progress toward more intelligible communication would be rapid."[806]

As you can imagine, this last article was ridiculed publicly, and Tesla's reputation among scientists and engineers plummeted. Despite this, Tesla continued to ask the New York elite for money for his projects. Eventually, Tesla convinced the financier J. P. Morgan that his system was superior and that he had patent priority over Marconi's system. In March of 1901, J. P. Morgan (who was still trying to take over Westinghouse's company) gave Nikola Tesla $150,000 to build a wireless station on Long Island, New York, and Tesla promised he would be able to communicate to London in six to eight months.[807] Tesla was positive that not only would he be able to send signals, but he'd also electrify the entire Earth and the atmosphere.

Immediately, Tesla began building a giant tower with the idea that he needed a big steel rod with 120 feet buried in the ground "to have a grip on the Earth so the whole of this globe can quiver."[808] However, in June, Marconi wrote an article for the *Electrical Review* talking about wireless telegraphy. This spooked Tesla, as it used a Tesla coil and had one end of the antennae grounded, which convinced Tesla that Marconi was trying to electrify the earth too. He now decided that his tower had to be even larger and went back to Morgan for more cash, as he "could not develop the business slowly in grocery-shop fashion."[809] However, there was another Wall Street stock market crash, causing the prices of everything to increase and resulting in millions of dollars lost for J. P. Morgan.[810] At first, Tesla blamed Morgan for the crash *while* he was asking for even more funding, which did not go over well with Morgan. Tesla just managed to smooth things over with Morgan when on December 12, 1901, Guglielmo Marconi said that he transmitted a wireless signal across the Atlantic.[811] By January 19, 1903, Marconi sent the first two-way transatlantic wireless signal from Roosevelt to King Edward and back, and Marconi was heralded as the winner of the wireless race.[812]

Tesla was undeterred, but Morgan was done with Tesla and his promises. Tesla continued as if nothing was wrong and built a 187-foot-tall mushroom-shaped tower with the hope that once Morgan saw the finished project, he would relent and start funding him again. By January 1904, Tesla wrote J. P. Morgan in desperation: "Since a year, Mr. Morgan, there has hardly been [a] night when my pillow was not bathed in tears."[813] But Morgan was unrelenting. Then, in June of that same year, the patent office reversed its 1900 decision and allowed Guglielmo Marconi a patent for a wireless transmitter with tuned oscillations, as he had an adjustable antenna and "the Stone patent does not show such an arrangement."[814]

By October, Morgan's secretary sent a curt message to another one of Tesla's financial pleas that said, "Mr. J. P. Morgan wishes me to inform you that it will be impossible for me to do anything on the matter."[815] Tesla replied that his life was like that of Job and "what chance have I to land the biggest Wall Street monster with the soul's spider thread?"[816] By 1906 Tesla had to lay off his employees at his tower. Then, in 1914, the Titanic sank with John Astor on board—

Tesla's last remaining wealthy investor—which left Tesla few resources for new funding.[817] Tesla continued to live a luxurious lifestyle at the exclusive New York hotel the Waldorf Astoria. In late 1915, the owner of the hotel became frustrated with the "peculiar odors" and the "inordinate amount of pigeon excrement" coming from Tesla's room and sent Tesla a bill for $19,000 in total rent due.[818] Tesla had to sign over the deed to his tower, Wardenclyffe, as collateral. In March of the following year, Tesla was humiliated and taken to bankruptcy court, as he couldn't pay $935 in back taxes. He claimed to have "scores" of debts, no money in the bank, and no physical assets and lived "mostly on credit."[819] Wardenclyffe was knocked down for scraps in July of 1917.[820]

Tesla still had his die-hard fans, but most people felt, as an article from 1902 put it, that "Aside from his polyphase work … Tesla has gradually sunk into oblivion and even his claims to the fatherhood of wireless telegraphy, both mundane and Martian, are not sufficient to bring him forth into the light of popular esteem in which he was formerly held."[821] In spite of this downfall, both Westinghouse and GE were blanketing the nation with alternating current power stations (two-phase for Westinghouse and three-phase for GE) that relied on Tesla's patents. Mikhail Dolivo-Dobrovolsky was rarely mentioned, and Tesla's reputation as the inventor of "polyphase current" and the induction motor was taken as fact, at least in America.

8.2 The Wizard of Schenectady

The reason that GE could go straight from DC to leading America's implementations of three-phase electricity was because, in December, 1892, GE bought a company called Osterheld and Eickemeyer, which gave GE some much-needed patents for motors for streetcars and the services of a rising star in the world of electrical engineering, 27-year-old Charles Proteus Steinmetz.[822] Steinmetz was more than a good three-phase electrician—he actually revolutionized the math and science behind electronics.

Steinmetz had immigrated to America in 1889 after he escaped Germany ahead of the authorities who wished to arrest him due to his strong belief in socialism.[823] When Steinmetz arrived in New York, he was almost refused entry—not because of his politics, which they didn't know about, but because of his physical appearance (Steinmetz had inherited a condition called achondroplasia with kyphosis, or a very short stature with an unusual curvature of the spine, from his father and grandfather).[824] Fortunately, an American friend convinced the immigration officials that he was a genius "whose presence would someday benefit all of America."[825] After pretending that his personal wealth was actually shared by the two men (and possibly a bribe), the customs officials reluctantly agreed to let him enter the US. At the time, Steinmetz was mostly a mathematician and, although he had written a few articles about electrical systems, he had never even seen a transformer before.[826]

Steinmetz was in debt, had no job, and spoke almost no English. However, he had a letter of introduction to meet a fellow German political immigrant named Rudolf Eickemeyer, who ran a company that made machines for producing hats and who also had a side interest in electric motors. Within a year, Steinmetz spoke fluent English and was Eickemeyer's right-hand man and he and Eickemeyer had designed a single-phase AC motor that they were sure would work well for streetcars.[827]

At the time, people were very confused about the physics of AC electricity, as an American electrician named George Prescott noted in 1887: "It is a well-known fact that alternating currents do not follow Ohm's law, and nobody knows what law they do follow."[828] Steinmetz had an instinct that AC *did* follow Ohm's law, and he felt that the explanation for the apparent discrepancy was because of something called magnetic hysteresis, or magnetic lag.

Back in 1861, a man named Philip Reis invented a crude telephone (the same one that was used by Edison to try to get around Bell's telephone). Four years later, a British American scientist and inventor named David Hughes improved it tremendously, although Hughes never patented it and instead used it for physics studies. By 1879 Hughes noted that "in experimenting with the microphone I had ample occasion to appreciate the exquisite sensitiveness of the telephone to minute induced currents," which inspired him to make a "perfect induction balance [which] allows us to obtain direct comparative measures of the force or disturbances produced by the introduction of any metal or conductor."[829] Hughes's results then inspired a Scottish engineer and professor named James Alfred Ewing to study magnetism in detail with the Hughes meter. This is how Ewing realized that metals in an electrified coil take a short amount of time to reach their full magnetic power and a similar amount of time for the metals to lose their magnetism when the current was removed— which is why he named it hysteresis, for the Greek "to be behind."[830]

Steinmetz immediately realized that since AC transformers have coils of wire wrapped around iron bars, AC transformers appeared to not follow Ohm's law because the magnetism of the iron lagged behind the current in the wires. In addition, he realized that this "magnetic lag" could affect how efficient the transformers were. By 1890 Steinmetz had made his first equation for power loss due to hysteresis, and in 1892, Steinmetz determined that due to hysteresis the transformer's efficiency was dependent on the frequency.[831] In addition, Steinmetz found that the amount of eddy currents (or currents swirling around the wrong direction) also depended on the frequency so that for a set voltage, the loss on a line was higher for AC then for DC.[832] These laws finally explained why so many had experimentally discovered that lower frequency had less loss in transmission.

Steinmetz's talk on hysteresis in January 1892 was a huge hit. The *Electrical Engineer* magazine said that they had seen many important papers there, "but we believe that none of more absorbing interest and practical utility has been presented to the Institute than that of Mr. Charles P. Steinmetz last week on the Law of Hysteresis."[833] Steinmetz was suddenly one of the leaders in the emerging engineering world, and we still use Steinmetz's laws to this very day.[834]

It was only a few months after Steinmetz's 1892 hysteresis talk that J.P. Morgan fired Edison and transformed Edison's General Electric to make plain old General Electric. Morgan then turned to purchasing as many electrical companies as he could. By December 1892, Eickemeyer sold his patents to GE, and Steinmetz, as well as all of Eickemeyer's employees, became GE workers.

Steinmetz seemed resigned to being part of a massive conglomerate. He wrote a friend in Germany, "That is the way it is here now—only the two giant companies, General Electric and Westinghouse can make use of inventions." Steinmetz added that he had preferred to work for Westinghouse, but he didn't fight it as he assumed that "it is only a matter of time as to when G.E. and Westinghouse will combine."[835]

GE was delighted with Steinmetz. Edwin Rice, the new technical director (and eventual president) of GE, recalled that Steinmetz "abolished the mystery and obscurity surrounding alternating current apparatus, and soon taught our engineers how to design such machines with as much ease and certainty as those employing the old familiar direct current."[836] The people at GE wisely realized what a prize they had in Steinmetz and gave him free rein. As Steinmetz told a friend, "[I] have unlimited power to work at what I wish, to go and come as I like, and only if I discover anything I inform the Company and let them have the patent."[837]

Steinmetz joined GE at an opportune time. On February 5, 1893, an engineer named Almarian Decker, who had been impressed with the three-phase Lauffen–Frankford transmission of 1891, insisted that a new plant in California use three-phase electricity.[838] Westinghouse only offered two-phase and, therefore, lost out on the contract. The new management of GE realized that there was an opening and put Steinmetz in charge of their new three-phase system. In 1893 GE became the first company to build a three-phase transmission system in America.[839] By January 1894, there were four three-phase systems built by GE and Steinmetz and none by Westinghouse. At this time, Steinmetz noted with pride that his 100-horsepower three-phase motors were popular, stating that "quite a number have been built and are now in successful operation."[840]

Steinmetz realized that most of the engineers he was working with could not keep up with his mathematics and did not have the skills to understand him. In July of 1893, Steinmetz created a new form of mathematics for studying AC systems. Steinmetz managed to simplify the difficult mathematics previously needed and with his new math stated that "the combination of sine waves is reduced to … elementary algebra."[841] What Steinmetz did was change the trig function of sine waves to a vector with a real and an imaginary part that could tell you both the amplitude of the wave (from the square root of the two parts squared) and the phase of the wave (from the inverse tangent of the ratio of the two parts). Steinmetz called it the symbolic method, but it is now called phasors, and it is still used to this day in electrical engineering design.[842]

The mathematics of phasors were to have an immediate effect on electrical distribution, as in February 1894 a Westinghouse employee named Lewis Stillwell told another engineer named Charles Scott that their two-phase four-wire system would cost $10,000 more to install to distribute electricity 10 miles than GE's three-phase three-wire system. Stillwell therefore wondered if they should just try three-phase, but Scott reminded him that their motors were two-phase. Scott had an insight that, for them, the "ideal arrangement would be a three-phase transmission line for supplying two-phase distributing circuits."[843]

Inspired, Scott sat down and drew a triangle with a line bisecting it. Thinking about the lines as vectors, as Steinmetz had suggested, Scott devised a method of changing three-phase power into two-phase or vice versa. Scott recalled, "When the commercial necessity was presented, the engineering problem was formulated, and a simple vector diagram was the key to the solution."[844]

The Scott-T transformer was a big hit, and soon Westinghouse's company was producing mixed three-phase and two-phase systems. For example, when they wanted to extend the electricity at Niagara to Buffalo in 1896, Westinghouse used the Scott-T transformer to transform the two-phase into three-phase to save money on the transmission of electricity and then another Scott-T transformer to transform it back to two-phase to use with their Tesla motors and light systems.[845]

Once Steinmetz heard of the Scott-T transformer, he immediately realized that he could sell three-phase motors to businesses electrified by Westinghouse if they worked at 60 Hz instead of 50 Hz, so he recommended "60 cycles as standard frequency for alternate current circuits for light and power distribution"[846] (although GE sometimes still used DC, 133 Hz, and 33 Hz depending on the situation).[847]

In 1894 Steinmetz was transferred to the Machine Works laboratory in upstate Schenectady, New York, which Edison had formed when he married his second wife but was no longer in charge of. In 1911 Steinmetz recalled that "Schenectady had a reputation at that time of being very similar to a cemetery. I was very agreeably disappointed to find that reputation underserved … and do not intend to live anywhere else."[848]

Steinmetz soon moved into a rented house, referred to as Liberty Hall, with his assistant Ernst Berg and Ernst's brother Eskil. Then, Ernst started adding strange pets—pets that Steinmetz formed a particular attachment to—and soon they had "a small-sized menagerie of queer pets," including "racoons, supposedly tame; an alligator or two, the special pets of Steinmetz; owls, squirrels, monkeys, and a pair of crows, with which Steinmetz … professed to be able to converse with."[849]

Steinmetz was particularly close to the crows, named Mary and John, and was heartbroken when a pet raccoon got free and ate them. They also had cranes, bald eagles, dogs, and more squirrels than anyone could count. They also formed the Mohawk River Aërial Navigation Club, which was America's first glider club. However, they couldn't really get any of their prototypes off the ground and made a few jumps; nothing they produced "could be dignified with the term 'flight.' "[850]

This wasn't as much as an all-boys club as you might think as there were several women and many children who would visit regularly, including a neighbor named Mrs. Krueger, her children, and Steinmetz's sister Clara, who would often stay for long periods until the craziness of the situation became too much, when she would escape to her own devices in New York.[851]

Then, in 1900, the club started to break up as the Berg brothers moved away to work at other jobs or to live less bohemian lives on their own. Still, Steinmetz continued to have a steady stream of visitors, both engineers and local families.

It was around this time that the president of GE, Edwin Rice, finally agreed to Steinmetz's idea that they should start a collaborative theoretical research group at GE, which they started at Steinmetz's stable that he was using as a home laboratory. After an accident in January of 1901, Steinmetz's home laboratory burned down and the GE research laboratory moved to its own building where the research groups flourished.[852]

Meanwhile, Steinmetz decided to build his own house, factory, and conservatory, which were described as a "Den of incomprehensible perplexity."[853] Steinmetz also bought a little shack on the side of a river, and soon he had groups of partiers visiting every summer weekend for long parties and constant attempts to dam the river. (He famously checked the stability of the shack by hosting a large party and putting the band and the punch bowl at the weak end. When it survived the night, Steinmetz figured it was stable enough to live in.)

By this time, Steinmetz's reputation was exploding, at least with engineers. In 1901 Steinmetz was elected president of the American Institute of Electrical Engineers, and in 1902, he was awarded an honorary degree from Harvard. When Steinmetz accepted his degree, the president of Harvard declared, in an American-centered way, that Steinmetz was "the foremost electrical engineer in the United States, and therefore the world."[854]

The following year, a liberal college in Schenectady called Union College gave Steinmetz an honorary doctorate and hired him as a professor of electrical engineering. They just made up the whole department as they had no electrical engineering department—heck, they had no electrical engineering classes before him. Steinmetz was excited about the job and decided to do it for free.[855]

It was around this time that the press started to get interested in Steinmetz. It started in March of 1903, when *Success* magazine ran a big article about Steinmetz where they said, "He is known and recognized by engineers everywhere as the man who probably knows more about the practical application of electricity than any other man in this country."[856] Soon the newspapers were full of articles about Steinmetz, which was pushed by Union College and GE. GE was particularly happy to have a flamboyant face to humanize their company, especially as it was awkward to promote Edison as he had been fired just 10 years earlier.

Steinmetz, who always liked to live communally, became particularly close to a young engineer named Joseph "Roy" Hayden. When Hayden married in 1903, Steinmetz invited the newly married couple to live with him, and the three people (which quickly grew to six with the arrival of Hayden's three children) lived in bohemian happiness for the rest of Steinmetz's life. In 1905 Steinmetz formally adopted Hayden and acted as a devoted and attentive grandfather to his grandchildren.

Steinmetz then decided that, as he was so often called to look at special problems, GE should form a special consulting department that was composed of the best specialist engineers so that they could swoop down and deal with any emergency. In 1909 GE created that department and made Steinmetz the head.[857] Now, of course, every tech company has such departments.

Meanwhile, Steinmetz continued to be an active socialist, if not a particularly radical one. He said that America "has given me everything I wanted… the only criticism which I can make is that I would far more enjoy my advantages if I knew that everybody else could enjoy the same."[858] Steinmetz was therefore delighted when, in 1911, Schenectady elected a socialist mayor named George Lunn. Steinmetz immediately offered his services and was nominated to be on the board of education, which immediately elected him president. Steinmetz learned that the town had quadrupled in size but that the schools had not increased enough in size and that there were over 3,000 students who were unable to get an education. Within two years, Steinmetz had built three new

Figure 3: Steinmetz and his adopted family in 1908

schools, enlarged two more, built numerous playgrounds, set up a system of school meals, set up systems of school doctors, and created an epidemic plan (which was good timing as the pandemic of 1918 was just about to arrive).[859] However, he was stymied by the board of apportionment, which never seemed to be willing to pay for all of this. Therefore, in 1913, he left his position at Union College to his old pal and former roommate Ernst Berg and ran to be on the board. Unfortunately, both Steinmetz and the mayor, Lunn, lost. It took two more years, but in 1915, both the mayor and Steinmetz won, and Steinmetz stayed on the board, focused on education issues, for the rest of his life. Steinmetz was also pushing for environmental conservation saying, "We have been a wasteful nation because of our great natural wealth … we have been destroying our forests to get lumber in the most extravagant way. We have taken out crops year after year and never put anything back in the earth. There has been no such thing as conservation. It has been destruction."[860]

You might wonder how his political and environmental feelings meshed with working for a giant energy conglomerate like GE. However, to Steinmetz, working at GE was part of his socialist and environmental beliefs. He felt like modern technology was the key, "to develop the most perfect civilization the world has ever seen. This civilization not for a minority depending on the labor of masses of slaves or serfs but a real civilization of benefit to all the members of the human race."[861]

But how could we reach this perfect society without destroying the environment? In 1913, Steinmetz believed he was working on the answer: "Electricity, my friend!...Electricity will take the place of coal, and will do the work a thousand fold better. The time is not far."[862]

Amusingly, Steinmetz was also a leader in electric cars. In January 1914, Steinmetz gave a talk with the title of "The Future of Automobiling Belongs to the Electic" as he said that gas cars were very expensive and, unlike a horse, an electric car "requires no attention."[863] Edison immediately asked Steinmetz if he could add that the electric car requires no attention "if equipped with an *Edison* battery."[864] Steinmetz agreed and even signed the ad. Edison used this endorsement and his image to promote the Edison battery.

Then soon after that (or perhaps before) Steinmetz bought a 1914 Duplex Drive Brougham Detroit electric car.[865] However, these early cars were very difficult to operate especially for Steinmetz with his physical limitations, so he started to tinker with it. By March, 1920, Steinmetz declared that he had made a better system and actually formed his own company, the "Steinmetz Electric Motor Car Company."[866] Some Steinmetz trucks were produced in 1922 and had very good press.[867]

Meanwhile, in April of 1921, Albert Einstein went on a tour of America to raise money for a Jewish college as he was starting to see "countless examples" of how Jewish students in Germany were being deprived of educational opportunities (not realizing that Germany was just getting started on that score).[868] This was just after the end of WWI, so the anti-German feeling was very strong, but Einstein was so famous that everyone flocked to see him and to use him to promote their cause or business. It was for that reason that the Radio Corporation of America had a big to-do with Einstein. GE took the opportunity to invite their top stars, like Irving Langmuir, Albert Hull, Steinmetz's old friend Ernst Berg, and of course, Charles Proteus Steinmetz, to the party (see figure 4).[869] *

Many years after the event, GE edited the picture so that it looked like it was just Einstein and Steinmetz and claimed that Steinmetz and Einstein "talked together for hours" about science, engineering, and socialism.[870] GE

---

* Note that, according to the *RCA News* article about this meeting, the man standing between Einstein and Steinmetz was an employee of AT&T named John Carson, not Tesla.

Figure 4: Steinmetz and Einstein in group photo, 1921

liked to exaggerate Steinmetz's popularity, but it is true that after the meeting, Steinmetz gave a series of lectures about Einstein's theory of relativity for laymen, to give people "a general knowledge and understanding of the new ideas on time and space."[871] Also, in February of 1922, Steinmetz wrote Lenin a letter offering his services to help out Russia with their electricity systems. Lenin politely declined but sent a signed picture and publicized their letters.[872] Steinmetz then put that portrait on the wall and insisted that every visitor had to admire it. GE was a little nervous about having Steinmetz doing this publicly, but he was just too famous for them to fire or reprimand.

Part of the reason for this fame is that in March 1922, mere weeks before Lenin published their letters, GE invited the press to see Steinmetz demonstrate the first artificial lightning bolt with power.[873]

Steinmetz had actually built his artificial lightning device in the fall of 1921 after his vacation cabin was struck by lightning two summers before. Steinmetz had already used his mathematical calculations to determine that lightning was not useful for commercial purposes, noting that it may have immense power (he calculated around 600 million horsepower), but it only lasted for two millionths of a second. So, "the electricity in a cloud that can hurl a thousand lightning-bolts is worth just ten dollars!"[874] However, this act of nature inspired Steinmetz to use "modern" technology to recreate lightning, which he did with two hundred of what were basically Leyden jars in the form of glass slabs, which would produce around 120,000 volts. This was just a fraction of a real lightning bolt, which Steinmetz estimated averaged between 50 to 100 million volts.

Steinmetz knew that higher voltages had been made before, specifically by Elihu Thomson and Nikola Tesla. But according to Steinmetz, "Mere high voltage is not lightning and has no similarity to lightning in its action and effects."[875] Instead, you need something that produces high voltage *and* high current to create a lot of power for a short period of time. Steinmetz's lightning produced over a million horsepower for a hundred-thousandth of a second. Steinmetz said that a small tree "is mechanically torn to pieces by the flash. A piece of wire struck by it vanishes in dust."[876]109 But Steinmetz wasn't just interested in a big flash. He was doing all this to actually test lightning arresters (the lightning protectors for electrical power lines) for the first time. The front page of the *New York Times* declared, "Modern Jove Hurls Lightning at Will."[877]

Then, in October of 1922, just 5 months after Steinmetz demonstrated his lightning device for the first time and 4 months after Lenin published their letters, GE held this big party to celebrate Thomas Edison visiting Schenectady for the first time after 30 years.[878] The cover story was that Edison showed up to see the latest GE marvels including Steinmetz's lightning device. However, it was also a way for Edison to support Steinmetz during the Lenin controversy as well as converting "General Electric" back to "Edison's General Electric" at least in theory. From then on GE used Edison's image as their unofficial spokesman and used Steinmetz's story as a way to talk about AC without involving people unrelated to GE like Gaulard, the ZBD group, Dolivo-Dobrovolsky, Westinghouse, Stanley, or Tesla.

There's also another story about Steinmetz that's too delicious to leave out. One time, Henry Ford had a problem with a generator that his engineers couldn't fix, so he hired Steinmetz to take a crack at it. Steinmetz refused all help and after two days of observing the giant machine, made a mark on the generator with some chalk and told the engineers that they needed to remove 16 windings from the field coil at that point. When the engineers complied, the generator was fixed! Ford was delighted until he got a bill for $10,000, at which point he demanded an itemized bill. Steinmetz responded with a note that simply said:

Making chalk marks on generator $1
Knowing where to make mark $9,999
Total Due $10,000[879]

In fall of 1923, Steinmetz was invited to give a talk at the American Institute of Electrical Engineers in Del Monte, California. Steinmetz was excited, as he had never been to the West Coast. The whole family went together, and in Hollywood, Steinmetz was given a studio tour by none other than the famous movie star Douglas Fairbanks. Steinmetz loved the trip but found it a bit tiresome and declared that their next one would be to the Mediterranean. When he woke up in the morning, he said he still felt a bit tired. His son, Hayden, offered to get him breakfast in bed, and by the time Steinmetz's grandson came up with the tray, Charles Proteus Steinmetz had died of a heart attack. He was 58 years old.[880] His car company folded soon after.[881]

Steinmetz's fame continued after his passing, so much so that in 1968 *Life* magazine wrote a memorial to mark the centennial of his birth where they described him as "the man who did most to tame electricity to consumer use."[882] But as the years passed, his role began to fade, especially for the general public. In a way, Steinmetz's story is typical in that, with the passage of time, the reputation of scientists and inventors and their influences comes from various sources, many of which have nothing to do with the scientist's actual contributions, or lack thereof. Nowhere is that more apparent than in the disparity between the myth and the actual accomplishments of (in chronical order by the date of their deaths) George Westinghouse, Mikhail Dolivo-Dobrovolsky, Thomas Edison, and of course, Nikola Tesla.

8.3 Men Die and Their Myths Are Born

The end of George Westinghouse Jr.'s life was sadder and more stressful than the rest, and it all had to do with the insurance company Equitable Life and the financier J. P. Morgan. This story arguably begins on May 2, 1899, when a businessman named Henry Baldwin Hyde died. Hyde had tried his best in his will to bequeath the insurance company that he had founded in 1859 to his 22-year-old son, James. The reason that this was important is that Hyde's company, Equitable Life Assurance, was the largest life insurance company in the world.[883] The board of directors, led by J. P. Morgan, had no interest in letting a child run their company and tried to convince James Hyde to take up more amusing activities (would he like to be ambassador to France?)[884] and leave the boring business stuff to them.

When Hyde refused, J. P. Morgan started a smear campaign against him with allegations of fraud and abuse that were fueled by the fact that the life insurance companies were *all* rife with fraud. This culminated when Hyde held a lavish Versailles-style party (which I assume involved people dressing up as Marie Antoinette and Louis XVI and eating a lot of cake) on January 31, 1905.[885] The scandal soon went out of control. People got spooked and started to take their money out of insurance companies, and the entire financial system seemed on the brink of collapse.

Because of the jeopardy to America's economy in June 1905, a businessman named Thomas Ryan bought the majority of the equitable stock. He put it into a trust with three men of honor with "no connection to Wall Street" so that insurance could be restored to public confidence.[886] The three men Ryan asked were the former president Grover Cleveland, a New York Supreme Court justice named Morgan O'Brian, and our friend George Westinghouse.[887] That wasn't enough, and in September, a legislative committee was appointed in New York to "investigate the conduct and the condition not only of the equitable but of other life insurance companies as well."[888] By 1906 the trustees had cleaned up the company, and new rules were created. For example, insurance companies were forbidden from holding stock in other companies, from contributing to political funds, from having hidden slush funds (called "yellow dog" funds), and more.[889]

Not surprisingly, Westinghouse's already fraught relationship with bankers went even further downhill after being a part of this financial reformation. Meanwhile, the reformations in the insurance companies weren't enough to protect Wall Street from the corrupt practices of businesses. In 1907 after a stock manipulation attempt went awry, the entire stock market fell off a cliff in what was called the Panic of 1907. The stock market was saved only when bankers, led by J. P. Morgan, used their collective private wealth to personally shore up the market. According to *Morgan: American Financier,* many people at the time thought that Morgan and his banker friends "deliberately brought on the late panic, to serve their own ends."[890] Westinghouse, like almost every other manufacturer, found himself in financial trouble after the crash. This time, no bankers were willing to step up and deal with the wrath of J. P. Morgan, and soon Westinghouse's company was run by a manager, although it took until July of 1911 for Westinghouse to lose all control.[891]

Westinghouse was devastated by this loss and soon found himself deteriorating physically due to heart problems possibly exacerbated by the stress.

As a coda to his work on electricity, in January of 1912, Westinghouse learned that the American Institute of Electrical Engineers (AIEE) was awarding him their highest honor for "meritorious achievement in connection with the development of the alternating-current system for light and power."[892] Ironically, at the time, their highest award was called the Edison Award and was initially formed by Edison's friends in 1904 in honor of the 25th anniversary of the light bulb (and Edison's 67th birthday), but by 1909 it had been administrated by the AIEE.[893] In his introduction, the scientist Michael Pupin acknowledged this apparent contradiction when awarding the honor, stating that "the medal named after the man Edison who twenty-two years ago was the chief opponent of the alternating-current system, goes to the man Westinghouse who twenty-two years ago was the chief defender of the alternating-current system."[894] However, Pupin felt that this was a sign that "the progressives and the conservatives of twenty-two years ago have become reconciled and they work as one unit."[895]

After the award, Westinghouse attempted to continue his work, but his poor health prevented this, and George Westinghouse died at the age of 67 on March 12, 1914. It seemed as if the entire city of Pittsburg mourned. Approximately 100,000 workers in Westinghouse factories halted work for an hour in honor of their founder,[896] 1,500 mourners attended his funeral, and a further 2,000 mourners attended his memorial.[897] He is still honored in Pittsburg to this very day, but outside that now-fair city, his reputation diminished over the years and was only revitalized in the 21st century as a character in the Tesla myth.

If Westinghouse's story was sad and stressful, poor Mikhail Dolivo-Dobrovolsky's was straight-up tragic. In 1914 Mikhail Dolivo-Dobrovolsky was the technical director of AEG and was leading Europe into three-phase systems. However, four months after Westinghouse's death, World War I began, and Dolivo-Dobrovolsky wisely decided that Germany wasn't a safe place to be for a Russian man and spent much of the war in Switzerland.[898] He returned to Germany in 1918, when Russia ended its participation in World War I (as they were busy with the Russian Revolution). However, by then Dolivo-Dobrovolsky was having health issues and died from heart problems in November 1919 at the age of 56.

The Germans, in the middle of losing World War I, weren't particularly interested in honoring the accomplishments of a Russian Polish man who'd abandoned them in their hour of need. The Russians were too busy with revolution to want to honor a man who had mostly accomplished things in Germany and hadn't participated in their revolution. As Americans were wholly invested in the story that Tesla had invented *all* of polyphase electricity (as Westinghouse and GE owned Tesla's patents), Dolivo-Dobrovolsky's influence and life story were mostly hidden, and his death mostly unremarked upon—especially considering his considerable influence on our electric world.

In the 1900s, while Mikhail Dolivo-Dobrovolsky's accomplishments disappeared from view and Westinghouse's reputation slowly faded, Edison's fame continued to grow and grow. Part of the reason for his stellar reputation was due to the eventual success of electric lights, record players, and movies—all fields that Edison announced early success with before others took them to financial and technical victories. The other source of Edison's renown was his very influential fan, Henry Ford.

Henry Ford met Thomas Edison at a dinner in 1896, but their relationship really took off in 1912 when Ford went to Edison with a pitch to design an electrical system for Ford's Model T. Edison wasn't interested but instead wondered if "Friend Ford" would "do a little gambling with me on the future of the storage battery" for an electric car.[899] Ford was more than agreeable, and by the end of 1913, Edison borrowed $700,000 from the young car manufacturer. It was the first of many gifts and loans, including more Ford cars for the Edison family than historians can count. In retrospect, it seems clear that Ford wasn't making business arrangements with Edison as much as propping up a hero, telling a reporter, "I think Mr. Edison is the greatest man in the world."[900] Ford remained Edison's closest friend and biggest fan for the rest of Edison's life.

Henry Ford always loved to collect old memorabilia. In 1919 after creating a lot of controversy by declaring that "history is more or less bunk," Ford decided to collect as many old shoes, watches, clocks, farm equipment, electrical devices, old cars, early planes, and as much old Americana as he could find and pronounced, "We're going to build a museum that's going to show industrial history, and it won't be bunk."[901] In 1928 Ford began a long-planned reconstruction of Edison's Menlo Park laboratory that was excruciatingly detailed and historically accurate, up to carting up seven railway cars full of New Jersey dirt.[902]

Ford decided to open the Edison Wing of his museum on October 21, 1929, to celebrate the 50th anniversary of Edison's manufacture of his first incandescent lamp. He called the celebration the Light's Golden Jubilee. This was an electric party to rival all electric parties, with John Rockefeller, Marie Curie, Orville Wright, Will Rogers, and over 500 other attendants.[903]

The party also featured live radio broadcasts, where people around the world were encouraged to listen with their lights off and only turn on the lights after Edison ceremonially flipped a switch to "give" them electricity. At the Ford Museum, a replica of the Liberty Bell was rung for the first time, and the president of the United States, Herbert Hoover, gave an enthusiastic speech that was followed by a radio address from Albert Einstein in Germany and then a small speech from the then ailing 82-year-old Thomas Edison.[904]

Edison died two years later in 1931 from complications from diabetes. Every paper was filled with accolades for Edison and his life. For example, the day he died the *New York Times* printed 22 articles about Edison.[905] After his death, Edison's fame and reputation continued unabated for 70 years. In one extreme example in 1997, *Life* magazine named Thomas Edison as the most important person on a list of "The 100 Most Important People in the Last 1,000 Years."[906] However, starting in 2000, Edison's reputation began to fall, as the rise of the Tesla myth painted Tesla as the world's greatest man while Edison was not just a man with serious faults but the world's greatest villain.[907]

In order to discuss the myth of Tesla, let's begin in May of 1917, when the American Institute of Electrical Engineers (AIEE) awarded Tesla an Edison Medal for inventing polyphase and for inspiring people with his coil. The introductions to the presentation of this medal were completely over the top. One address said that Tesla's introduction of his two-phase motor and generator was the creation of a "great experimental truth" and that Tesla "left nothing to be done for those who followed him." Moreover, without Tesla, "the wheels of industry would cease to turn, our electric cars and trains would stop, our towns would be dark, our mills would be dead and idle. Yea, so far-reaching is this work that it has become the warp and wolf of industry."[908]

The articles about Tesla's award were gobbled up by conspiracy theorists, including an editor of a radio magazine (and science fiction writer) named Hugo Gernsback. In 1919 Gernsback declared that the "present-day notions on wireless are totally erroneous and not based upon actual fact."[909] Gernsback then invited Tesla to correct the "scientific illusions" in his magazine, as well as in a series of autobiographical sketches that Tesla eventually published as a book. In this, Tesla stated that his discovery of the two-phase motor occurred while in a period of anxiety when his self-professed abilities to hear and see better than average people became heightened to a point that he "had the sense of a bat, and could detect the presence of an object at a distance of twelve feet by a peculiar creepy sensation on the forehead."[910] Tesla's words gained him more fans who were interested in denying "traditional science" as well as more disdain from people who knew that lightning does not cause the rain and bats do not see with their foreheads.

When Tesla compiled these articles into his autobiography in 1919, he still had nothing but kind words to say about Edison, writing that "[my first] meeting with Edison was a memorable event in my life. I was amazed at this wonderful man who, without early advantages and scientific training, had accomplished so much."[911] However, when Henry Ford held the celebration for Edison's 50th anniversary of the light bulb in 1929, Tesla became jealous of all the accolades that Edison was receiving. Tesla then wrote a letter to the

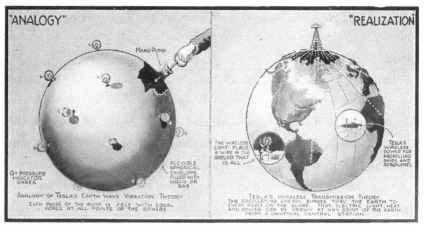

Figure 5: Hugo Gernsback's interpretation of how Tesla would "tap into" the earth's infinite energy

editor with a version of history that erased Westinghouse entirely from the narrative and pretended that Tesla had invented AC. Tesla wrote that Edison's "primitive scheme of lighting was subject to fatal economic limitations and could never proved [*sic*] a commercial success [and] it has been displaced by a more practical and efficient system based on my rotating magnetic field."[912] In addition, Tesla claimed that the war of the currents was between Edison and himself, writing that "Edison and his associates bitterly opposed the introduction of my system, raising a clamor against the 'deadliness' of the alternating current." Tesla even went as far as to claim that "had the Edison companies not finally adopted my invention they would have been wiped out of existence. … In truth, my system has not only provided energy for all purposes throughout the world but also revolutionized electric lighting and made it a great commercial success."[913]

Finally, Tesla said that most of the billions of dollars that electricity provided "can be traced to my system" and that Edison just took what was known and reformed it while "what I contributed constitutes a new and lasting addition to human knowledge… [that] will live as long as science itself."[914]

There's yet another disturbing event in Tesla's life. In the 1920s, Tesla met a young German American poet whom he had long admired named George Viereck, and they became close friends. A lawyer named Elmer Gertz recalled meeting Tesla at a party and recalled that Tesla "knew the entire body of Goethe's poetry by heart [and] all of Viereck's … and he talks of birds, pigeons, and ESP, all sorts of what seemed to me at the time unreal things."[915]

As the 1930s started, Viereck became more and more enamored of Nazi Germany, and Tesla became more and more enamored of Viereck, dedicating his one and only published poem to Viereck on December 31, 1934.[916] In February 1935, Viereck interviewed Tesla, and Tesla pontificated about eugenics with views that were fully aligned with the Nazi ethos. Here's what Tesla said:

> The year 2100 will see eugenics universally established. In past ages, the law governing the survival of the fittest roughly weeded out the less desirable strains. Then man's new sense of pity began to interfere with the ruthless workings of nature. As a result, we continue to keep alive and to breed the unfit. The only method compatible with

our notions of civilization and the race is to prevent the breeding of the unfit by sterilization and the deliberate guidance of the mating instinct. Several European countries and a number of states of the American Union sterilize the criminal and the insane. This is not sufficient. The trend of opinion among eugenists is that we must make marriage more difficult. Certainly no one who is not a desirable parent should be permitted to produce progeny. A century from now it will no more occur to a normal person to mate with a person eugenically unfit than to marry a habitual criminal.[917]

Seven months later, Tesla's wishes of making marriage more difficult for "undesirables" were fulfilled when the Nazis enacted the anti-Semitic and racist Nuremberg Laws, which were followed by international outrage and silence from Nikola Tesla.

In 1939 George Viereck continued to push Nazi propaganda, calling Hitler "a dynamic genius ... first in war, first in peace, first in the hearts of his country-men."[918] By 1941 Viereck was convicted by the US government for failing to register as a Nazi agent. (Viereck was so famous that in 1941 a senator named Alva Adams reminded his fellow senators that the Foreign Agent Registration Act was "the act under which George Sylvester Viereck was just recently indicted.")[919] Tesla didn't publicly speak up about Viereck, nor did he speak up against fascism when his hometown of Smiljan, Croatia, was taken over by a fascist group called the Ustaše in 1941, which was a Nazi puppet state. Tesla didn't even speak up when this new government, in the name of eugenics, killed hundreds of thousands of Tesla's fellow Serbs (as well his Jewish and Romani countrymen).[920]

Toward the end of his life, Tesla started to be followed around all day by a Pulitzer Prize–winning science journalist named John O'Neill. O'Neill had met Tesla when he was just a child working at the New York City library and had been a superfan ever since.[921] And like the superfans before him, whatever Tesla said was spun as brilliant, no matter how surreal or physically impossible. Thinking that lightning could make rain? Not correct but still "genius."[922] Spending months designing a ring made of dirt to be built around the equator of Earth like the rings of Saturn that would have its scaffolding removed and then be slowed to a stop to allow one to "travel around the Earth in a single day"? That was just an "excellent opportunity to use all of the mathematical techniques available to him."[923] Feeding pigeons because he was hoping that a pigeon that he had loved 20 years previously, "as a man loves a woman," would be reincarnated as another pigeon? That was "a fantastic situation, probably without parallel in human annals ... the love story of Tesla's life."[924] O'Neil went as far as to declare that "even the gods of old, in the wildest imaginings of their worshipers, never undertook such gigantic tasks of world-wide dimension as those which Tesla attempted and accomplished."[925]

When Tesla died in January 1943, O'Neill published a biography of Tesla that has been described as "pure hagiography" (pure idiolatry).[926] As the years progressed, Tesla gained a small but vocal cult following from both anti-science crusaders and engineers who loved his beautiful coil and were amazed by the power of three-phase motors and transmission (which they thought was invented by Tesla).

Five months after Tesla's death, on June 21, 1943, the United States Government sued the Marconi Wireless Telegraph Company of America as they had new letters from John Stone Stone that they felt proved that "Stone had conceived of the idea of tuning all four circuits prior to the date of Marconi's invention."[927] (This was also after the death of Guglielmo Marconi, John Stone Stone, and Oliver Lodge, but the whole point was for the US government to get around the Marconi wireless patent.) With this new information, the judge determined that "Stone anticipated Marconi, and that Marconi's patent did not disclose invention over Stone." Also, the judge declared that if they included the patents of Lodge and Tesla as well, "Marconi's patent involved no invention over Lodge, Tesla, and Stone."[928] Despite the fact that majority of the lawsuit was about Stone's patent, Tesla fans have taken this as proof that Tesla invented all of radio.[929]

Then, in October of 1960, a Slovenian electrical engineer named France Avčin suggested the name Tesla for a unit of magnetic flux density, which was accepted.[930] After that, there was a growing interest in the Tesla coil, especially by hardcore, do-it-yourself tinkerers who wanted to challenge themselves by trying to build Tesla's spectacular coil. By June 1964, *Popular Mechanics Magazine* had a five-page, step-by-step article on how to "Make Your Own Fantastic Tesla Coil."[931] Soon there was a cottage industry of DIY Tesla coils and renewed interest in Nicola Tesla and his story.

It was at this time that a few amateur scientists discovered the story of Edison and Brown and the public demonstrations killing animals. Several authors then folded it into the myth of Tesla and the Tesla-Edison "feud" that Tesla had created. For example, in March of 1967, *Amateur Radio Magazine* published an expose on Edison with no mention of Brown. The attack on Edison was focused on his interactions with Tesla (based on O'Neill's version of events) with the addition that Edison, "demonstrated the horrible dangers of alternating currents by electrocuting cats and dogs."[932] (Note that Nikola Tesla never mentioned the animal killing experiments. It seems as though the public view of animal experimentation was far different in the 1800s than it was in the 1900s to today.)

By the 1980s, Tesla had reached a bit of cult status in several circles, and there were multiple biographies written about him, all promoting the idea that Tesla invented AC, fought Edison and was responsible for all of modern technology. Despite this, Tesla was basically not mentioned in popular culture in the 1900s. That all started to change on December 12, 2000, when the American Public Broadcasting Station (PBS) published a documentary called *Tesla: Master of Lightning*. It began with the following: "This is the story of a modern Prometheus, who changed the world with electricity. It was Nikola Tesla who captured the power of Niagara Falls with his alternating current system and made it possible to transmit electricity to all of America and the world … He worked and locked horns with some of the most powerful people of his day: Thomas Edison, who resented his ideas, Guillermo Marconi, who capitalized on his inventions, [and] George Westinghouse, who created the Westinghouse Electric Company with Tesla's patents."[933] Despite the false narrative that this was presenting, this movie was to have a fundamental impact on our cultural and historical understanding, and it created a myth of Tesla that seems to grow as the years pass.

Why was this movie so influential? I can think of six reasons. First, it was a well-made documentary on a fabulous learning channel with clips from professors claiming all that was in it was true. Second, very few people know the details of the origin of electricity (or radio, as the movie states that Tesla invented all of radio as well, due to the Marconi patent loss of 1943), so it makes sense that Tesla was the lone genius behind everything. Third, the story told was satisfying to viewers, as it fit a comfortable and cinematic narrative of the lone genius David battling the evil corporate Goliath.

Fourth, it's easy to vilify a person who would do something as terrible as torture animals. In fact, the director decided that Edison's actual involvement in finding horses and dogs to kill with alternating current wasn't enough. The filmmakers therefore deceptively added a short film from Edison's film company from 1903 showing the death of a circus elephant that was being electrocuted *while* the narrator talked about how "Edison's employees demonstrated the dangers of alternating current by electrocuting animals in public demonstrations."[934] However, the elephant's gruesome death had nothing to do with the war of the currents and nothing to do with Edison. The elephant, Topsy, was killed because the circus decided that the elephant was dangerous.[935] The original idea was to have a public hanging, but the SPCA fought against it, so the circus owners decided to electrocute the elephant instead. They then sold tickets to the event, and although Edison's employees did have the bad taste to film and market it, Edison and his crew had no influence on deciding to kill an elephant nor in choosing electrocution.[936] In fact, this film was made 11 years after the war of the currents was over. However, one cannot stomach the horrific video of a terrible death of such a majestic animal without feeling that Edison was beyond evil.

Fifth, Tesla made a lot of wild statements about what he had accomplished, and some of these things have eventually been accomplished. If framed it the right way, it looks like Tesla *predicted* these events or even inspired them. For example, the filmmakers took Tesla's claim from 1898 that he had made a remote-controlled torpedo that could revolutionize warfare to say that Tesla's work led to the strategic defense system.[937] Finally, even well over 100 years after its invention, Tesla coils are really, really cool, and it's hard to not believe that a man who could invent such a fascinating "lightning" machine could be behind everything.

The PBS movie was widely popular, and soon Tesla clubs and Tesla books started to pop up all over the place. Two years after the Tesla documentary, in July 2003, two American entrepreneurs named Martin Eberhard and Marc Terpenning named their electric car company Tesla Motors after Nikola Tesla. (Elon Musk joined the company soon after.)[938] It became good PR to promote the story of Nikola Tesla as it also promoted their car.

Also, that same year, a historian named Jill Jonnes wrote the bestselling book *Empires of Light*. This was not a book by a Tesla fanatic but a well written and well researched historical study by a noteworthy historian. For example, in O'Neill's book Tesla claimed that when Westinghouse first met Tesla in 1888, Westinghouse instantly offered "one million dollars cash for your alternating current patents, plus royalty."[939] Jonnes didn't just accept that as fact and discovered that the numbers were actually $20,000 in cash, $50,000 in notes, and $2.50 per horsepower.[940]

However, Jonnes never informed the reader about any of Tesla's exaggerations or illogical statements. In addition, Jonnes fell for the whole story that Tesla invented all of AC, that he had a rivalry with Edison, and that Edison had kept Tesla from achieving all of his dreams of free electricity. I am not claiming any type of conspiracy here. Jonnes is clearly an excellent researcher and historian, which is actually the root of the problem. It seems to me that this combination of one misunderstanding propped up with true facts honestly told caused more long-term harm than all the fanfiction produced by Nikola Tesla sycophants combined.

Soon, Tesla was popping up all over the place in popular media as a genius, and Edison had morphed from the Father of Electricity into the ultimate villain. You can see this transformation by comparing the 1985 movie *Back to the Future* to the 2006 movie *The Prestige*. In *Back to the Future*, when a crazy scientist hears that he needs 1.21 gigawatts of power to return his friend to the future, he pours out his troubles to a picture and says, "1.21 gigawatts! Tom, how am I going to generate that kind of power?" The picture is of Thomas Edison, and the character then places the picture next to his other personal heroes, Isaac Newton, Benjamin Franklin, and Albert Einstein, with no Tesla in sight.[941] Fast-forward to the 2006 movie *The Prestige*, where Nikola Tesla is an actual character in the plot (played by the infinitely charismatic David Bowie) who had magical electrical powers and was being constantly hounded by an unseen Thomas Edison.[942]

One of the most damaging misconceptions to come out of Jill Jonnes's book, and the linchpin of the whole Tesla myth, was her parroting O'Neill's book regarding a story that Westinghouse and Tesla renegotiated their contract in 1891. Recall that, in 1891, Westinghouse had been convinced to use more money and manpower to attempt to finally make Tesla's motors work on an industrial scale at 60 Hz and that Tesla was paid royalties for his motor until 1896, when he was paid a lump sum of $216,600 so that GE and Westinghouse could use polyphase motors freely. However, according to O'Neill and Jonnes, the royalties were dropped in 1891 for free. In this telling, Westinghouse went to Tesla in desperate straits and begged Tesla to drop the contract for money per horsepower for his two-phase motor, stating that his decision "determines the fate of the Westinghouse Company," and adding, "I believe your polyphase system is the greatest discovery in the field of electricity."[943]

O'Neill also declared that Tesla ripped up the contract on the spot and that this act of generosity was a "gift" to Westinghouse that was worth a whopping $12 million, which probably caused Tesla to be "without funds with which to develop his discoveries."[944] In 2003 Jonnes upped the ante a bit more and declared, "Tesla should have been rich just from the royalties on AC, but, ever the idealist, he gave them up to save the Westinghouse Electric Company in a time of dire financial peril. Without his AC royalties, which would have been $17 million, Tesla never had enough capital to launch his expensive and ambitious projects."[945]

One cannot read O'Neill's or Jonnes's book, especially on that meeting, without concluding that Tesla invented all of AC, that Westinghouse's entire company was founded on Tesla's inventions, and that Tesla's other odd ideas were all possible if he hadn't been hampered by his personal generosity toward Westinghouse.

To figure this out, let's do a thought experiment. Imagine that Westinghouse was *not* convinced to restart the two-phase motor research in 1891. What would have happened? Tesla would still have demonstrated his coil and still have been famous for it. Benjamin Lamme would have been disappointed to not work on the induction motor, and the Westinghouse Company would be a bit behind in the electric motor "game." However, they still would have gotten the contract for the world's fair in Chicago (the contract was all about lighting not motors) and still impressed everyone with their now single-phase AC power.

Without Westinghouse's support for Tesla's patents, it seems very likely that Dolivo-Dobrovolsky would have won his three-phase patents. His name and influence would have been remembered, and GE, along with

Westinghouse, would have purchased his patent. Meanwhile, Dolivo-Dobrovolsky in Germany and Steinmetz in America (and others), would have perfected their three-phase induction motors, and GE and AEG would have pushed three-phase. In fact, the biggest difference as far as I can see in terms of the customers is that without Westinghouse pushing two-phase at 60 Hz, Steinmetz would have probably just copied Dolivo-Dobrovolsky in using the lowest frequency that didn't blink unpleasantly and used 50 Hz. In this scenario, the entire world would use the same frequency.

However, that didn't happen. Tesla's name was placed on most Westinghouse devices, and we are stuck with using two different frequencies depending on whether the area was initially electrified by a US or a European company. That brings up one more point: why are there so many different electrical standards for voltages, where a minority use between 100 and 127 volts and the majority use between 220 and 240 volts? The answer has to do with the Wallace-Farmer dynamo, Edison's three-wire DC system, tungsten light bulbs, and the city of Chicago.

8.4 A World of Electrical Dependence

In order to understand why every country seems to have its own unique electrical system of voltages, we need to start with Thomas Edison on September 8, 1878. That was the day that Edison visited William Wallace's factory and decided that Wallace's machines could be better used to light up thousands of incandescent lamps instead of a handful of too-bright arc lamps. Wallace's machine was designed to be at 110 volts, presumably because his DC arc lamps also worked at this voltage (or they worked at 55 volts, and he put two in series; it is unclear). Then, by the time that Edison decided that the Wallace-Farmer dynamos were not efficient enough, he determined that thin platinum would glow pleasantly at 110 volts and had his team design an improved generator to be at that same number. From then on, all Edison generators were set at 110 volts.[946]

After Edison started to electrify parts of New York from the first electrical power station in September of 1882, he noticed that some of his customers had brighter lamps than others. He realized that some people were on "popular" lines in locations where more people had turned on more lamps and had dimmer lights while the less popular lines would have brighter lamps.[947] In

November, Edison came up with an ingenious solution to balance out two lines and make them equal—use two DC generators in series with a "neutral" wire between them (see figure 6). In this way, the current from one generator would flow out of the positive electrode to the negative electrode, and the current from the other generator would do the same. No current will run in the center "neutral" wire if the system is in balance, but you can still connect between the "live" wire and the "neutral" wire to make a circuit for your lamp at 110 volts.

If the system is out of balance, however, current will run in the central wire. Edison could measure that with a current meter and then rearrange the connections (with a switch) to bring the system back into balance so that all lamps would have basically the same brightness. By using this system, you can electrify with three wires what used to take four, and as the center neutral wire had little to no current in it, it could be made with a very thin wire. In this way, Edison reduced the total amount of copper wire by over 60%.[948] Finally, if you wanted more power for a something like a motor, you could just connect to the two live wires and get 220 volts instead of 110 volts, which is exactly what Edison did.[949]

The only metal filament that Edison could make work in a bulb was made of platinum. Since that was too expensive to mass produce, he used bamboo or carbonized cotton filaments, even though they would burn out at 220 volts. Edison's competitors used similar filaments, and many (but not all) companies copied his 110 volts for bulbs and 220 volts for motors standard.

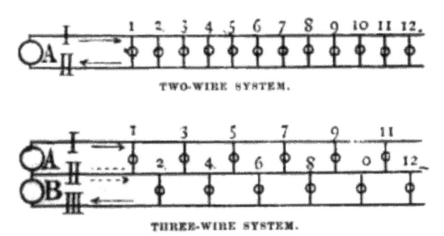

Figure 6: Edison's two-wire system compared to the three-wire system

Then, in 1904, inventors named Sándor Just and Franjo Hanaman filed a patent for a light bulb that used the metal tungsten instead of carbonized cotton or bamboo.[950] These could be used at far higher temperatures and voltages and lasted far longer. Then, in 1906, a man working at GEs research laboratory named William Coolidge patented a method to mass produce the filaments. Although the tungsten lamp was superior, and GE, it still took a little while to ramp up the manufacture of a new, complicated device and re-place all of the old cotton lamps.[951] Despite that, several companies in Europe paid their customers to change their light bulbs to the new type of metal that would work at high voltages. This was still profitable because the transform-ers used a lot less wire to step down to 220 V rather than 110 V. Also, with the higher voltage (and lower current), it was easier to transmit the electricity from the transformer. This required fewer transformers and allowed for thin-ner wires. Europe, despite its wealth, had very few indoor electric lights to switch, as the wealthy tended to live in castles and were often loath to attempt a new electricity system that might involve tearing up history. Furthermore, businesses in Europe tended to be older and more well-established with less need for flashy things like electric lights to drive attention and sales.[952] In that way, European lighting was often at 220 V and 50 Hz, and all the countries that were supplied by Europeans in Africa and Asia followed suit. (Note that this is a simplification, and there was an odd assortment of voltages and fre-quencies and even a mix of DC and AC in every country at this time.)[953]

However, in America, the need for incandescent lamps was so high that the new bulbs couldn't keep up, let alone replace all the old lamps. In the US in 1909, 14 million metal lamps that could handle higher voltage were manufactured, but the demand was so high that 53 million new carbon lamps that could only work up to 110 volts were sold as well. Ten years later, the US had ramped up production of metal lamps by a whopping 1,500%, which was finally enough to cover all the lighting needs.[954] But by this time, there were too many electrical systems set up to change all those transformers to 220 volts.[955] You might ask why America had so many more incandescent lights than Europe or anywhere else in the world, and that has to do with the city of Chicago, which in the mid-to late-1800s was the fastest growing city in history.

In 1835 Chicago had an approximate population of 70 souls. Five years later, when Chicago was designed as a city, it was a pretty small town with a population of around 4,800.[956] Then, in 1847, a canal was built to connect the river from Lake Michigan to the Mississippi river, which caused the town to blossom as a hub of transportation. A local judge prophetically remarked that this canal, which was only 100 miles long, would "at once, and by magic, change the condition and prospects of our city."[957]

Just after this transformation, gold was discovered in California in 1849. This sent a rush of people from the populated East Coast to try to strike it rich in the West, and Chicago became the last spot of "civilization" to stock up for the trip. Meat-drying and meatpacking industries flourished. Then, the growth of railroads caused Chicago to be an even bigger hub of industry fueled by the forests of Wisconsin and populated by waves of immigrants mostly from Ireland and Germany. When the Civil War started in 1861, it fueled even more industrialization and transportation, which helped Chicago grow economically and physically. All of this meant that by 1870 the population had increased to almost 300,000 with no end in sight.[958] With the sudden population growth, the houses were built fast and cheap and without thought for hygiene or safety. That was when a cow kicked over a lamp (or a cooking fire got out of control), and the entire downtown burned to the ground in what was called the Great Chicago Fire of 1871.[959]

Suddenly, the architects of Chicago had a blank space to build and build tall. Space was still at a premium, as the city was hemmed in by the lake, river, and railyards. The population of Chicago was still rising, and this included all the office workers who needed to deal with the infrastructure of so much transportation and insurance. However, brick buildings are heavy and need ridiculously thick walls, which wasted space. Wooden buildings can't be built very tall and were outlawed anyway. Cast-iron buildings weaken in fire and therefore were not popular in Chicago for obvious reasons.

This problem was solved by an architect named William Jenny. The story is that one night Jenny's wife put a book that she was reading on the top of a birdcage when welcoming her husband home. That's when William Jenny came up with an ingenious idea of using a metal skeleton to hold up the building instead of using a load-bearing wall, which meant that the walls could be significantly lighter.[960] This allowed people to build much taller structures, and in 1884, Jenny designed what is considered to be the world's first skyscraper with the 10-story-tall Home Insurance Building. By 1893

POPULATION OF CHICAGO.

1835,	70	1896	1,616,635
1840	4,853	1898	1,851,588
1845	12,088	1900 United States census	1,698,575
1850	29,963	1901 U. S. Census Bureau (estimated)	1,757,010
1855	60,627	1902 U. S. Census Bureau (estimated)	1,815,445
1860	112,172	1903 U. S. Census Bureau (estimated)	1,873,880
1865	178,900	1904 U. S. Census Bureau (estimated)	1,932,315
1870	298,977	1905 U. S. Census Bureau (estimated)	1,990,750
1871 (June)	334,270	1906 U. S. Census Bureau (estimated)	2,049,185
1872 (October)	364,377	1907 U. S. Census Bureau (estimated)	2,139,713
1880	503,185	1908 U. S. Census Bureau (estimated)	2,195,273
1890	1,208,669	1908 Chicago Bureau of Statistics	
1892	1,438,010	(estimated)	2,535,154
1894	1,568,727		

Figure 7: The ridiculous population growth in Chicago between 1835 and 1908

Chicago had 12 skyscrapers between 16 and 20 stories tall, and New York had only four skyscrapers, despite a far larger population.[961]

I mention 1893 in particular because that's when the city of Chicago (after vigorous debate and many bribes) hosted the Columbian World's Exhibition. It's hard to overemphasize the effect of this fair on Americans in every walk of life. For one, the fair had over 28 million visitors,[962] most of whom were Americans when the population of America was just 63 million.[963] Many were influenced by the architectural style displayed and started the city beautiful movement to build parks and attempt to make other cities as beautiful as Chicago.[964] In addition, after the success of the fair, many industrialists decided that it was a symbol of city pride (as well as product placement) to build skyscrapers in their hometown, which was particularly powerful in New York City, where rich New Yorkers were not going to let a hog-butchering city get all the accolades. By 1899 the US had a whopping 62 skyscrapers, and the rest of the world combined had only four: one in Japan, one in the Netherlands, one in Australia, and one in the UK.[965] Most of these skyscrapers were electrified, often with generators in the basement, as gas lamps could not safely be piped to great heights.[966]

The fair was also influential because, as described in chapter 8, it was lit by AC electricity by George Westinghouse, and with so many electric lights, it was the first exposition that was successfully kept open at night.[967] At the time, a poet declared that just the electricity alone "would be well worthy of the attention of the world. ... The spectacle is more resplendent than the capitals of Europe ever saw."[968] Because of the fair, everyone in America wanted electric lights, and the desire for electricity grew not just from the rich individuals but from many up-and-coming businesses. The fair is often described as a win for AC over DC, but most of the population had no interest or idea about phases of AC or DC. They just knew that lights were a sign of wealth, and therefore, they wanted them. This is why America had too many light bulbs to easily switch to tungsten bulbs and 220 volts. Ironically, they were too invested in electric lights to move to a more advanced electric light system and stuck to 110 volts.

As time passed, different countries declared countrywide standards, usually based on what was commonly used in the country at the time—either 110 volts or 220 volts. After this, many electric companies slowly tried to get permission to legally increase the voltage a bit to save a little bit on wires for transformers. So, for example, companies in the US went from 110 volts to 120 volts, and companies in Turkey went from 220 volts to 240 volts. The outlier is the country of Japan, where the government was so frightened of fire (for good reason, considering Tokyo's history) that they *lowered* the voltage to the plugs to 100 volts and kept it there. It's the only country in the world to have a potential of less than 110 volts. In addition, Japan is the only country to be half-electrified at 50 Hz and half at 60 Hz, one of the quirks left after a European company (Dolivo-Dobrovolsky's AEG) provided the electricity for Tokyo in 1895 and an American company (Steinmetz's GE)

Figure 8: The 1893 Chicago World Exposition at night

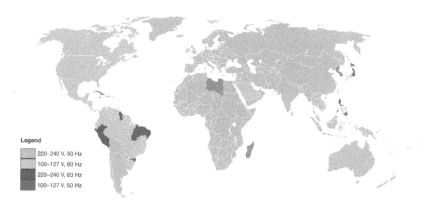

Figure 9: World Map of Voltages and Frequencies

provided the electricity for Osaka in 1896.[969]

In this way, the world was electrified. We have become so dependent on it that it's hard to imagine a world without it. And all of it, every single part, can be traced back, step by step, to when a sailor told an English doctor that compasses don't always point to the North Star. And that, dear reader, is how we tamed electricity, or honestly, how electricity tamed us.

Chapter Summary

✧ **1871:** The Great Fire of Chicago burns down almost all of downtown.

✧ **1884:** William Jenny begins construction of the world's first skyscraper in Chicago.

✧ **1890:** Charles Steinmetz creates an equation for how hysteresis in magnets increases the power loss in transformers due to the frequency. Tesla learns of Hertz's experiment.

✧ **1891:** Nikola Tesla displays his coil for the first time, making him internationally famous.

✧ **1893:** Charles Steinmetz creates new mathematics for AC systems. Chicago hosts the World's Exposition, which influences many to build skyscrapers and to install electricity.

✧ **1894:** Heinrich Hertz dies, and Oliver Lodge gives a talk on the work of Hertz, where it's apparent that Hertz's waves could be used for wireless communication.

✧ **1895:** Wilhelm Röntgen discovers X-rays.

- **1896:** In March, Edison creates an X-ray screen, the fluoroscope. In May, Edison patents a fluorescent X-ray light bulb. Tesla claims he has a better X-ray bulb but does not display it.
- **1897:** Guglielmo Marconi files his first patent for wireless telegraphy based on Lodge's demonstration in 1894. Tesla files for a patent for wireless energy transfer. Westinghouse and GE pay Tesla for his "polyphase" patents.
- **1900:** John Stone Stone files for a patent that uses Tesla coils in wireless telegraphy. Marconi files for a similar patent nine months later.
- **1901:** Tesla states that he communicated with Martians, then receives money from J. P. Morgan to make the whole Earth vibrate with electricity. Marconi sends a wireless signal across the Atlantic.
- **1903:** Marconi has the first two-way wireless communication across the Atlantic between Roosevelt and King Edward.
- **1904:** The tungsten light bulb is discovered. Marconi wins his wireless patent after showing that his system was different from Stone's. J. P. Morgan officially tells Tesla that he's no longer supporting him.
- **1905:** Westinghouse is on a three-man committee to clean up insurance companies.
- **1906:** Tesla has to fire his employees.
- **1907:** The stock market crashes. Westinghouse starts to lose control of his company.
- **1912:** George Westinghouse receives the Edison Award for his work on AC electricity.
- **1914:** George Westinghouse dies.
- **1917:** Tesla receives the Edison Award for polyphase current and his Tesla Coil.
- **1919:** Tesla writes a series of articles for a radio magazine and makes them into an autobiography. Mikhail Dolivo-Dobrovolsky dies and is barely mentioned. The US finally produces enough tungsten lamps to no longer produce cotton-filament lamps.
- **1921:** Charles Steinmetz creates first powerful artificial lightning.
- **1929:** Henry Ford hosts the Light's Golden Jubilee to celebrate the 50th anniversary of Edison's light bulb. Tesla becomes jealous and declares that he invented AC and made electricity possible.

✧ **1931:** Edison dies.

✧ **1935:** Tesla writes about the importance of racist and ablest eugenics for his friend and Hitler-supporter George Viereck.

✧ **1943:** Tesla dies, and John O'Neill writes a very influential biography of him. The US government wins a patent lawsuit against Marconi's radio patent.

✧ **1960:** The unit of magnetic flux density is named a Tesla after Nikola Tesla.

✧ **1964:** *Popular Mechanics Magazine* published an article on how to "Make Your Own Fantastic Tesla Coil," which inspires legions of DIY coils.

✧ **2000:** PBS airs the documentary *Tesla: Master of Lightning*, which creates the narrative that Tesla invented AC, Edison was an elephant-killing monster who was hounding Tesla, Westinghouse based his entire company on Tesla, and that Tesla invented all modern electricity and radio and even modern warfare but was suppressed by evil corporations.

✧ **2003:** Tesla Motor Company is founded. Jill Jonnes publishes *Empires of Light*, which emphasizes the false narrative that Tesla was the lone genius behind Westinghouse's company and that Tesla would have accomplished all that he said he could and more if it wasn't for his charity toward Westinghouse.

Author's Note

You might be surprised to learn that despite the fact that I just wrote an entire book on the history and physics of electricity with almost no mathematics (and I have four more science history books with almost no math on the way),*i I actually like math. I love puzzles, and I find math comforting. There is a wrong answer and a right answer, and there are many ways to get there. So, even after I've solved a problem, I still want to look at it and see if I can find a more beautiful solution.

When I started teaching high school, my best teacher friend was a fellow physics teacher named Billy Caudy. We used to spend every lunch together complaining about the administration, the unruly classes, and the sorry state of the equipment while we discussed constructive co-planning of how to teach physics to 13-year-olds. A significant portion of our time together, however, was spent solving challenging physics problems, which we both adored to an obsessive degree. In particular, I remember spending a lot of time trying to solve the total resistance of a system of resistors across a 10-by-10 grid and then trying to expand it to any size. Why did we do this? Because we are the kind of people who find that fun!

It has occurred to me that science education, at least in America, caters almost exclusively to people like me and Billy who love math puzzles. People who find mathematics challenging or are scared by mathematics are excluded

---

* I am finishing a book on the history of wireless communication, which starts with Newton sticking a long wooden needle in his eye and goes through the history of inferred, radio, television, radar, microwaves, transistors, and cell phones. I am also working on a book about the early history of quantum mechanics focusing on Max Planck. I also want to write a history of spectroscopy in astronomy and a biography of a scientist whom I love named Hertha Aryton. And, yes, I do suffer from more ideas than I can handle, which is better than the alternative, I guess.

by our education system. I used to work to help those students with their fears, but I didn't question the idea that math is *the* tool that was needed to understand physics. I used to say that "math is the grammar and physics the poetry of life." However, after writing this book and seeing how different scientists and inventors made their discoveries, I'm starting to think that math isn't *the* tool, it's just *a* tool, albeit a powerful tool.

Just think back to all of the people I've discussed in these pages: some were math geniuses, and some were mathematically illiterate, but they all changed the way we see our world. In fact, irrespective of their mathematical skills, it's rare to find a significant invention or discovery that was purely motivated by mathematics. You might think that's because of a quirk of the subject of electricity and not true for other branches of science, but I disagree.

For example, the Danish physicist Niels Bohr (1885–1962) was a leader of the Copenhagen interpretation of quantum mechanics and an astonishingly influential scientist, but Bohr felt unsteady with advanced mathematics, once saying, "You know, I am really an amateur. And if they go really into high mathematics I can't follow."[970] In 1963 his student Werner Heisenberg recalled that "Bohr was not a mathematically minded man. He was, I would say, Faraday but not Maxwell."[971] How many Niels Bohrs and Michael Faradays are we missing out on with our current learning system?

Moreover, by teaching the history of science, people can learn how science is never "proved" or settled. A student could see how scientific views change over time and some of the historical challenges that scientists have faced when presenting new ideas. I'm not at all saying we should drop mathematics from science. As I said before, I love math, and I feel it's a powerful tool that can be used to present solutions for complex problems. In addition, students should be tested on their understanding of the concepts and their ability to use those concepts to solve problems, not on their recall of historical figures. What I am saying (and I admit this is deeply self-serving) is that we should stop teaching the concepts through math and instead teach the concepts through the actions of the *people* who discovered them.

I contend that this method would help everyone and, surprisingly, would be especially helpful for people who love mathematics and end up being researchers in scientific fields. First, it's quite rare for anyone, even those of us who love math, to remember pure mathematics as well as we remember stories. I can recall the plot to many movies I enjoyed in high school, but I cannot recall a single equation or concept from my chemistry class taken at the same time. If the purpose of a single science class is not, in general, to make one an expert in that field but to give the student methods to approach science questions and a framework for how that particular branch of science works, how can that happen if we cannot remember what we were taught?

Second, our traditional math-based, context-free education means that almost every experimentalist, theoretician, and inventor is starting from scratch. In general, our understanding of how things are discovered is that they are found "by accident," or nothing at all. However, every discovery is in a way "by accident," or it wouldn't be new, while an accidental discovery can have a lot of information that is important. What exactly was the accident? What was the person looking for when they discovered something they weren't expecting? Did they immediately see the full impact of their discovery? How did other scientists and the public react to it? In the present day, how do we know if we have discovered something new if we have no reference to how discoveries were made and received in the past?

Third, although all discoveries are made in a chain of human discovery, those chains are not always in a straight line. By that I mean that many discoveries, especially many technological ones, are new adaptations from old technology. It's ironic that the image we use for a sudden idea is an incandescent light bulb when that invention took so many years to be commercially viable.

Another example is the use of semiconductors, upon which our entire electronic world depends. Most people would put the origin of semiconductor technology as December of 1947 when John Bardeen and Walter Brattain discovered the semiconducting transistor. However, the first semiconductor diode, or object that used semiconductors as a one-way switch, dated back to 1901 when the Indian scientist Jagadish Chandra Bose discovered that a semiconducting material could be used for a radio detector, as the "warm and damp climate of Bengal" caused "special difficulties" with the commonly used detectors at the time.[972] Who knows what great new technological marvel could come from a new perspective of an outdated technology if we only look?

Fourth, and finally, I think that these stories are quite inspiring. None of these people had an easy path to discovery and acceptance. It was fascinating to see how people tried (or did not try) to balance their scientific obsessions with their personal life. I was quite moved by how, for example, George Westinghouse was so devoted to his wife and family, all the while going on with his endless inventions, or how Laura Bassi discovered and taught while having so many children in a world that did not appreciate her having any kind of personal life or any scientific interests of her own. Science is personal because scientists and inventors are people. Sometimes scientists are delightful, sometimes they are selfish, and some are delusional, poetic, crude, kind, or cruel. It's time—past time—we start to tell their stories.

References for Figures

Chapter 1: Small Beginnings

Figure 1: Cropped Ernest Board oil painting of Gilbert and Queen Elizabeth from *Handbook of the Historical Medical Museum Organized by Henry Wellcome* (1913), 22; Wikimedia commons: "William Gilbert demonstrating the magnet before Queen Elizab Wellcome V0018144.jpg."

Figure 2a: *Loadstone*, photograph by Fred Anzley Annet in *Electrical Machinery: A Practical Study* (1921), 11; **Figure 2b:** "Amber" author's photograph.

Figure 3: Otto von Guericke chasing feathers with electric repulsion from *The New (So-Called) Magdeburg Experiments of Otto Von Guericke* (2012), 228; Wikimedia Commons: "The first electrical machine invented by Otto von Guericke. Wellcome M0012621.jpg."

Figure 4: Hauksbee's electricity and glowing machine from *Physico-mechanical Experiments on Various Subjects* (1719), Table VII, 193 (cropped).

Figure 5: *Gray's Charity Boy* in Dopplemayr *Neu-ent Phaen* (1744) referenced in Heilbron, *Electricity in the 17ᵗʰ and 18ᵗʰ Centuries* (1979), 247.

Chapter 2: Electricity Party

Figure 1: Author with crazy hair. Author's photograph.

Figure 2: 17ᵗʰ century woman being electrified from Boulard, and Alglave, *The Electric Light* (1884), 17.

Figure 3: J Flipart Sculp from Watson, *Expériences et observations* (1748), Plate III.

Figure 4: Author lighting alcohol on fire. Author's picture.

Figure 5: *Experiment of Cuneus*, found in Privat-Deschanel, *Electricity and Magnetism* (1878), 570.

Figure 6: Madame du Barry and two servants demonstrate electrical experiment, engraving by J. F. Beauvarlet after painting by C. A. Vanloo, ca. 1770, from Abbé Dairaine, "Catalogue de l'oeuvre de Jacques-Firmin Beauvarlet, précédé d'une notice sur sa vie et ses ouvrages," *Mémoires de la Société impériale d'émulation d'Abbeville* 90

Figure 7a: Franklin in 1746, painting by Robert Feke in the Harvard University Portrait (1860), Wikimedia commons: "Benjamin Franklin Robert Feke.jpg."

Figure 7b: Benjamin Franklin's electro-static generator, Watercolor painting, Wikimedia commons: "Electricity; Benjamin Franklin's electro-static generator. W Wellcome V0025410.jpg."

Figure 8: Guilutt, *Dalibard at Marly*; Figuier, *Les Merveilles de la science, 1867–1891* 1, 21.

Chapter 3: The Birth of the Battery

Figure 1: Painting of Laura Bassi, from Wikimedia Commons: "Laura Bassi.jpg."

Figure 2: Galvani's experiment, as portrayed in Galvani, *De Viribus Electricitatis* (1792), 418.

Figure 3a: Luigi Galvani painting, from Wikimedia Commons: "Luigi Galvani oil-painting (CardioNetworks ECGpedia).jpg."

Figure 3b: Lucia Galvani painting, from Wikimedia Commons: "Гальвани Лючия Галеацци.jpg."

Figure 4: Alessandro Volta by Garavaglia Giovita, from Wikimedia Commons: "Volta A.jpg."

Figure 5a: Volta, "On the Electricity excited by the mere contact of conducting substances of different kinds," *The Philosophical Magazine* vii (1800), plate *xvii*; 430 (cropped).

Figure 5b: Author's picture.

Figure 6a: Aldini's line drawings of electrified corpses, from Wikimedia Commons: "Giovanni Aldini, Essai … sur le galvanisme … Wellcome L0023895.jpg." (cropped).

Figure 6b: Aldini's line drawings of electrifying depressed patients, from Wikimedia Commons: "Giovanni Aldini, galvanism experiments Wellcome L0011096.jpg." (cropped).

Figure 7: Oil painting of Humphry Davy by Sir Thomas Lawrence from the National Portrait Gallery; Wikimedia commons: "Sir Humphry Davy, Bt by Sir Thomas Lawrence.jpg." (cropped).

Chapter 4: A Galvanized World

Figure 1a: Michael Faraday, painted by Henry Pickersgill, found on Wikipedia Commons: "Portrait of To His Grace the Duke of Somerset this portrait of Michael Faraday (4670717).jpg."

Figure 1b: Electromagnetic rotation experiment, in Faraday, *Experimental Researches in Electricity* 2 (1844), plate 4.

Figure 2a: André-Marie Ampère in 1825 drawn by Ambrose Tardieu, found in

Brackett, *Electricity in Daily Life* (1891), 32.

Figure 2b: Figure of pancake coils, from Ampère, "Suite du Memoire sur l'Action mutuelle entre deux courans électriques …" in *Annales de Chimie et de Physique* 15 (1820), plate 5; fig. 1.

Figure 3: Sturgeon's electromagnet, by Sturgeon, "Improved Electro Magnetic apparatus," *Transactions of the Royal Society of Arts, Manufactures and Commerce* 43 (1824), plate 3; fig. 13.

Figure 4a Faraday's induction ring, from Collins, *The Design and Construction of Induction Coils* (1909), 6.

Figure 4b: Photograph of Faraday's Induction Ring, found in "Faraday Medal," *Proc. Of the Institution of Electrical Engineers* 60, no. 308 (April 1922): 499.

Figure 5: Faraday's generator, from Boulard and Alglave, *The Electric Light* (1884), 224.

Figure 6: Sturgeon's motor and Jacobi's motor both from Sturgeon, *Annals of Electricity* 1 (1827), plate II and plate XIII.

Chapter 5: The Mighty Telegraph

Figure 1: Frame for testing strength of electromagnet, found in Henry, *Writings of Joseph Henry* (1887), 43, Smithsonian Miscellaneous Collections.

Figure 2: Graph of current versus external resistance, author's own.

Figure 3: Joseph Henry in the 1840s, from Wikimedia Commons: "Joseph Henry (1840s).jpg."

Figure 4a: Portrait of Lucretia Morse and her two children, by Samuel Morse, from the High Museum of Art, Wikimedia Commons: "Portrait of Mrs. Morse and Two Children by Samuel F. B. Morse, 1824, High Museum of Art.jpg."

Figure 4b: Self portrait of Samuel Morse, Wikimedia Commons: "Samuel-finley-morse 1.jpg"

Figure 5a: Diagram of Morse's 1835 telegraph, Wikimedia Commons: "Morse telegraph.jpg"

Figure 5b: Daguerreotype of Samuel Morse in Paris, Wikimedia Commons: "Samuel Morse 1840.jpg."

Figure 5c: Samuel Morse drawing of his block letters (1870) found in Edward L. Morse "The Dot-and-Dash Alphabet" *The Century Magazine* vol. 83 (1912), 704.

Figure 5d: Drawing of a 1870s Morse telegraph system, from *Popular Science Monthly* 3 (1873).

Figure 6a: Photograph of Mabel Hubbard, from Waite, *Make a Joyful Sound* (1961), 58.

Figure 6b: Alexander Graham Bell, photographed by E. A. Holton from Library of Congress's Gilbert H. Grosvenor Collection of Photographs, www.loc.gov/item/00652770/.

Figure 7: A. G. Bell, US Patent 174,465, "Telegraphy," March 7, 1876 (cropped).

Chapter 6: Edison and Westinghouse

Figure 1a: Schematic of carbon microphone, from Wikimedia Commons, "Carbon microphone.svg."

Figure 1b: Button carbon microphone, photographed by Olli Niemitalo, Wikimedia Commons: "Ericsson carbon microphone opened.jpg."

Figure 2: Edison and his early phonograph, photographed by Levin Handy, from Library of Congress, Digital ID: cwpbh 04044, https://hdl.loc.gov/loc.pnp/cw-pbh.04044 (cropped).

Figure 3: Pixii Generator from Fontaine, *Electric Lighting* (1878), 57.

Figure 4: Alliance generator electrifying an arc lamp, from Julian Lefèvre, *Dictionnare d'electricite* (1895), 451.

Figure 5a: DC generator with separate exciter, from *Hawkins Electrical Guide* 1 (1917), 196.

Figure 5b: Wilde machine by William Sawyer, in Sawyer, *Electric Lighting* (1881), 14.

Figure 6a: Pavel Yablochkov (or Jablochkoff), from Wikimedia Commons "Яблочков Москва.jpg."

Figure 6b: Drawing of a demonstration of the power of Yablochkov candles as compared to gas lamps in 1878 from Wikimedia Commons, "Jablochkoff Candles on the Victoria Embankment, December 1878.jpg."

Figure 7: Edison's machine by William Sawyer, in Sawyer, *Electric Lighting* (1881), 42.

Figure 8a: George Westinghouse circa 1884, found in Wikimedia Commons, "George Westinghouse 1884.png."

Figure 8b: Marguerite Erskine Westinghouse, found in Leupp, *George Westinghouse: His Life and Achievements* (1919), 135.

Chapter 7: War of the Currents

Figure 1: Sturgeon's Induction Machine from Fleming, *The Alternate Current Transformer in Theory and Practice*, vol. 2.

Figure 2: Ruhmkorff coil schematic, from Wikimedia Commons, "Ruhmkorff coil schematic 1.svg."

Figure 3a: Gaulard and Gibbs's Secondary Generator, from "Gaulard and Gibbs' System," *Engineering* 38 (1885), 454.

Figure 3b: William Stanley Jr., "Induction Coil," US 349,611, September 21, 1886.

Figure 4: Thomas Edison to Edward Johnson, November 1886, The Thomas A. Edison Papers [X710A].

Figure 5: Ferraris's motor, from Thompson, "Polyphase Electric Currents" (1895), 89.

Figure 6a: Photograph of Tesla circa 1896 Wikimedia Commons: "N.Tesla.jpg."

Figure 6b: Nikola Tesla patent US 382,279, "Electro Magnetic Motor," May 1, 1888 (cropped).

Figure 7a: Baily's motor, by Silvanus Thompson from Thompson, "Polyphase Electric Currents" (1895), 85.

Figure 7b: Deprez's motor by Silvanus Thompson, from Thompson, "Polyphase Electric Currents" (1895), 87.

Figure 8a: How three phases combine, from Mikhail Dolivo-Dobrovolsky, US 422,746, "Electrical Induction Apparatus or Transformer," March 4, 1890 (cropped).

Figure 8b and c: Delta transformers and star transformer, from Dolivo-Dobrovolsky, "Transmission of power by rotary-phase alternate currents," Electrical Engineer 7 (April 1891), 407.

Figure 9: Diagram of the Lauffen–Frankfort Transmission by Silvanus Thompson, found in Thompson, "Polyphase Electric Currents" (1895), 107.

Figure 10a: Mikhail Dolivo-Dobrovolsky in around 1883 by Magnus, found in Wikimedia Commons: "Mikhail Ossipovitch Dolivo Dobrovolski à 22 ans.jpg."

Figure 10b: Mikhail Dolivo-Dobrovolsky, US 422,746, "Electrical Induction Apparatus or Transformer," March 4, 1890 (cropped).

Figure 10c: Nikola Tesla patent, US 382,280, "Electrical Transmission of Power," May 1, 1888 (cropped).

Chapter 8: Our Electric World

Figure 1: Tesla with his coils, photographed by Dickenson Alley, 1899. Wikimedia Commons: "Nikola Tesla, with his equipment Wellcome M0014782.jpg."

Figure 2a: Drawing of Roentgen discovering X-rays by author.

Figure 2b: Drawing of a patient getting an X-ray in 1909 from Edwin Houston, "Elementary Electricity," in *Popular Electricity* 2, no. 1 (May 1908): 6.

Figure 3: Steinmetz with his family from **"Charles Proteus Steinmetz,"** *The Mentor-World Traveler* 13 (May 1925), 9.

Figure 4: RCA News, Volume 2 By Radio Corporation of America (1921), 7.

Figure 5: Diagram of Tesla's theory of wireless transfer of energy drawn by Hugo Gernsback found in Tesla, "Famous Scientific Illusions" *Electrical Experimenter* (February 1919), 693.

Figure 6: Edison's 3-wire system schematic, drawn by H. M Paul in "Edison's Three-wire System of Distribution" *Science* 4 (1884), 477.

Figure 7: "Population of Chicago," *Annual Report of the Board of Trade of the City of Chicago* 51 (1909), 140.

Figure 8: Agricultural building at night, from northwest, with spotlight or beacon of light shining across the lagoon. Large photographic print from *The White City (As It Was)*. Photographs by William Henry Jackson; World's Columbian Exposition, 1893, image from The Field Museum Library.

Figure 9: Map of main voltages and frequencies from Wikimedia Commons: "World Map of Mains Electricity Voltages and Frequencies.png."

References

Preface

1   Marie Curie, *Pierre Curie* (New York: Macmillan, 1921), 69.

Chapter 1: Small Beginnings (1600–1733)

2   Henry B. Jones, *The Life and Letters of Faraday*, vol. 2 (London: Longmans, Green & Co, 1870), 403.

3   Astrid Kander, Paolo Malanima, and Paul Warde, *Power to the People* (London: Princeton University Press, 2015), 303.

4   Lynn Hoogenboom, *Sir Francis Drake: A Primary Source Biography* (New York: PowerKids Press, 2006), 7.

5   Samuel Bawlf, *The Secret Voyage of Sir Francis Drake* (Vancouver: D&M Publishers, 2009), 211.

6   Marie Boas Hall, *The Scientific Renaissance 1450–1630* (Mineola, NY: Dover Publications, 1994), 159.

7   William Gilbert, *De Magnete* (On Magnets), trans. P. Fleury Mottelay (London: Bernard Quaritch,1893), *x*.

8   Ibid., 54.

9   Ibid., 77.

10 Ibid., 1.

11 Olav Hammer, *Claiming Knowledge: Strategies of Epistemology from Theosophy to the New Age* (Leiden, Netherlands: Koninklijke, 2001), 211.

12 Gilbert, *De Magnete, xvii*.

13 Ibid., 333.

14 Ibid., *xv*.

15 Ibid., 79.

16 Thomas Brown, *Pseudodoxia Epidemica* (London: Nath Ekins, 1646), 51.

17 Gilbert, *De Magnete, xi*.

18 Park Benjamin, *A History of Electricity* (New York: J. Wiley & Sons, 1895), 264.

19 Emerson Thomas McMullen, *William Harvey and the Use of Purpose in the Scientific Revolution* (Lanham, MD: University Press of America, 1998), 42.

20 Thomas E. Conlon, *Thinking about Nothing: Otto Von Guericke and the Magdeburg Experiments on the Vacuum* (Morrisville, NC: Lulu.com, 2011), 21.

21 Ibid., 290.

22 G. Mortimer, *Eyewitness Accounts of the Thirty Years War 1618–48* (London: Palgrave Macmillan UK, 2002).

23 Tryntje Helfferich, *The Thirty Years War: A Documentary History* (Indianapolis, IN: Hackett Publishing Inc., 2009), 48.

24 Hans Schimank and Arthur Ritter von Vincenti, eds., *Otto von Guericke, Bürgermeister von Magdeburg* (Magdeburg, Germany: Stadt Magdeburg, 1936), 19.

25 Conlon, *Thinking about Nothing*, 287.

26 Otto von Guericke, *The New (So-Called) Magdeburg Experiments of Otto Von Guericke*, trans. Margaret Glover Foley Ames (Philadelphia: International Archives of the History of Ideas, 1994), 228.

27 Conlon, *Thinking about Nothing*, 21.

28 Guericke, *The New (So-Called) Magdeburg Experiments*, 278.

29 Jed Z. Buchwald and Robert Fox, *Oxford Handbook of the History of Physics* (Oxford: Oxford University Press, 2013), 104.

30 Ibid.

31 Nadia Nedzel, *The Rule of Law, Economic Development, and Corporate Governance* (London: Edward Elgar Publishing, 2020), 23.

32 Ibid.

33 "History of the Royal Society," The Royal Society, accessed December 9, 2021, https://royalsociety.org/about-us/history/.

34 Tina Skouen and Ryan J. Stark, *Rhetoric and the Early Royal Society: A Sourcebook* (Leiden, the Netherlands: Brill, 2014), 257.

35 Angela Saini, *Inferior: How Science Got Women Wrong and the New Research That's Rewriting the Story* (Boston: Beacon Press, 2017), 7.

36 Anne Whitman, I. Bernard Cohen, and Julia Budenz, "A Brief History of the Principia," in *The Principia: The Authoritative Translation* (Oakland, CA: University of California Press, 2016), 1.

37 William H. Cropper, *Great Physicists: The Life and Times of Leading Physicists* (Oxford: Oxford University Press, 2004), 31.

38 Susan Meyer, *Isaac Newton* (New York: Rosen Publishing Group, 2017), 87.

39 Edward Dolnick, *The Clockwork Universe: Isaac Newton, the Royal Society, and the Birth of the Modern World* (New York: HarperTorch, 2011), 207.

40 *Oxford Dictionary of National Biography*, s.v. "Francis, Hauksbee," by Larry Stewart, May 21, 2009, https://www.oxforddnb.com/view/10.1093/ref:odnb/9780198614128.001.0001/odnb-9780198614128-e-12619?rskey=d0EjdF&

result=3.

41 M. Picard, "Experience Faite a L'Observatoire sur la barometer simple touchant un nouveau phonomene qu'on y a decouvert," *Le Journal des Sçavans* (1676), 112.

42 Francis Hauksbee, *Physico-mechanical Experiments on Various Subjects* (London: R. Brugis, 1719), 36.

43 *Oxford Dictionary of National Biography*, s.v. "Hauksbee, Francis," by Stephen Pumfrey, May 21, 2009, https://www.oxforddnb.com/view/10.1093/ref:odnb/9780198614128.001.0001/odnb-9780198614128-e-12618.

44 David Clark and Lesley Murdin, "The Rehabilitation of Stephen Gray," *New Scientist Magazine*, May 1979, 653.

45 Joseph Keithley, *The Story of Electrical and Magnetic Measurements* (Oxford: Wiley, 1999), 15.

46 John L. Heilbron, *Electricity in the 17ᵗʰ and 18ᵗʰ Centuries: A Study of Early Modern Physics* (Berkeley, CA: University of California Press, 1979), 243.

47 Clark and Murdin, "The Rehabilitation of Stephen Gray," 653.

48 M. Peck, "Review of Newton's Tyranny: The Suppressed Scientific Discoveries of Stephen Gray and John Flamsteed," *Journal of Guidance, Control, and Dynamics* 27, no. 4 (2004): 734, https://doi.org/10.2514/1.11197.

49 Clark and Murdin, "The Rehabilitation of Stephen Gray," 653.

50 Ibid.

51 *Oxford Dictionary of National Biography*, s.v. "Gray, Stephen" by Michael Ben-Chaim, September 23, 2004, https://www.oxforddnb.com/view/10.1093/ref:odnb/9780198614128.001.0001/odnb-9780198614128-e-11354/.

52 Robert A. Chipman, "The Manuscript Letters of Stephen Gray," *Isis* 49, no. 4 (1958): 419.

53 Jill Jonnes, *Empires of Light: Edison, Tesla, Westinghouse, and the Race to Electrify the World* (Toronto: Random House, 2003), 21.

54 Stephen Gray, "A Letter to Cromwell Mortimer," *Philosophical Transactions* 37, no. 417 (1731): 20, https://doi.org/10.1098/rstl.1731.0005.

55 Ibid., 21.

56 Ibid., 26.

57 Ibid., 27.

58 Ibid.

59 Heilbron, *Electricity in the 17ᵗʰ and 18ᵗʰ Centuries*, 292.

60 Gray, "A letter to Cromwell Mortimer," 33.

61 Ibid., 39.

62 S. Gray and C. Mortimer, "An Account of Some Electrical Experiments Intended to Be Communicated to the Royal Society by Mr. Stephen Gray, F. R. S. Taken from His Mouth by Cromwell Mortimer, M.D.R.S. Secr. on Feb 14, 1735-6. Being the Day before He Died," *Philosophical Transactions* 39 (1735): 402–3,

https://doi.org/10.1098/rstl.1735.0082.

63 Benjamin, *A History of Electricity*, 478.

64 Charles Du Fay, "A Letter from Mons. Du Fay," *Philosophical Transactions* 38 (1733): 258.

65 Ibid.

66 Ibid., 259.

67 D. V. Subba Rao, *Textbook of Mineral Processing* (Jodhpur, India: Scientific Publishers, 2017), 257.

68 Ibid., 262–3.

69 Ibid., 263.

70 Ibid., 263.

71 Frederick Collier Bakewell, *Electrical Science: Its History, Phenomena, and Applications* (London: Ingram, Cooke, & Co.,1853), 12.

72 Du Fay, "A Letter from Mons. Du Fay," 263–4.

73 Benjamin, *A History of Electricity*, 487.

Chapter 2: Electrical Party (1736–1792)

74 Joseph Priestley, *The History and Present State of Electricity, with Original Experiments* (London: C. Bathurst et al., 1775), 548–9.

75 Benjamin, *A History of Electricity*, 491.

76 Heilbron, *Electricity in the 17th and 18th Centuries*, 264.

77 Ibid., 265.

78 Ibid.

79 Benjamin, *A History of Electricity*, 495.

80 Priestley, *The History and Present State of Electricity*, 156.

81 Benjamin, *A History of Electricity*, 495.

82 Ibid., 498.

83 Heilbron, *Electricity in the 17th and 18th Centuries*, 267.

84 Priestley, *The History and Present State of Electricity*, 84.

85 Nick Tucker et al., "The History of Science and Technology of Electrospinning from 1600 to 1995," *Journal of Engineered Fibers and Fabrics* 7, no. 2 (2012): 65, https://doi.org/10.1177/155892501200702S10.

86 Benjamin, *A History of Electricity*, 514.

87 Ibid., 516.

88 Heilbron, *Electricity in the 17th and 18th Centuries*, 313.

89 Ibid., 314.

90 Priestly, *History and Present State of Electricity*, 84.

91 Heilbron, *Electricity in the 17th and 18th Centuries*, 317.

92 Priestly, *History and Present State of Electricity*, 97.

93 Heilbron, *Electricity in the 17th and 18th Centuries*, 318.

94 Ibid., 79.

95 Ibid., 320.

96 Henry Smith Williams, *A History of Science: Vol. II* (Freiburg im Breisgau, Germany: Outlook Verlag, 2018), 169.

97 Heilbron, *Electricity in the 17th and 18th Centuries*, 314.

98 Benjamin, *A History of Electricity*, 536.

99 Benjamin Franklin, *Experiments and Observations on Electricity* (London: E. Cave, 1751), 2.

100 Walter Isaacson, *Benjamin Franklin: An American Life* (New York: Simon & Schuster, 2003), 59, 118.

101 Ibid., 13–15.

102 Phillip Dray, *Stealing God's Thunder: Benjamin Franklin's Lightning Rod and the Invention of America* (New York: Random House Trade, 2005), 47.

103 Franklin, *Experiments and Observations on Electricity*, 37.

104 Ibid., 6.

105 Ibid., 8–9.

106 Ibid., 17.

107 Ibid., 9.

108 Ibid., 34-5.

109 Dray, *Stealing God's Thunder* (2005), *xii*.

110 Franklin, *Experiments and Observations on Electricity*, 65–6.

111 Ibid., 66.

112 William Burns, *Science in the Enlightenment* (Oxford: ABC-CLIO, 2003), 215.

113 Benjamin, *A History of Electricity*, 517.

114 Tom Tucker, *Bolt of Fate: Benjamin Franklin and His Fabulous Kite* (New York: PublicAffairs, 2009), 27.

115 Jaques Roger, *Buffon: A Life in Natural History* (Ithaca: Cornell University Press, 1997), 7.

116 Bill Bryson, *A Short History of Nearly Everything* (London: Black Swan, 2004), 80.

117 Ernst Mayr, *The Growth of Biological Thought: Diversity, Evolution, and Inheritance* (Cambridge, MA: Harvard University Press, 1981), 330.

118 J. A. Leo Lemay, *The Life of Benjamin Franklin, Vol. 3* (Philadelphia, PA: University of Pennsylvania Press, 2014), 87.

119 Tucker, *Bolt of Fate*, 27.

120 Roger, *Buffon,* 212.

121 Heilbron, *Electricity in the 17th and 18th Centuries*, 349.

122 Celine Cherici, *From Clouds to the Brain* (Oxford: Wiley, 2020), 58.

123 Heilbron, *Electricity in the 17th and 18th Centuries*, 348.

124 Thomas-François Dalibard, "Report of an Experiment with Lightning," Founders Online National Archives, May 13, 1752, 110–1.

125 Heilbron, *Electricity in the 17th and 18th Centuries*, 349.

126 Franklin, *Experiments and Observations on Electricity*, 111.

127 Ibid., 112.

128 Priestley, *The History and Present State of Electricity*, 178–9.

129 Michael Brian Schiffer, *Draw the Lightning Down: Benjamin Franklin and Electrical Technology in the Age of Enlightenment* (Oakland, CA: University of California Press, 2006), 165.

130 Priestley, *The History and Present State of Electricity*, 84.

131 Heilbron, *Electricity in the 17th and 18th Centuries*, 349.

132 Franklin, *Experiments and Observations on Electricity*, 162.

133 Benjamin Franklin, *The Papers of Benjamin Franklin*, vol. 4 (London: Yale University Press, 1961), 408.

134 I. B. Cohen, *Benjamin Franklin's Science* (Cambridge, MA: Harvard University Press, 1990), 141.

135 Dray, *Stealing God's Thunder*, 96.

136 Benjamin Franklin, *The Writings of Benjamin Franklin*, vol. 1 (New York: Macmillan, 1907), 104.

137 "Lightning and Protection from Lightning," *Proceedings of the Colorado Scientific Society* (1907), 399.

138 Gerald Molloy, *Lightning, Thunder and Lightning Conductors* (New York: Humboldt Publishing Company, 1890), 38.

139 Carla J. Mulford, *Benjamin Franklin and the Ends of Empire* (Oxford: Oxford University Press, 2015), 289.

140 Charles Francis Adams, ed., *The Works of John Adams*, vol. 1 (Boston: Little, Brown & Co., 1856), 660.

141 Dray, *Stealing God's Thunder*, xvi.

142 C. Stewart Gillmor, *Coulomb and the Evolution of Physics and Engineering in Eighteenth-Century France* (Princeton, NJ: Princeton University Press, 2017), 16.

143 Gillmor, *Coulomb and the Evolution of Physics*, 5.

144 Ibid.

145 Ibid.

146 Encyclopedia.com, s.v. "Coulomb, Charles Augustin," updated May 23, 2018, https://www.encyclopedia.com/people/science-and-technology/chemistry-biographies/charles-coulomb.

147 Gillmor, *Coulomb and the Evolution of Physics,* 24.

148 Ibid., 25.

149 Ibid.

150 Isaac Elishakoff, *Safety Factors and Reliability: Friends or Foes?* (Heidelberg, Netherlands: Springer, 2004), 266.

151 Joseph F. Keithley, *The Story of Electrical and Magnetic Measurements: From 500*

BC to the 1940s (New York: Wiley, 1999), 42.

152 Clifford Pickover, *Archimedes to Hawking: Laws of Science: Laws of Science and the Great Minds Behind Them* (Oxford: OUP USA, 2008), 157.

153 Heilbron, *Electricity in the 17th and 18th Centuries*, 469–70.

154 F. F. Centore, *Robert Hooke's Contributions to Mechanics* (Heidelberg, Netherlands: Springer Netherlands, 2013), 4.

155 David Deming, *Science and Technology in World History*, vol. 3 (Jefferson, NC: McFarland & Co., 2014), 236.

156 John Munro, *Pioneers of Electricity: Or, Short Lives of the Great Electricians* (London: Religious Tract Society, 1890), 81.

157 Heilbron, *Electricity in the 17th and 18th Centuries*.

158 Henry Cavendish, "Experiments to Determine the Density of the Earth," *Philosophical Transactions* 88 (1798): 469.

159 M. Coulomb, "Premier mémoire sur l'électricité et le magnétisme" *Histoire de L'Académie Royale des Sciences* (1785), 572.

160 *The Edinburgh Encyclopedia,* vol. 7., s.v. "Coulomb, Charles Augustus."

Chapter 3: The Birth of the Battery (1732–1812)

161 Hertha Ayrton, *The Electric Arc* (New York: D. Van Nostrand Co., 1902), 2.

162 John Davy, ed., *The Collected Works of Sir Humphry Davy* (London: Smith, Elder & Co., 1839–1840), 116–7.

163 *The Philosophical Magazine*, vol. *xxxv* (Jan–June 1810), 463.

164 Paula Findlen, "Science as a Career in Enlightenment Italy: The Strategies of Laura Bassi," *Isis* 84, no. 3 (September 1993): 449.

165 Ibid., 449.

166 Ibid.

167 Ibid., 445–50.

168 Ibid., 451.

169 Ibid., 450.

170 Ibid.

171 Monique Frize, *Laura Bassi and Science in 18th Century Europe: The Extraordinary Life and Role of Italy's Pioneering Female Professor* (Berlin: Springer, 2016), 35.

172 Findlen, "Science as a Career in Enlightenment Italy," 450.

173 Gabriella Berti Logan, "The Desire to Contribute: An Eighteenth-Century Italian Woman of Science," *The American Historical Review* 99, no. 3 (1994): 795, https://doi.org/10.1086/ahr/99.3.785.

174 Ibid.

175 Frize, *Laura Bassi and Science in 18th Century Europe*, 40.

176 Ibid.

177 Marta Cavazza, "Laura Bassi and Giuseppe Veratti: An Electric Couple during

the Enlightenment," *Contributions to Science* 4, no. 1 (2009): 121.

178 Luisa Cifarelli and Raffaella Simli, eds., *Laura Bassi—The World's First Woman Professor in Natural Philosophy: An Iconic Physicist in Enlightenment Italy* (New York: Springer International Publishing, 2020), 76–79.

179 Frize, *Laura Bassi and Science in 18th Century Europe*, 65–66, 85.

180 Ibid., 70.

181 Cavazza, "Laura Bassi and Giuseppe Veratti: An Electric Couple," 123.

182 Ibid., 75.

183 Robert Klitzman, *Designing Babies: How Technology Is Changing the Ways We Create Children* (Oxford: OUP USA, 2019), 4.

184 B. L. Saini, *Introduction to Biotechnology* (Delhi, India: Laxmi Publications, 2010), 96.

185 Alberto Elena, " 'In lode della filosofessa di Bologna': An Introduction to Laura Bassi" *Isis* 82, no. 3 (1991): 513, https://doi.org/10.1086/355839.

186 Cavazza, "Laura Bassi and Giuseppe Veratti: An Electric Couple," 121.

187 Elena, "An Introduction to Laura Bassi," 514.

188 Ibid.

189 Cavazza, "Laura Bassi and Giuseppe Veratti: An Electric Couple," 117.

190 Albrecht von Haller, *A Dissertation on the Sensible and Irritable Parts of Animals* (Farmington Hills, MI: Gale ECCO, 2010).

191 Frize, *Laura Bassi and Science in 18th Century Europe*, 66.

192 Priestley, *The History and Present State of Electricity*, 472.

193 Logan, "The Desire to Contribute," 810.

194 Maria Cieslak-Golonka and Bruno Morten, "The Women Scientists of Bologna," *American Scientist* 88, no. 1 (January 2000): 68, http://www1.doi.com/10.1511/2000.15.761/.

195 Catherine M. C. Haines and Helen M. Stevens, *International Women in Science* (Oxford: ABC-CLIO, 2001), 23.

196 John Heilbron, *The Oxford Companion to the History of Modern Science* (Oxford: Oxford University Press, 2003), 323.

197 Frank N. Magill, *The 17th and 18th Centuries: Dictionary of World Biography, Vol. 4* (Milton Park, UK: Taylor & Francis, 2013), 523.

198 Ibid.

199 "Galeazzi Galvani Lucia," Scienza a Due Voci, accessed December 9, 2021, http://scienzaa2voci.unibo.it/biografie/76-galeazzi-galvani-lucia.

200 Luigi Galvani, *Commentary on the Effect of Electricity on Muscular Motion* (Cambridge, MA: Elizabeth Licht, 1953), *ix*.

201 Marco Bresadola, "Medicine and Science in the Life of Luigi Galvani (1737–1798)," *Brain Research Bulletin* 5, no. 5 (July 1998): 367–380, https://www.doi.org/10.1016/s0361-9230(98)00023-9.

202 Aloysii Galvani, *De Viribus Electricitatis in Motu Musculari (1792)* (Whitefish, MT: Kessinger Publishing, 2010), 361.

203 Ibid.

204 Ibid., 364.

205 Heilbron, *Electricity in the 17ᵗʰ & 18ᵗʰ Centuries*, 492.

206 Galvani, *De Viribus Electricitatis*, 368.

207 Ibid.

208 Marco Piccolino and Marco Bresadola, *Shocking Frogs: Galvani, Volta, and the Electric Origins of Neuroscience* (Oxford: Oxford University Press, 2013), 23.

209 Ibid., 141.

210 Galvani, *De Viribus Electricitatis*, 368.

211 Heilbron, *Electricity in the 17ᵗʰ & 18ᵗʰ Centuries*, 492.

212 Edwin J. Houston, *Electricity in Every-Day Life* (Berkeley, CA: University of California Libraries, 1905), 345.

213 Heilbron, *Electricity in the 17ᵗʰ & 18ᵗʰ Centuries*, 492.

214 Aé Parent and G. Aldini, "Giovanni Aldini: From Animal Electricity to Human Brain Stimulation," *Le Journal Canadien Des Sciences Neurologiques* 31, no. 4 (November 2004): 578.

215 Celine Cherici, *From Clouds to the Brain: The Movement of Electricity in Medical Science* (Hoboken, NJ: Wiley, 2020), 141.

216 "Award Winners: Copley Medal," The Royal Society, accessed December 9, 2021, https://docs.google.com/spreadsheets/d/1dsunM9ukGLgaW3HdG9cvJ_QKd7pWjGI0qi_fCb1ROD4/pubhtml?gid=1336391689&single=true.

217 John Munro, *Pioneers of Electricity; Or, Short Lives of the Great Electricians* (London: Religious Tract Society, 1890), 98.

218 Electrochemistry Encyclopedia, s.v. "Volta and the 'Pile,'" by Franco Decker, January 2005, https://knowledge.electrochem.org/encycl/art-v01-volta.htm.

219 Alessandro Volta, "On the Electricity Excited by the Mere Contact of Conducting Substances of Different Kinds," *The Philosophical Magazine* 7 (January 1832): 289.

220 Lyle D. Feisel, "Why Do We Call It a … Volt?," *The Bent of Tau Beta Pi* (Summer 2017): 19, https://www.tbp.org/pubs/Features/Su17Feisel.pdf.

221 Franklin, *Experiments and Observations on Electricity*, 38.

222 Volta, "On the Electricity Excited by the Mere…"

223 Ibid., 305.

224 John Aldini, *An Account of the Late Improvements in Galvanism* (London: Cuthell and Martin, 1803), *i*.

225 Ibid., 53.

226 Parent and Aldini, "Giovanni Aldini," 580.

227   Aldini, *An Account of the Late Improvements in Galvanism*, 113.

228   Ibid., 114–5.

229   Alan Weiss, *The Electroconvulsive Therapy Workbook: Clinical Applications* (Oxford: Taylor & Francis, 2018).

230   Aldini, *An Account of the Late Improvements in Galvanism*, 196–8.

231   Caroline Jowett, *The History of Newgate Prison* (Barnsley, UK: Pen & Sword Books, 2017).

232   Andrew Knapp, *The Newgate Calendar*, vol. 3 (London: J. Robins and Co., 1825), 317.

233   Mary Shelley, *Frankenstein: Or, the Modern Prometheus* (London: Lackington, Hughes, Harding, Mavor & Jones, 1818), 11.

234   William Nicholson, "Account of the New Electrical or Galvanic Apparatus of Sig. Alex. Volta, and Experiments Performed with the Same," *Journal of Natural Philosophy, Chemistry, & the Arts* 4 (1801): 179, https://archive.org/details/cbarchive_121695_accountsofthenewelectricalorga9999/page/n1/mode/1up.

235   Ibid., 182.

236   Ibid., 186.

237   Alan W. Hirshfeld, *The Electric Life of Michael Faraday* (London: Walker & Co., 2009), 8–9.

238   Harriet Martineau, *A History of the Thirty Years Peace*, vol. 2 (Newbridge, Ireland: Irish University Press, 1877), 370.

239   John Ayrton Paris, *The Life of Sir Humphry Davy: Volume 1* (London: Henry Colburn and Richard Bentley, 1831), 1–2.

240   Davy, *The Collected Works of Sir Humphry Davy*, 32.

241   Ibid.

242   *Oxford Dictionary of National Biography*, s.v. "Davy, Humphry," by Robert Hunt, 1888, accessed February 28, 2022, https://www.oxforddnb.com/view/10.1093/odnb/9780192683120.001.0001/odnb-9780192683120-e-7314. (access 3/5/2022)

243   W. Bourne and J. Duncan, "Morbidity and Mortality in Obsteterics," *Current Researches in Anesthesia* 1 (1922): 27.

244   June Z. Fullmer, *Young Humphry Davy: The Making of an Experimental Chemist* (Philadelphia: American Philosophical Society, 2000), 86.

245   Bourne and Duncan, "Morbidity and Mortality in Obsteterics," 27.

246   Humphry Davy, *Researches, Chemical and Philosophical; Chiefly Concerning Nitrous Oxide* (London: J. Johnson, 1800).

247   Davy, *The Collected Works of Sir Humphry Davy*, 83.

248   Ibid., 84.

249   "Proceedings of Learned Societies," *The Philosophical Magazine of London* IX (1905): 281.

250 Davy, *The Collected Works of Sir Humphry Davy*, 88–89.

251 Humphry Davy, "An Account of Some Galvanic Combinations," *Philosophical Transactions of the Royal Society* (June 1801), 399.

252 "Proceedings of Learned Societies," 281.

253 Paris, *The Life of Sir Humphry Davy: Volume 1*, 87.

254 John Timbs, *Curiosities of London* (London: D. Bogue, 1855), 654.

255 Davy, *The Collected Works of Sir Humphry Davy*, 109.

256 Ibid., 130.

257 Humphry Davy, *Elements of Chemical Philosophy* (London: J. Johnson, 1812), 153.

258 Hertha Ayrton, *The Electric Arc* (Cambridge: Cambridge University Press, 2012), 24.

259 Ibid., 28.

260 Raymond Lamont-Brown, *Humphry Davy: Life Beyond the Lamp* (Cheltenham, UK: History Press, 2004).

261 Davy, *The Collected Works of Sir Humphry Davy*, 136.

262 Ibid., 96.

Chapter 4: A Galvanized World (1820–1846)

263 Alfred Smee, *Elements of Electro-Metallurgy* (London: Brown, Green, and Longmans, 1843), 128.

264 E. Rutherford, *Proceedings of the Royal Institute of Great Britain Vol. 27* (London: Royal Institution of Great Britain, 1931), 39.

265 John Tyndall, *Faraday as a Discoverer* (London: Longmans, Green, and Co.,1868), 147.

266 Silvanus Phillips Thompson, *Michael Faraday: His Life and Work* (London: Cassell, 1898), 1–2.

267 Ibid., 280.

268 Hirshfeld, *The Electric Life of Michael Faraday*, 47.

269 In 1811, Davy told his mother that tickets to his lecture were going from "ten to twenty guineas" (10.5 to 21 pounds) Davy, *The Collected Works of Sir Humphry Davy.* 129.

270 Thompson, *Michael Faraday: His Life and Work*, 4.

271 *The Westminster Review*, vol. 96 (1871), 363.

272 Hirshfeld, *The Electric Life of Michael Faraday*, 5.

273 Ibid., 8.

274 Jane Marcet, *Conversations in Chemistry Intended More Especially for the Female Sex* (London: Longman, Hurst, Rees, Orme & Brown, 1809).

275 Hirshfeld, *The Electric Life of Michael Faraday*, 13–4.

276 Ibid., 11.

277 Davy, *The Collected Works of Sir Humphry Davy*, 136.

278 L. Pearce Williams, ed., *The Selected Correspondence of Michael Faraday Volume 1* (Cambridge: Cambridge University Press, 1971), 5.

279 Ibid.

280 Thompson, *Michael Faraday: His Life and Work*, 11.

281 Ibid., 12.

282 Williams, *The Selected Correspondence of Michael Faraday Volume 1*, 40.

283 John Gribbin, *The Scientists: A History of Science Told Through the Lives of the Greatest Inventors* (New York: Random House, 2004), 415.

284 Tyndall, *Faraday as a Discoverer*, 149.

285 Thompson, *Michael Faraday: His Life and Work*, 18.

286 Williams, *The Selected Correspondence of Michael Faraday Volume 1*, 62.

287 Hirshfeld, *The Electric Life of Michael Faraday*, 53.

288 Ibid., 47

289 Williams, *The Selected Correspondence of Michael Faraday Volume 1*, 86–7.

290 Hirshfeld, *The Electric Life of Michael Faraday*, 53.

291 Henry Bonce Jones, *The Life and Letters of Faraday Volume 1* (Cambridge: Cambridge University Press, 1870), 170.

292 Walter Jerrold, *Michael Faraday: Man of Science* (London: Partridge, 1893), 52.

293 Thompson, *Michael Faraday: His Life and Work*, 44.

294 Jones, *The Life and Letters of Faraday, Volume 1*, 222.

295 Thompson, *Michael Faraday: His Life and Work*, 47.

296 Jones, *The Life and Letters of Faraday, Volume 1*, 317.

297 Ibid., 324.

298 Thompson, *Michael Faraday: His Life and Work*, 50.

299 John Tyndall, *Fragments of Science for Unscientific People: A Series of Detached Essays, Lectures and Reviews* (New York: D. Appleton, 1872), 337.

300 Jones, *The Life and Letters of Faraday, Volume 1*, 363.

301 Robert M. Brian et al., eds, *Hans Christian Oersted and the Romantic Legacy in Science: Ideas, Disciplines, Practices* (New York: Springer-Verlag, 2007), 2.

302 Hans Oersted, *Selected Scientific Works of Hans Christian Ørsted* (Princeton, NJ: Princeton University Press, 2014), 417.

303 Ibid., 418–9.

304 Davy, *The Collected Works of Sir Humphry Davy*, 260–1.

305 Michael Faraday, "On Some New Electro-Magnetical Motions," *Quarterly Journal of Science* 12 (1822): 92.

306 Jones, *The Life and Letters of Faraday, Volume 1*, 356.

307 J. H. Gladstone, *Michael Faraday* (New York: Harper & Brothers, 1872), 20.

308 A. J. Frank and L. James, *The Correspondence of Michael Faraday* (London: Institution of Engineering and Technology, 1991), 233.

309 Ibid., 235.

310 John Davy, *Memoirs of the Life of Sir Humphry Davy* (Cambridge: Cambridge University Press, 2011), 280.

311 Catherine de Lange, *10 Voyages Through the Human Mind* (London: Michael O'Mara, 2019).

312 Hirshfeld, *The Electric Life of Michael Faraday*, 109.

313 Peter Day, *The Philosopher's Tree: A Selection of Michael Faraday's Writings* (Boca Raton, FL: CRC Press, 2019), 75.

314 J. P. Edwards, ed., *Lives of the Illustrious*, vol. 7 (London: Partridge and Oakey, 1855), 163.

315 Ibid., 164.

316 Ibid.

317 Ibid.

318 Ibid.

319 Ibid.

320 Ibid., 166.

321 A. K. T. Assis and J. P. M. C. Chaib, *Ampère's Electrodynamics* (Berlin: Apeiron, 2015), 23.

322 Ibid., 59.

323 Ibid., 55.

324 Ibid., 55.

325 Ibid., 62.

326 Ibid., 119.

327 André-Marie Ampère, *Correspondance du Grand Ampère*, vol. 2 (1936), 576–7.

328 Assis and Chaib, *Ampère's Electrodynamics*, 101.

329 Ibid., 106.

330 Ibid., 101.

331 S. Ross, *Nineteenth-Century Attitudes: Men of Science* (Dordrecht, Netherlands: Springer Netherlands, 2012), 96.

332 Joseph Louis Gay-Lussac, *Annales de chimie et de physique*, vol. 27 (1824), 363.

333 Assis and Chaib, *Ampère's Electrodynamics*, 517–8.

334 *Memoirs and Proceedings* (Manchester: Manchester Literary and Philosophical Society, 1857), 54.

335 Ibid.

336 Iwan Rhys Morus, *When Physics Became King* (Chicago: University of Chicago Press, 2005), 99.

337 William Sturgeon, "The Large Silver Metal and Thirty Guineas Were This Session Presented to Mr. W. Sturgeon," *Transactions of the Society of Arts* 43 (1825): 37.

338 Ibid., 40.

339 Hirshfeld, *The Electric Life of Michael Faraday*, 112.

340 Ibid., 119.

341 Faraday, *Experimental Researches in Electricity: Vol 1*, 149.

342 Jones, *The Life and Letters of Faraday*, 10.

343 Williams, *Michael Faraday*, 196.

344 Michael Faraday, *Experimental Researches in Electricity, Volume 1* (London: R. and J. E. Taylor, 1839), 32.

345 Ibid.

346 Frank and James, *The Correspondence of Michael Faraday*, 277.

347 Richard R. Yeo, *Defining Science: William Whewell, Natural Knowledge, and Public Debate in Early Victorian Britain* (Cambridge: Cambridge University Press, 2003), 3.

348 Michael Faraday, "Experimental Researches in Electricity—Seventh Series," *Philosophical Transactions* vol. 124, (January 1834): 79.

349 Faraday, *Experimental Researches in Electricity, Volume 1*, 104.

350 Ibid.

351 Ibid., 364.

352 Ibid., 365.

353 Ibid.

354 Ibid.

355 Mike Elgan, "Easy Mobile Security the Faraday Way," Computerworld, May 19, 2018, https://www.computerworld.com/article/3273491/easy-mobile-security-the-faraday-way.html.

356 Faraday, *Experimental Researches in Electricity, Volume 1,* 521.

357 "Obituary Notices of Deceased Fellows: George Simon Ohm," *Proceedings of Royal Society of London* 7 (January 1856): 599.

358 Georg Ohm, *The Galvanic Circuit Investigated Mathematically* (Boston: C. J. Peters & Son, 1891), 15.

359 Christa Jungnickel and Russell McCormmach, *Intellectual Mastery of Nature: Theoretical Physics from Ohm to Einstein, Volume 1* (Chicago: University of Chicago Press, 1990), 52.

360 Georg Ohm, "Ueber Elektricitätsleiter," *Journal für Chemie und Physik* 44 (1825): 12.

361 Morton L. Schagrin, "Resistance to Ohm's Law," *American Journal of Physics* 31, no. 7 (February 1963): 542.

362 Ibid., 545.

363 Niels Hugh de Vaudrey Heathcote, "A Translation of the Paper in Which Ohm First Announced His Law of the Galvanic Circuit," *Science Progress in the Twentieth Century* 26, no. 101 (July 1931): 69.

364 Ibid.

365 Schagrin, "Resistance to Ohm's Law," 72.

366 Rollo Appleyard, *Pioneers of Electrical Communication* (London: Macmillan and Co., 1968), 199.

367 Jungnickel and McCormmach, *Intellectual Mastery of Nature*, 53.

368 John Tyndall, "Reports on the Progress of the Physical Sciences," *The London, Edinburgh, and Dublin Philosophical Magazine and Journal of Science* (May 1852): 322.

369 "Resistance to Ohm's Law," *American Journal of Physics* 31, no. 7 (July 2005): 540.

370 Lloyd William Taylor, *Physics: The Pioneer Science* (Mineola, NY: Dover, 1959), 668.

371 Ibid.

372 "Obituary Notices of Deceased Fellows: George Simon Ohm," 600.

373 Jungnickel and McCormmach, *Intellectual Mastery of Nature*, 57–8.

374 W. Sturgeon, "Prospectus," *The Annals of Electricity* 1 (1836): *ii*.

375 W. Sturgeon, "Description of an Electro-magnetic Engine," *The Annals of Electricity* 1 (1836): 78.

376 M. Jacobi, "On the Application of Electro-Magnetism to the Moving of Machines," *The Annals of Electricity, Magnetism, and Chemistry* (1837): 422.

377 Ibid.

378 Donald S. L. Cardwell, *James Joule: A Biography* (Manchester: Manchester University Press, 1989), 30.

379 James Joule, "Description of an Electro-Magnetic Engine," *Annals of Electricity* 2 (January 1838): 122.

380 James Joule, "Investigations in Magnetism and Electro-Magnetism" *Annals of Electricity* 4 (May 1839): 135.

381 Ibid., 131.

382 James Joule, "On the Heat Evolved by Metallic Conductors of Electricity," *The Scientific Papers of James Prescott Joule*, vol. 1 (1884): 61.

383 Ibid., 65.

384 *Encyclopedia Britannica Online*, s.v. "Joule's law," accessed January 12, 2022, https://www.britannica.com/science/Joules-law.

385 Cardwell, *James Joule*, 37.

386 Robert H. Kargon, *Science in Victorian Manchester: Enterprise and Expertise* (Piscataway, NJ: Transaction Publishers, 1977), 40.

387 Ibid., 41.

388 James Joule, "Obituary: William Sturgeon," *American Journal of Science* 61 (1851): 444–6.

389 William Thomson, *Mathematical and Physical Papers* (Cambridge: Cambridge University Press, 1882), 102.

390 James Joule, "On the Calorific Effects of Magneto-Electricity," *The Scientific Papers of James Prescott Joule*, vol. 1 (1884): 157.

391 P. K. Nag, *Basic and Applied Thermodynamics* (New York: McGraw-Hill, 2002), 46.

392 Brian Bowers, *Sir Charles Wheatstone FRS* (New York: Institution of Electrical Engineers, 2001), 8.

393 Ibid., 70.

394 *Proceedings of the Royal Society*, vol. 3 (December 1837): 366.

395 British Association for the Advancement of Science, "On the Translation of Foreign Scientific Memoirs," *Report of the Annual Meeting* 10 (1841): 446.

396 Brian Bowers, *Sir Charles Wheatstone FRS, 1802–1875* (London: Institution of Engineering and Technology, 2001), 102.

397 Richard Taylor, *Scientific Memoirs, Selected from the Transactions of Foreign Academies of Science and Learned Societies, and From Foreign Journals* 2 (1841): 401.

398 "Award Winners: Copley Medal."

399 Charles Wheatstone, "The Bakerian Lecture," *Philosophical Transactions* 133 (1843): 303.

400 Karl Alois Keller, *Christianity and the Leaders of Modern Science* (Whitefish, MN: Kessinger Publishing, 1911), 132–3.

401 Dr. J. Lamont, "Obituary Notices of Deceased Fellows: George Simon Ohm," *Proceedings of Royal Society of London* 7 (1856): 602.

402 *Report of the British Association for the Advancement of Science* (1865), 348–9.

403 "Thomson on Electrical Units of Measurement," *The Practical Applications of Electricity* (London, Institution of Civil Engineers, 1884), 171.

404 Thompson, *Michael Faraday: His Life and Work*, 223.

405 Frank and James, *The Correspondence of Michael Faraday*, vol. 3 (1991), 146.

406 Michael Faraday, *Experimental Researches in Electricity* (2012), 19.

407 Hirshfeld, *The Electric Life of Michael Faraday*, 165.

408 Faraday, *Experimental Researches in Electricity: Vol 3*, 447.

409 J. M. Thomas and John I. Thomas, *Michael Faraday and the Royal Institution* (Milton Park: Taylor & Francis, 1991), 115.

410 "Peter Zeeman: Facts," the Nobel Prize, accessed January 12, 2022, https://www.nobelprize.org/prizes/physics/1902/zeeman/facts/.

411 Jones, *The Life and Letters of Faraday*, 455.

412 Ibid., 458.

413 Ibid., 478.

414 Thomas Fothergill Cooke, *Authorship of the Practical Electric Telegraph of Great Britain* (Bath: R. E. Peach,1868), xxxi.

Chapter 5: The Mighty Telegraph (1826–1876)

415 Jones, *The Life and Letters of Faraday*, vol. 1, 218.

416 Samuel Morse, *Samuel F. B. Morse: His Letters and Journals,* vol. 2 (Boston, MA: Houghton Mifflin, 1914), 186.

417 Alfred M. Mayer, *A Memorial of Joseph Henry* (Washington, DC: Government Printing Office, 1880), 500.

418 Ibid., 505.

419 Nathan Reingold, *Science in Nineteenth-Century America: A Documentary History* (Chicago: University of Chicago Press, 1985), 71.

420 Joseph Henry, *Scientific Writings of Joseph Henry* (Washington, DC: Smithsonian Institute, 1886), 3.

421 Ibid., 45.

422 Reingold, *Science in Nineteenth-Century America*, 67.

423 Ibid., 63.

424 Henry, *Scientific Writings of Joseph Henry*, 42.

425 Ibid.

426 Geoffrey Hubbard, *Cooke and Wheatstone* (London: Routledge, 1965).

427 Henry, *Scientific Writings of Joseph Henry*, 42.

428 Henry, *The Papers of Joseph Henry*, 578.

429 Ibid., *xxi*.

430 E. Shippen et al., "Some Notes about Princeton," *The Princeton University Library Chronicle* 59 (1997): 30, https://doi.org/10.25290/prinunivlibrchro.59.1.0015.

431 Henry, *The Papers of Joseph Henry*, vol. 5 (1981), 29.

432 Henry, *The Papers of Joseph Henry*, vol. 4 (1972), 452.

433 Neil Kagan, *Smithsonian Civil War; Inside the National Collection* (Washington, DC: Smithsonian, 2013), 16

434 Shippen, "Some Notes about Princeton," 49.

435 Ibid.

436 Henry, *A Memorial of Joseph Henry* (Washington, DC: Government Printing Office, 1880), 150.

437 Henry, *The Papers of Joseph Henry*, vol. 4 (1972), 452.

438 David Bodanis, *Electric Universe: How Electricity Switched on the Modern World* (New York: Crown Publishing Group, 2005), 20.

439 David McCullough, *The Greater Journey: Americans in Paris* (New York: Simon & Schuster, 2011), 83.

440 David McCullough, "Samuel Morse's Reversal of Fortune," *Smithsonian Magazine*, September 2011, https://www.smithsonianmag.com/history/samuel -morses-reversal-of-fortune-49650609/.

441 Morse, *Samuel F. B. Morse: His Letters and Journals,* vol. 2 (1914), 4.

442 Ibid., 12.

443 Ibid., 17.

444 Ibid.

445 Edward L. Morse "The Dot-and-Dash Alphabet" *The Century Magazine* vol. 83 (1912), 696.

446 Ibid., 26.

447 Samuel Morse, *Confessions of a French Catholic Priest* (New York: John S. Taylor, 1837), 163.

448 McCullough, "Samuel Morse's Reversal of Fortune."

449 Kenneth Silverman, *Lightning Man: The Accursed Life of Samuel F. B. Morse* (Boston, MA: Da Capo Press, 2004).

450 Morse, *Samuel F. B. Morse: His Letters and Journals,* vol. 2, 39.

451 Christopher N. Phillips, *Epic in American Culture,* (Baltimore, MA: Johns Hopkins University Press, 2012), 114.

452 Morse, *Samuel F. B. Morse: His Letters and Journals,* vol. 2, 31.

453 Robert Marion La Follette, *The Making of America,* vol. 7 (Chicago: De Bower, Chapline & Company, 1906), 118.

454 Franklin Leonard Pope, "The American Inventors of the Telegraph," *The Century Magazine* 35 (1887), 935.

455 Silverman, *Lightning Man*, 167.

456 William T. Jeans, *Lives of the Electricians* (New Kensington, PA: Whitaker & Company, 1887), 265.

457 John Jenkins, *The Untold Story of the Telegraph* (Bellingham, WA: Spark Museum, 2018).

458 Samuel Prime, *The Life of Samuel F.B. Morse* (New York: D. Appleton and Company,1875), 358.

459 Ibid., 395.

460 Reingold, *Science in Nineteenth-Century America*, 83.

461 Prime, *The Life of Samuel F.B. Morse*, 421.

462 Ibid., 418.

463 Ibid., 423.

464 Ibid., 462.

465 Ibid., 463.

466 Morse, *Samuel F. B. Morse: His Letters and Journals*, vol. 2 (2014), 224–6.

467 T. Comerford Martin, "The Indirect Control of Telegraphs," *The Electrical Journal* 32 (1893): 89.

468 Laurence Turnbull, *The Electro Magnetic Telegraph* (Philadelphia: A. Hart, 1853), 115.

469 Antony Dugdale, *Yale, Slavery and Abolition* (New Haven, CT: Amistad Committee, 2001), 26.

470 "Yale, Slavery & Abolition," accessed December 9, 2021, www.yaleslavery.org.

471 Bodanis, *Electric Universe*, 225.

472 Frank P. Bachman, *Great Inventors and Their Inventions* (New York: American Book Company, 1918), 230.

473 Ibid., 231.

474 Edwin S. Grosvenor, *Alexander Graham Bell* (Novato, CA: New Word City, 2016), 23.

475 Naomi Pasachoff, *Alexander Graham Bell: Making Connections* (Oxford: OUP USA, 1996), 17.

476 Bachman, *Great Inventors and Their Inventions*, 233.

477 Walter Lefferts, *Our Country's Leaders* (Philadelphia: J. B. Lippincott, 1924), 217.

478 A. Graham Bell, "Visible Speech as a Means of Communicating Articulation to Deaf Mutes," *American Annals of the Deaf and Dumb* 17, no. 1 (1872), https://www.jstor.org/stable/44460666.

479 Ibid., 5.

480 "Letter from Alexander Melville Bell to Alexander Graham Bell, May 28, 1870," PICRYL, accessed December 9, 2021, https://picryl.com/media/letter-from-alexander-melville-bell-to-alexander-graham-bell-may-28-1870.

481 Robert V. Bruce, *Bell: Alexander Graham Bell and the Conquest of Solitude* (Ithaca, NY: Cornell University Press, 1990), 79.

482 Tony Foster, *The Sound and the Silence: The Private Lives of Mabel and Alexander Graham Bell* (Bloomington, IN: iUniverse, 2000), 112.

483 Helen E. Waite, *Make a Joyful Sound* (Philadelphia: Macrae Smith Co., 1961), 32.

484 Gardiner Greene Hubbard, *The Story of the Rise of the Oral Method in America* (Washington, DC: Press of W. F. Roberts, 1898), 23.

485 Waite, *Make a Joyful Sound*, 45.

486 Ibid., 59.

487 Jennifer Groundwater, *Alexander Graham Bell: The Spirit of Innovation* (Halifax, Canada: Formac Publishing, 2018), 42.

488 Seth Shulman, *The Telephone Gambit: Chasing Alexander Graham Bell's Secret* (New York: W. W. Norton & Company, 2009), 67.

489 Bachman, *Great Inventors and Their Inventions*, 235.

490 Ibid., 238.

491 "Letter from Alexander Graham Bell to Alexander Melville Bell, Eliza Symonds Bell, Carrie Bell, November 23, 1874," Library of Congress, accessed December 9, 2021, https://www.loc.gov/item/magbell.00410226/.

492 Waite, *Make a Joyful Sound*, 117.

493 Bodanis, *Electric Universe*, 30.

494 Bachman, *Great Inventors and Their Inventions*, 240.

495 E. Curnick, "The Emperor Gave the Telephone a Chance," *The Epworth Herald* 23 (1912): 810.

496 Waite, *Make A Joyful Sound*, 148.

497 "Letter from Alexander Graham Bell to Gertrude McCurdy Hubbard, August 25, 1875," Library of Congress, accessed December 9, 2021, https://www.loc.gov/item/magbell.08500112/.

498 Bruce, *Alexander Graham Bell and the Conquest of Solitude*, 160.

499 "Letter from Alexander Graham Bell to Gardiner Greene Hubbard, November 23, 1875," Library of Congress, accessed December 9, 2021, https://www.loc.gov/item/magbell.07900221/.

500 Ibid.

501 Bruce, *Alexander Graham Bell and the Conquest of Solitude*, 161.

502 Ibid., 165.

503 Ibid., 168.

504 "Letter from Alexander Graham Bell to Alexander Melville Bell, March 10, 1876," Library of Congress, accessed December 9, 2021, https://www.loc.gov/resource/magbell.00500211/?st=gallery.

505 "Letter from Alexander Graham Bell to Alexander Melville Bell and Eliza Symonds Bell, May 5, 1876," Library of Congress, accessed December 9, 2021, https://www.loc.gov/item/magbell.00500220/.

506 Charlie Cullen, *Learn Audio Electronics with Arduino* (Milton Park, Oxford: Taylor & Francis, 2020), 79.

507 Bachman, *Great Inventors and Their Inventions,* 242.

508 Ibid., 244.

509 Ibid., 245.

510 Ibid., 246.

511 Ibid.

512 Waite, *Make A Joyful Sound*, 192.

513 Ibid., 191.

514 "Bell Telephone Co.," Federal Communications Commission (Washington, DC: Government Printing Office, 1938), 7.

515 Michael A. Schuman, *Alexander Graham Bell: Scientist and Inventor* (Berkeley Heights, NJ: Enslow Publishing, 2015), 44.

516 Bruce, *Bell: Alexander Graham Bell and the Conquest of Solitude*, 31.

517 Alexander Graham Bell, *Memoir Upon the Formation of a Deaf Variety of the Human Race* (Washington, DC: National Academy of the Sciences, 1884), 3.

518 Alexander Graham Bell, "A Few Thoughts Concerning Eugenics," *Annual Report of the American Genetic Association* 4 (1904): 214.

519 William Ayers et al., *Handbook of Social Justice in Education* (Milton Park, UK: Routledge, 2009), 195.

520 George Veditz, dir., *The Preservation of the Sign Language* (1913), 14 mins.

521 Helen Keller, *The Story of My Life* (New York: Grosset and Dunlap, 1905), 19.

522 Waite, *Make A Joyful Sound*, 247.

523 Olivia B. Waxman, "Co-Founding the ACLU, Fighting for Labor Rights and Other Helen Keller Accomplishments Students Don't Learn in School," *Time*, December 15, 2020, https://time.com/5918660/helen-keller-disability-

history/?utm_source=twitter&utm_medium=social&utm_campaign=editorial&utm_term=history.

524 Ibid.

525 Waite, *Make A Joyful Sound*, 293.

526 "National Geographic and the U.S. National Parks," National Geographic, May 26, 2010, https://www.nationalgeographic.com/travel/national-parks/article/society-history.

527 Waite, *Make A Joyful Sound*, 293.

528 Bruce, *Bell: Alexander Graham Bell and the Conquest of Solitude*, 491.

529 Charlotte Gray, *Reluctant Genius: Alexander Graham Bell and the Passion for Invention* (New York: Arcade Publishing, 2011), 421.

530 Ibid.

Chapter 6: Edison and Westinghouse (1862–1886)

531 William Thomson, "Westinghouse Obituary," *The New International Year Book* (1915), 785.

532 Charles Steinmetz, "Edison: The Genius," *Illuminating Engineering* 11 (1917): 634.

533 Neil Baldwin, *Edison: Inventing the Century* (Chicago: University of Chicago Press, 2001), 25.

534 Randall E. Stross, *The Wizard of Menlo Park* (New York: Three Rivers Press, 2007), 4.

535 Baldwin, *Edison: Inventing the Century*, 30.

536 Randall Stross, "The Incredible Talking Machine," *Time*, June 23, 2010, http://content.time.com/time/specials/packages/article/0,28804,1999143_1999210_1999211,00.html.

537 Baldwin, *Edison: Inventing the Century*, 47.

538 Ibid., 51.

539 "[D7110B], Letter from Daniel H. Craig to Thomas Alva Edison, January 18, 1871," Rutgers School of Arts and Sciences, accessed December 9, 2021.

540 James Baird McClure, *Edison and His Inventions* (Chicago: Rhodes & McClure,1879), 67.

541 "[NE1676031A], Technical Note, Thomas Alva Edison, February 1st, 1872," Rutgers School of Arts and Sciences, accessed December 9, 2021.

542 "[NE1678059], Technical Note, Thomas Alva Edison, February 14th, 1872," Rutgers School of Arts and Sciences, accessed December 9, 2021.

543 Irvin D. Solomon, *Thomas Edison: The Fort Myers Connection* (Mount Pleasant, SC: Arcadia, 2001), 83.

544 "[SB178C], Publication, Edison and Murray, 1874," Rutgers School of Arts and Sciences, accessed December 9, 2021.

545 Stross, *The Wizard of Menlo Park*, 18.

546 Robert Silverberg, *Light for the World: Edison and the Power Industry* (Princeton, NJ: Van Nostrand, 1967), 62.

547 "The Judgement in the Telephone Case," *The Telegraphic Journal and Electrical Review* (April 16, 1886), 353.

548 United States Patent Office, No. 222,390, "Carbon Telephone," December 9, 1879, https://patentimages.storage.googleapis.com/4e/a7/16/dfa7b0705005e9/US222390.pdf.

549 "Carbon Transmitter," *IEEE Global History Network*, August 13, 2008.

550 Bodanis, *Electric Universe*, 41.

551 Russell W. Burns, *Communications: An International History of the Formative Years* (London: Institution of Engineering and Technology, 2004), 178.

552 "[QP001585] American Graphophone Company v. Edison's Phonograph Works," The Thomas A. Edison Papers, April 20, 1896, 586.

553 Charles Batchelor, "[MBJ00757] My Recollections of Al Edison," The Thomas A. Edison Papers, 1906.

554 Thomas Edison, "[NV12026] Technical Note, July 18, 1877," The Thomas A. Edison Papers, 1877.

555 Edward Johnson, "Letter to the Editor," *Scientific American*, November 6, 1877.

556 "Mr. Edison at Home in Menlo Park," *Daily Evening Traveler*, May 23, 1878.

557 Stross, *The Wizard of Menlo Park*, 67.

558 Leslie J. Newville, *Development of the Phonograph at Alexander Graham Bell's Volta Laboratory* (Washington, DC: Smithsonian Institution, 1959), 71.

559 Maury Klein, *The Power Makers: Steam, Electricity, and the Men Who Invented Modern America* (New York: Bloomsbury USA, 2003), 139.

560 "Inventions Big Triumph," *The New York Sun*, September 10, 1878.

561 Ibid.

562 Ibid.

563 "Edison's Electric Light," *The New York Sun*, October 20, 1878.

564 "Edison's Newest Marvel," *The New York Sun*, September 16, 1878.

565 Ibid.

566 Christopher Cooper, *The Truth about Tesla: The Myth of the Lone Genius in the History of Innovation* (London: Race Point Publishing, 2018), 92.

567 Émile Alglave and J. Boulard, *The Electric Light: Its History, Production and Applications* (New York: D. Appleton and Company, 1884), 233.

568 W. J. King, *Development of Electrical Technology in the 19th Century* (Washington, DC: Smithsonian Institution, 1962), 356.

569 Alglave and Boulard, *The Electric Light*, 233.

570 Ibid., 234.

571 Francis Bacon Crocker, *Electric Lighting: A Practical Exposition of the Art, for the Use of Engineers, Students and Others Interested in the Installation or Operation of Electrical Plants* (New York: D. Van Nostrand, 1906), 10.

572 H. Wilde, "Experimental Researches in Magnetism and Electricity," *Philosophical Transactions* 157 (January 1867): 106.

573 Ibid.

574 "The Varley Testimonial," *Nature* 46, no. 25 (August 1892): 369.

575 Antonio Pacinotti, *Descrizione di una macchinetta elettro-magnetica,* trans. S. P. Thompson (Bergamo, Italy: Instituto Italiano d'Arti Grafiche, 1912), 45.

576 Harold Schobert, *Energy and Society* (Milton Park, UK: Taylor & Francis, 2014), 205.

577 *Encyclopedia Britannica Online,* s.v. "Hippolyte Fontaine," updated December 6, 2021, https://www.britannica.com/biography/Hippolyte-Fontaine.

578 Ibid.

579 Loren Graham, *Lonely Ideas: Can Russia Compete?* (Cambridge, MA: MIT Press, 2013), 32–3.

580 Ibid., 34.

581 *The New Encyclopedia Britannica,* vol. 12 (Chicago: Encyclopedia Britannica, 1998), s.v. "Yablochkov, Pavel."

582 Ainissa Ramirez, *The Alchemy of Us: How Humans and Matter Transformed One Another* (Cambridge, MA: MIT Press, 2021), 126.

583 "Report of the Committee on Dynamo-Electric Machines," *Journal of the Franklin Institute* cv, no. 5 (May 1878): 21.

584 Frank Lewis Dyer and Thomas Commerford Martin, *Edison: His Life and Inventions* (New York: Harper & Brothers, 1929), 248.

585 "[LB003390] Edison to Grosvenor Lowrey," The Thomas A. Edison Papers, October 3, 1878.

586 Mark Essig, *Edison and the Electric Chair: A Story of Light and Death* (New York: Walker & Co., 2009), 30.

587 "[MBN004025] Charles Batchelor, 'Technical Notes and Drawings,'" The Thomas A. Edison Papers, January 2, 1879.

588 "[MU021] Francis Upton to His Father," The Thomas A. Edison Papers, July 6, 1869.

589 Paris, *The Life of Sir Humphry Davy: Volume 1,* 87.

590 *Journal of the Society of Telegraph Engineers* 8 (1878), 250–2.

591 "[NE1695] Caveat for Electric Light Spirals," The Thomas A. Edison Papers, September 1878, 49–63.

592 Bodanis, *Electric Universe,* 44.

593 Dyer and Martin, *Edison: His Life and Inventions,* 256.

594 "Wanted, a Platinum Mine," *New York Sun*, July 7, 1879.

595 "[N052015] Notebook Entry," The Thomas A. Edison Papers, October 22, 1879.

596 United States Patent Office, No. US223898A, "Electric Light," January 27, 1880, https://patents.google.com/patent/US223898A/en.

597 "A Malicious Visitor," *New-York Daily Tribune*, January 2, 1880.

598 "Mr. Edison and His Critics," *The Sun*, January 24, 1880.

599 Jonnes, *Empires of Light*, 67.

600 Alglave and Boulard, *The Electric Light*, 158.

601 Jonnes, *Empires of Light*, 63.

602 Ibid., 68

603 Bodanis, *Electric Universe*, 46.

604 "Edison's Electric Light," *New York Times*, March 1, 1881.

605 Dyer and Martin, *Edison: His Life and Inventions*, 243.

606 Jonnes, *Empires of Light*, 71.

607 "The Edison Lamp in Germany," *The Electrical World* vol 3–4 (January 1884), 29.

608 Rayvon Fouché, *Black Inventors in the Age of Segregation: Granville T. Woods, Lewis H. Latimer, and Shelby J. Davidson* (Baltimore, MD: The John Hopkins University Press, 2003), 105.

609 George M. Chinn, *The Machine Gun: Volume 1* (Washington, DC: US Government Printing Office, 1951), 128.

610 "[D7802ZUQ] Stockton Griffin to Thomas Edison," The Thomas A. Edison Papers, August 5, 1878.

611 "[D7802ZVP] Stockton Griffin to Thomas Edison," The Thomas A. Edison Papers, August 16, 1878.

612 "Sorrow at Menlo Park," *New York World*, August 17, 1884.

613 Ibid.

614 "[D8214C] Dr. Leslie Ward to Thomas Edison," The Thomas A. Edison Papers, January 18, 1882.

615 "[D8414O1] Robert Lozier to John Tomlinson," The Thomas A. Edison Papers, August 9, 1884.

616 Paul Israel, *Edison: A Life of Invention* (New York: John Wiley & Sons, 2003), 230.

617 Stephen Fiske, *Off-hand Portraits of Prominent New Yorkers* (New York: G. R. Lockwood & Sons, 1884), 108, 113.

618 Dagobert Runes, *The Diary and Sundry Observations* (New York: Philosophical Library, 1948), 17.

619 "[NA011005] Thomas Edison to James Wright," The Thomas A. Edison Papers, August 1887.

620 "Edison's Newest Marvel," *The Sun*, September 16, 1878.

621 Stross, *The Wizard of Menlo Park*, 167.

622 "[D8736AEL] Samuel Insull to Thomas Edison," The Thomas A. Edison Papers, November 5, 1887.

623 Forrest McDonald, *Insull: The Rise and Fall of a Billionaire Utility Tycoon* (Fairless Hills, PA: Beard Books, 2004), 28.

624 Ibid.

625 "[X120CAN] Frank Julian Sprague to Edward Johnson," The Thomas A. Edison Papers, September 13, 1886.

626 Francis E. Leupp, *George Westinghouse: His Life and Achievements* (Boston: Little, Brown & Company, 1919), 287.

627 Ibid., 10.

628 Essig, *Edison and the Electric Chair*, 106.

629 Ibid.

630 Quentin R. Skrabec, *George Westinghouse: Gentle Genius* (New York: Algora Publishing, 2007), 35.

631 Leupp, *George Westinghouse: His Life and Achievements*, 45.

632 Haig Gordon Garbedian, *George Westinghouse: Fabulous Inventor* (New York: Mead Dodd, 1943), 58.

633 Jonnes, *Empires of Light*, 124.

634 Skrabec, *George Westinghouse: Gentle Genius*, 39.

635 George Westinghouse Jr., "The Development of the Air Brake," *Railroad Men Magazine* 24 (April 1911): 209.

636 Ibid., 210.

637 Skrabec, *George Westinghouse: Gentle Genius*, 43.

638 C. Wohleber, " 'St. George' Westinghouse," *Invention and Technology Magazine* 12, no. 3 (Winter 1997).

639 Garbedian, *George Westinghouse: Fabulous Inventor*, 72.

640 Skrabec, *George Westinghouse: Gentle Genius*, 47.

641 Ibid., 58.

642 "George Westinghouse Commemoration," *American Society of Mechanical Engineers* (1937), 49.

643 Wohleber, " 'St. George' Westinghouse."

644 Leupp, *George Westinghouse: His Life and Achievements*, 107.

645 Ibid.

646 Arthur Warren, *George Westinghouse, 1846–1914* (Pittsburgh, PA: Westinghouse Electrical Corp., 1946), 18.

647 Jonnes, *Empires of Light*, 125.

648 Ibid.

649 Leupp, *George Westinghouse: His Life and Achievements*, 111.

650 Richard Moran, *Executioner's Current* (New York: Knopf Doubleday Publishing, 2007), 48.

651   Skrabec, *George Westinghouse: Gentle Genius*, 117.

652   "Gaulard and Gibbs' System," *Engineering* 39 (May 1885): 459.

Chapter 7: War of the Currents (1880–1893)

653   "[X710A] Thomas Edison to Edward Johnson," The Thomas A. Edison Papers, November 1886.

654   Leupp, *George Westinghouse: His Life and Achievements*, 149.

655   Faraday, *Experimental Researches in Electricity*, 6.

656   N. Callan, "A Description of an Electro-Magnetic Repeater," *Annals of Electricity* 1 (March 1837): 230.

657   Ibid.

658   Samuel Howard Monell, *High Frequency Electric Currents in Medicine and Dentistry* (Houston, TX: William R. Jenkins Company, 1910), 217.

659   Gregory Malanowski, *The Race for Wireless* (Bloomington, IN: AuthorHouse, 2011), 15.

660   Thomas P. Hughes, *Networks of Power: Electrification in Western Society, 1880–1930* (Baltimore, MD: The John Hopkins University Press, 1993), 88.

661   Ibid.

662   "Gaulard and Gibbs' System," 459.

663   Jonnes, *Empires of Light*, 120.

664   Harold C. Passer, *The Electrical Manufacturers, 1875–1900: A Study in Competition, Entrepreneurship, Technical Change, and Economic Growth* (Cambridge, MA: Harvard University Press, 1953), 132.

665   George T. Ferris, *Our Native Land: Or, Glances at American Scenery and Places with Sketches of Life and Character* (New York: D. Appleton & Company, 1882), 518.

666   "George Westinghouse Commemoration," 22.

667   Passer, *The Electrical Manufacturers*, 132.

668   Leupp, *George Westinghouse: His Life and Achievements*, 138.

669   Jonnes, *Empires of Light*, 134.

670   Skrabec, *George Westinghouse: Gentle Genius*, 120.

671   Rotary Club Plaque, "William Stanley: 1858–1916," erected by The Rotary Club of Great Barrington on its Fiftieth Anniversary, May 18, 1974.

672   "IEEE Milestone in Electrical Engineering and Computing: Alternating Current Electrification, 1886," Institute of Electrical and Electronics Engineers, October 2004.

673   K. Zipornowsky, M. Déri, and O. T. Blathy, "Secondary Generators or Transformers," *The Telegraphic Journal of Electrical Review* (October 10, 1885): 324.

674   "M. Lucien Gaulard," *The Electrical Engineer* 1 (February 1888): 147.

675   Hughes, *Networks of Power*, 94.

676 United States Patent Office, No. 349,611, "Induction Coil," September 21, 1886.

677 "[X710A] Thomas Edison to Edward Johnson," The Thomas A. Edison Papers, November 1886.

678 Ibid.

679 Leupp, *George Westinghouse: His Life and Achievements*, 140.

680 Randy Alfred, "Aug. 14, 1888: I Sing the Meter Electric," *Wired*, August 14, 2008, https://www.wired.com/2008/08/dayintech-0814/.

681 William R. Huber *George Westinghouse: Powering the World* (US; McFarland, 2022), 171.

682 "Ricerche Teoriche e Sperimentali sul Generatore Secondario Gaulard e Gibbs," *The Electrician*, April 11, 1885, 450.

683 William Stanley, "Tesla Split-Phase Decisions," *Electrical World and Engineer* xli, no. 12 (March 1903): 486.

684 Ibid.

685 W. Bernard Carlson, *Tesla: Inventor of the Electrical Age* (Princeton: Princeton University Press, 2015), 108.

686 Silvanus P. Thomson, "Polyphase Electric Currents and Alternate-Current Motors," *Nature* 53, no. 293 (1900).

687 "Mr. Nikola Tesla on Alternating Current Motors," *The Telegraphic Journal and Electrical Review* xxiv (June 1889), 648.

688 "Mr. Tesla's Address of Acceptance," *Electrical Review and Western Electrician* 70 (May 1917): 881.

689 "The Tesla Patents," *Electrical Review* 37, no. 12 (September 1900): 288.

690 C. Babbage and J. Herschel, "Account of the Repetition of M. Arago's Experiments on the Magnetism Manifested by Various Substances during the Act of Rotation," *Philosophical Transactions* 115 (June 1825): 480–1.

691 W. Baily, "A Mode of Producing Arago's Rotation," *Journal of Physics A* 3–4 (June 1879): 115.

692 Thomson, "Polyphase Electric Currents," 437.

693 Ibid., 440 and 69–70.

694 United States Pension Office, No. 382,280A, "Electrical Transmission of Power," October 12, 1887.

695 Ibid.

696 "Westinghouse Electric v. New England Granite," *The Federal Reporter* 103 (1900): 966 and 972.

697 Carlson, *Tesla: Inventor of the Electrical Age*, 111.

698 Harold Presser, *The Electrical Manufacturers, 1875–1900* (New York: Arno Press, 1972), 278.

699 Ibid.

700 Ibid.

701 "Tesla's Tribute to Westinghouse," *The Age of Steel* lxxxviii, no. 10 (September 1900): 9.

702 *Engineering News*, 279.

703 Skrabec, *George Westinghouse: Gentle Genius*, 130.

704 Ibid., 123.

705 "Edison vs. Westinghouse," *Electrical World* v9 (1887), 8.

706 "[D8704AEP] Alfred Porter Southwick to Thomas Alva Edison," The Thomas A. Edison Papers, November 8, 1887.

707 "[D8704AFJ] Alfred Porter Southwick to Thomas Alva Edison," The Thomas A. Edison Papers, December 5, 1887.

708 Jonnes, *Empires of Light*, 142.

709 "[LB026116] Thomas Alva Edison to Alfred Porter Southwick," The Thomas A. Edison Papers, December 19, 1887.

710 Edison Electric Light Co., "A Warning from the Edison Electric Light Co.," 1888.

711 Stross, *The Wizard of Menlo Park,* 124.

712 Leupp, *George Westinghouse: His Life and Achievements*, 143.

713 "Reply to Mr. Edison's letter," *North American Review*, December 1889.

714 Jonnes, *Empires of Light*, 166.

715 "[D8828ABV] George Westinghouse to Thomas Edison," The Thomas A. Edison Papers, June 7, 1888.

716 Harold P. Brown, *The Electrical Engineer* 8 (February 1889): 74.

717 "[LB026273] Thomas Edison to Henry Bergh," The Thomas A. Edison Papers, July 13, 1888.

718 "[D8828ACI] Henry Bergh to Thomas Edison," The Thomas A. Edison Papers, July 14, 1888.

719 "Mr. Brown's Rejoinder," *Electrical Engineer* vii (August 1888): 369.

720 "Surer Than the Rope," *New York Times*, December 6, 1888.

721 "[D8954ADC] Sherburne Eaton to Thomas Edison," The Thomas A. Edison Papers, October 7, 1889.

722 Moran, *Executioner's Current,* 160.

723 Tom McNichol, *AC/DC: The Savage Tale of the First Standards War* (New York: John Wiley & Sons, 2011), 120.

724 "Far Worse Than Hanging: Kemmler's Death Proves an Awful Spectacle," *New York Times*, August 7, 1890, 1.

725 Ibid.

726 Jonnes, *Empires of Light*, 213.

727 Ibid., 223.

728 David Glasner, ed., *Business Cycles and Depressions: An Encyclopedia* (Milton Park, UK: Routledge, 1997).

729 Leupp, *George Westinghouse: His Life and Achievements*, 159.

730 S. Vavilov, *People of Russian Science: Essays on Outstanding Figures of Natural Science [Люди русской науки: Очерки о выдающихся деятелях естествознания и техники]* (1948).

731 Edvard Radzinsky, *Alexander II: The Last Great Tsar* (New York: Free Press, 2005), *xi*.

732 Ibid., 426.

733 Vavilov, *People of Russian Science*.

734 M. Dolivo-Dobrovolsky, "Transmission of Power by Rotary-Phase Alternate Currents," Electrical Engineer 7 (April 1891): 369.

735 Ibid.

736 Ibid.

737 "The Invention of the Electric Motor 1856–1893," Elektrotechnisches Institut (ETI), https://www.eti.kit.edu/english/1390.php.

738 Vavilov, *People of Russian Science*, 173; Silvanus P. Thompson, *Elementary Lessons in Electricity and Magnetism* (New York: Macmillan and Co, 1895), 507.

739 Thomson, *Elementary Lessons in Electricity and Magnetism*, 507.

740 Vasily Y. Ushakov, *Electrical Power Engineering: Current State, Problems, and Perspectives* (New York: Springer, 2017), 16.

741 Adam Allerhand, "The Earliest Years of Three-Phase Power," *Proceedings of the IEEE* 108 (January 2020): 215–6.

742 "Frankfort Electrical Exhibition," *Western Electrician* (June 1891), 355.

743 Ibid.

744 Herausgegeben vom Vorstand der Ausstellung, *Offizieller Bericht über die Internationale elektrotechnische Ausstellung in Frankfurt am Main, 1891* (Frankfurt, Germany: J. D. Sauerländer, 1894), 324.

745 *Lightning: Volume 1* (April 1892), 509.

746 Ibid.

747 "The Transmission of Power at Frankfort," *The Electrical Engineer* (September 1891), 286.

748 Silvanus P. Thompson, "The Frankfort Congress of 1891," *The Electrician* (September 1891), 581.

749 Dolivo-Dobrovolsky, "Transmission of Power by Rotary-Phase Alternate Currents," 368.

750 Charles Brown, "Reasons for the Use of the Three-Phase Current in the Lauffen–Frankfort Transmission," *The Electrical World* xviii, no. 19 (November 1891), 345.

751 United States Pension Office, No. 382,280, "Electrical Transmission of Power," May 1, 1888.

752 Dolivo-Dobrovolsky, "Transmission of Power by Rotary-Phase Alternate Currents," 336.

753 Benjamin Lamme, "The Story of the Induction Motor," *Electrical Engineering* xl (March 1921), 205.

754 Benjamin G. Lamme, *Benjamin Garver Lamme, Electrical Engineer, An Autobiography* (New York: G. P. Putnam & Sons, 1926), 60.

755 Lamme, *Benjamin Garver Lamme, Electrical Engineer, An Autobiography*, 61.

756 Jean Strouse, *Morgan: American Financier* (New York: Random House, 2014), 313.

757 "Mr. Edison Is Satisfied," *New York Times*, February 21, 1893.

758 Alfred O. Tate, *Edison's Open Door: The Life Story of Thomas A. Edison, a Great Individualist* (New York: E. P. Dutton, 1938), 278.

759 Skrabec, *George Westinghouse: Gentle Genius*, 149.

760 Ibid.

761 Lamme, "The Story of the Induction Motor," 212.

762 Lamme, *Benjamin Garver Lamme, Electrical Engineer, An Autobiography*, 61

763 C. F. Scott, "Exhibit of Tesla's Polyphase System at the World's Fair," *Western Electrician* (September 1893), 126.

764 L. J. Davis, *Fleet Fire: Thomas Edison and the Pioneers of the Electrical Revolution* (New York: Arcade, 2012).

765 Lamme, *Benjamin Garver Lamme, Electrical Engineer, An Autobiography*, 61.

766 Ibid.

767 Ibid.

Chapter 8: Our Electric World (1890–Present)

768 "Tesla's Tribute to Westinghouse," *Age of Steel* 88, no. 10 (September 1900): 9.

769 Jonnes, *Empires of Light*, 421.

770 Carlson, *Tesla: Inventor of the Electrical Age,* 120.

771 Nikola Tesla, "Experiments with Alternating Currents of Very High Frequency," *The Electrical Engineer* (July 1891): 35.

772 "Mr. Tesla's Experiments," *Electrical Engineer* 13–14 (April 1892): 350.

773 L. Hawkins, "Nikola Tesla, His Work and Unfulfilled Promises," *Electrical Age* 30, no. 2 (February 1903): 102.

774 A. Brisbane, "Our Foremost Electrician," *New York World*, July 22, 1894.

775 Thomas Commerford Martin, *The Inventions, Researches and Writings of Nikola Tesla* (New York: The Electrical Engineer, 1894), 4.

776 "[D8828AAG] William Carman to Thomas Edison," The Thomas A. Edison Papers, February 3, 1888; "[D8818AIM] Thomas Edison to Edison Machine Works," The Thomas A. Edison Papers, April 12, 1888.

777 "[X120CBN] Frank Sprague to Sprague Executive Board (leaked to Edison)," The Thomas A. Edison Papers, April 29, 1890.

778 H. Dam, "The New Marvel in Photography," *McClure's Magazine* vi, no. 5 (April 1896): 413.

779 Ibid.

780 Otto Glasser, *Wilhelm Conrad Roentgen and the Early History of the Roentgen Rays* (Novato, CA: Norman Publishing, 1993), 67.

781 Bern Dibner, *The New Rays of Professor Roentgen* (Norwalk, CN: Burndy Library, 1963), 23.

782 "[D9631ABG] William Morton to Thomas Edison," The Thomas A. Edison Papers, February 20, 1896.

783 "[LB062322] Thomas Edison to Nikola Tesla," The Thomas A. Edison Papers, March 13, 1896.

784 "X-ray Spectacles, Now," *Guy's Hospital Gazette*, April 11, 1896.

785 United States Census Bureau, No. 865,367, "Fluorescent Electric Lamp," May 19, 1896.

786 "Edison Fears Hidden Perils of the X-rays," *New York World*, August 3, 1903.

787 "Edison and Tesla Rivals" *New York Journal*, May 22, 1896.

788 Ibid.

789 *Electrical Age* 17, no. 22, 285.

790 "[LB062498] Edison to the Editor of the Electric Review," The Thomas A. Edison Papers, May 29, 1896.

791 "Annual Report of the Board of Directors of the Westinghouse Electric," *Electricity* vol. 12, No. 25 (June 1897): 387.

792 "Wonders Never Cease," *Electricity* xv, no. 19, 290.

793 Ibid.

794 Erik Larson, *Thunderstruck* (New York: Crown, 2006), 14.

795 Ibid., 11.

796 United States Census Bureau, No. 586,193, "Transmitting Electrical Signals," July 13, 1897.

797 United States Census Bureau, No. 645,576, "System of Transmission of Electrical Energy," March 20, 1900.

798 Ibid.

799 Skrabec, *George Westinghouse: Gentle Genius*, 214.

800 United States Census Bureau, No. 714756, "Method of Selective Electric Signaling," December 2, 1902.

801 Nikola Tesla, "The Problem of Increasing Human Energy," *The Century Magazine* vol. 60 (June 1900): 178.

802 "Science and Fiction," *Popular Science Monthly* 57 (1900), 326.

803 "A Marconi Wireless Telegraph Company for America," *Electrical World and Engineer* vol. 34, no. 23 (December 1899): 870.

804 Gavin Weightman, *Signor Marconi's Magic Box* (New York: Hachette Books, 2009).

805 Nikola Tesla, "Talking with Planets," *Collier's Weekly* (February 1901), 359.

806 Ibid.

807 Carlson, *Tesla: Inventor of the Electrical Age*, 317 and 347.

808 Nikola Tesla, *Nikola Tesla on His Work with Alternating Currents* (Pawcatuck, CT: Sun Publishing, 1992), 177.

809 Elizabeth Rauscher and Toby Grotz, *Proceedings of the Tesla Centennial Symposium* (Colorado Springs, CO: International Tesla Society, 1985), 35.

810 Edwin Palmer Hoyt, *The House of Morgan* (New York: Dodd, Mead & Company, 1966), 237.

811 "Wireless Signals Across the Ocean," *New York Times*, December 15, 1901.

812 "Word Is Flashed from Roosevelt to King Edward," *The World*, January 19, 1903.

813 Rauscher and Grotz, *Proceedings of the Tesla Centennial Symposium*, 37.

814 "Marconi Wireless Telegraph Co. of America v. Kilbourne and Clark MFG Co.," *The Federal Reporter* 265 (May 1920): 659.

815 Jonnes, *Empires of Light*, 363.

816 Margaret Cheney and Robert Uth, *Tesla: Master of Lightning* (New York: Barnes & Noble Books, 1999), 106.

817 Carlson, *Tesla: Inventor of the Electrical Age*, 361.

818 H. Secor, "Tesla No Money Wizard," *The New York World*, March 18, 1916.

819 Ibid.

820 Cooper, *The Truth About Tesla*, 59.

821 F. Collins, "Signaling Through Space Without Wires," *Electrical World and Engineer* xl, no. 13 (September 1902): 486.

822 "The Thunderer's Legacy," *Life* 58, no. 16 (April 1965): 57.

823 "Charles Proteus Steinmetz," *The Mentor-World Traveler* 13 (May 1925): 8.

824 Bill Buell, *Historic Schenectady County: A Bicentennial History* (San Antonio, TX: Historical Publishing Network, 2009), 49.

825 Gilbert King, "Charles Proteus Steinmetz, the Wizard of Schenectady," *Smithsonian Magazine*, August 16, 2011, https://www.smithsonianmag.com/history/charles-proteus-steinmetz-the-wizard-of-schenectady-51912022/.

826 J. W. Hammond, *Charles Proteus Steinmetz: A Biography* (Merchant Books, 2008), 257.

827 Ronald R. Kline, *Steinmetz: Engineer and Socialist* (Lexington, MA: Plunkett Lake Press, 2019).

828 William Stanley, "Phenomena of Retardation in the Induction Coil," *American Institute of Electrical Engineers* v, no. 4 (January 1888): 132.

829 D. Hughes, "On an Induction-Currents Balance," *Proceedings of the Royal Society of London* 29 (May 1879): 56.

830 J. Ewing, "On the Production of Transient Electric Currents and Iron and Steel Conductors …" *Proceedings of the Royal Society of London* 33 (November 1881): 22.

831 Charles Proteus Steinmetz, *Theoretical Elements of Electrical Engineering* (London: McGraw Hill Publishing, 1909), 53.

832 Ibid.

833 "The Law of Hysteresis," *The Electrical Engineer* (January 1892): 86.

834 Kline, *Steinmetz: Engineer and Socialist.*

835 Ibid.

836 Hammond, *Charles Proteus Steinmetz: A Biography*, 206.

837 Kline, *Steinmetz: Engineer and Socialist.*

838 "Almarian William Decker," *The Journal of Electricity, Power, and Gas* vol. 8, no. 1 (January 1903): 98.

839 A. Allerhand, "The Earliest Years of Three-Phase Power," *Proceedings of the IEEE* 108 (January 2020): 215–6.

840 Bell, "On Polyphase Apparatus," *Transactions of the American Institute of Electrical Engineers* 35 (January 79 1894).

841 Charles Proteus Steinmetz, *Theory and Calculation of Alternating Current Phenomena* (New York: Electrical World and Engineer, 1900), 38.

842 Joseph E. Fleckenstein, *Three-Phase Electrical Power* (Boca Raton, FL: CRC Press, 2017), *xiii.*

843 Charles Scott, "The Development of the Two-Phase, Three-Phase Transformation," *The Electric Journal* 16 (1919): 28.

844 Ibid.

845 Thomas Blalock and Craig Woodworth, "25-Hz at Niagara Falls," *IEEE Power & Energy Magazine* (Jan/Feb 2008), 88.

846 Charles Steinmetz, "Communicated after Adjournment," (Feb 1894); Bell "On Polyphase Apparatus" *Transactions of the American Institute of Electrical Engineers*, vol. XL, 48.

847 "A New Electric System" *Electrical Review* (Oct 10, 1894) 171.

848 Charles Steinmetz, "The Vitality of Schenectady," *Schenectady Board of Trade*, April 7, 1911.

849 J. W. Hammond, "Charles Proteus Steinmetz," *The Mentor-World Traveler* 13 (May 1925): 14.

850 Tom D. Crouch, *A Dream of Wings* (New York: W. W. Norton, 2002), 172.

851 Hammond, *Charles Proteus Steinmetz*, 239.

852 Guy Bartlett, "The General Electric Research Laboratory, What It Is and What It Has Accomplished," *Journal of Chemical Education*, vol. 6. No. 10 (1929), 1619.

853 Ibid., 400.

854 Ibid., 272.

855 Ibid., 283–4.

856 Herbert Wallace, "A Man Who Knows," *Success Magazine* 6 (March 1903): 145.

857 Hammond, *Charles Proteus Steinmetz*, 296.

858 Charles Steinmetz, *America and the New Epoch* (New York: Harper & Brothers, 1916), *ix.*

859 Hammond, *Charles Proteus Steinmetz*, 314.

860 Sender Garlin, *Charles P. Steinmetz, Scientist and Socialist* (New York: American Institute for Marxist Studies, 1977), 12.

861 "Steinmetz speaks on WGY radio" miSci - Museum of Innovation and Science, https://nyheritage.contentdm.oclc.org/digital/collection/schmuse/id/269/rec/167

862 Steinmetz quoted by H. Bedford-Jones "The Wonder-Work of the Mohawk Valley" *Popular Electricity* vol. 5, No. 10 (Feb 1913), 1020.

863 Charles Steinmetz "The Future of Automobiling Belongs to the Electric" delivered Jan 28, 1914, found in *Automobile Topics* (Feb 7, 1914), 1091.

864 For example, *The Automobile* (Feb 26, 1914), 532.

865 "Photos: 1914 electric car" (April 9, 2014) *Times Union* (Schenectady).

866 "The New Steinmetz Electric" *The Central Station* (March, 1920), 302-3.

867 "Steinmetz Electric Truck Called Marvel by Experts" *The American Monthly* vol. 14 (1922), 26.

868 Siegfried Grundmann, "Einstein to Fritz Haber" in *The Einstein Dossiers* (Berlin: Physica-Verlag, 2006), 123.

869 Pierre H. Boucheron, "Einstein Visits High Power Radio," *RCA News* 2 (1921): 6.

870 Grundmann, *The Einstein Dossiers*, 125.

871 Charles Steinmetz, *Four Lectures on Relativity and Space* (New York: McGraw-Hill, 1923), *v.*

872 Kathlyn Gay, *American Dissidents* (Santa Barbara, CA: ABC-CLIO, 2012), 579–80.

873 "Man-Made Lightning Under Control" *Schenectady Works,* vol. 6 (March 3, 1922), 1-3.

874 Steinmetz quoted in "Still Greater Developments" *The Mining Congress Journal,* vol. 8-9, (June 1923), 207.

875 "Tamed Lightning" *Scientific American* vol. 127 (July, 1922), 26.

876 Ibid.

877 "Modern Jove Hurls Lightning at Will," *New York Times,* March 3, 1922.

878 "Thomas A. Edison, Welcomed Back to General Electric Plant, Renews Acquaintance with Early Associates" *Schenectady Works News* (Nov 3, 1922), 6.

879 Jack B. Scott "Letter to the Editor: Charles Steinmetz" *Life*, May 14, 1965, 27.

880 Hammond, *Charles Proteus Steinmetz*, 465–476.

881 Denis Hamill "John McCain has something to learn about the electric car's history" (July 7, 2008) *The Daily News.*

882 "The Thunderer's Legacy," *Life* 58, no. 16, April 23, 1965.

883 *Henry Baldwin Hyde: A Biographical Sketch* (New York: De Vinnes Press, 1901), 190.

884 *Testimony Taken before the Joint Committee of the Senate of the State of New York,* vol. iv (New York: Brandow Print Company, 1905), 3196.

885 Strouse, *Morgan: American Financier,* 544.

886 Henry G. Prout, *A Life of George Westinghouse* (New York: American Society of Mechanical Engineers, 1921), 283–4.

887 "Nomination of Directors," *The Insurance Press* 21 (December 1905): 3.

888 "The Present Status of the Equitable," *The World's Work* (1905), 6581.

889 *The World Almanac and Encyclopedia* (New York: Press Publishing Co., 1906), 17–8.

890 Robert Bruner and Sean Carr, *The Panic of 1907: Lessons Learned from the Market's Perfect Storm* (Hoboken, NJ: Wiley, 2009); Strouse, *Morgan: American Financier.*

891 Skrabec, *George Westinghouse: Gentle Genius,* 32–3.

892 "Acknowledgment of the Award," *Electrical Engineering* 31 (1912): 333.

893 *Electrical Review and Western Electrician* 70 (May 1917): 771.

894 Michael Pupin, "Electrical Engineering," *Electrical Engineering* 31 (1912): 327.

895 Ibid.

896 Skrabec, *George Westinghouse: Gentle Genius,* 249.

897 "George Westinghouse Dead," *Electrical Review and Western Electrician* 64 (March 1914): 565.

898 Vavilov, *People of Russian Science.*

899 Stross, *The Wizard of Menlo Park,* 237 and 242.

900 Henry Ford, *Quotations from the Unusual Henry Ford* (Redondo Beach, CA: Quotamus Press, 1978), 51.

901 Gerry Boehme, *Henry Ford: Assembly Line and Automobile Pioneer* (New York: Cavendish Square Publishing, 2019), 89.

902 "Edison Young Again as He Relives Past in Old Laboratory," *New York Times,* October 21, 1929.

903 "Light's Golden Jubilee Honors Thomas Edison and Dedicates a Museum," October 9, 2019, https://www.thehenryford.org/explore/blog/light-s-golden-jubilee-honors-thomas-edison-and-dedicates-a-museum.

904 Ibid.

905 Stross, *The Wizard of Menlo Park,* 284.

906 "The 100 Most Important People in the Last 1,000 Years," *Life,* Fall 1997, 135.

907 Alex Knapp, "Nikola Tesla Wasn't God and Thomas Edison Wasn't the Devil" *Forbes,* May 18, 2012.

908 "Address by B. A Behrend," *Electrical Review and Western Electrician* 70 (May 1917): 880.

909 H. Gernsback, "Editorial: The New Wireless," *Electric Experimenter* (February 1919): 682.

910 Nikola Tesla, *My Inventions and Other Writings* (New York: Experimenter Publishing Co., 1919), 27.

911 Ibid., 36.

912 "Mr. Tesla Speaks Out," *New York World*, November 29, 1929.

913 Ibid.

914 Ibid.

915 Cheney and Uth, *Tesla, Master of Lightning*, 137.

916 Margaret Cheney, *Tesla: Man Out of Time* (New York: Simon & Schuster, 2011), 299.

917 Nikola Tesla, "A Machine to End War," *Liberty Magazine*, February 9, 1935.

918 Marc Seifer, *Wizard: The Life and Times of Nikola Tesla: Biography of a Genius* (New York: Citadel, 2016), 442.

919 Alva Adams in *Second Supplemental National Defense Appropriation Bill for 1942: Hearings Before the Subcommittee ...* (Washington, DC: US Government Printing Office, 1941), 69.

920 Rory Yeomans, *Visions of Annihilation: The Ustasha Regime and the Cultural Politics of Fascism* (Pittsburgh, PA: University of Pittsburgh, 2012), 18.

921 Ralph Bergstresser, *Dr. Nikola Tesla: The Forgotten Super Man* (Mokelumne Hill, CA: Mokelumne Hill Press, 1996), 15.

922 John Joseph O'Neill, *Prodigal Genius: The Life of Nikola Tesla* (Philadelphia, PA: Ives Washburn, 1944), 30.

923 Ibid., 37.

924 Ibid.

925 Ibid., 3.

926 A. David Wunsch, "The Truth about Tesla: The Myth of the Loan Genius in the History of Innovation," *Technology and Society,* July 28, 2017, https://technologyandsociety.org/the-truth-about-tesla-the-myth-of-the-lone-genius-in-the-history-of-innovation/.

927 "Marconi Wireless Telegraph v. The United States" (June 21, 1943) US Patent Office *Decisions of the Commissioner of Patents* (1944), 339.

928 Ibid., 350.

929 Christopher A. Harkins, "Tesla, Marconi, and the Great Radio Controversy," *Missouri Law Review* 73, no. 3 (Summer 2008): 759.

930 *Comptes Rendus des Séances de la Onzièmee Conférence Générale des Poids et Mesures*, Paris, 11–20 Octobre, 1960.

931 Harold P. Strand "Make Your Own Fantastic Tesla Coil" *Popular Mechanics* (June, 1964), vol. 121, No. 6, 169.

932 J. L Elkhorne "Edison – The Fabulous Drone" *Amateur Radio* vol. 46, issue 3, (March 1967), 53.

933 Robert Uth, dir., *Tesla: Master of Lightning* (2000), 87 mins.

934 Ibid.

935 "'Tops' and the Press Agent," *The Brooklyn Daily Eagle*, December 13, 1902, 5.

936 Michael Daly, *Topsy: The Startling Story of the Crooked-Tailed Elephant, P. T. Barnum, and the American Wizard, Thomas Edison* (New York: Grove Press,).

937 Uth, dir., *Tesla: Master of Lightning*.

938 Alex Davies, "Here's Why Tesla Motors Is Named for a Famous Serbian Inventor," Insider, August 8, 2013, https://www.businessinsider.com/who-is-tesla-named-for-2013-8?r=US&IR=T.

939 O'Neill *Prodigal Genius*, 74.

940 Jonnes, *Empire of Light*, 162.

941 *Back to the Future*, directed by Robert Zemeckis (1985), 116 mins.

942 *The Prestige*, directed by Christopher Nolan (2006), 130 mins.

943 O'Neill, *Prodigal Genius: The Life of Nikola Tesla*, 82–3.

944 Ibid.

945 Jonnes, *Empires of Light*, 421.

946 George Westinghouse, "The Dangers of Electric Lighting: A Reply to Mr. Edison," *The Electrical Engineer* 9 (January 1890): 15.

947 H. M. Paul, "Edison's Three-Wire System of Distribution," *Science* 4 (1884): 477.

948 Nehemiah Hawkins, *Hawkins Electrical Guide*, no. 3 (New York: Theo Audel & Co., 1917), 711.

949 Westinghouse, "The Dangers of Electric Lighting," 15.

950 Eugene Shteyn and Max Shtein, *Scalable Innovation: A Guide for Inventors, Entrepreneurs, and IP Professionals* (Boca Raton, FL: CRC Press, 2016), 81.

951 Ibid.

952 "The History of Electric Lighting," *Country Life,* September 20, 2011.

953 Lawrence D. Batson, *Trade Promotion Series* 136 (Washington, DC: US Government Printing Office, 1932).

954 Raymond Kane and Heinz Sell, *Revolution in Lamps: A Chronicle of 50 Years of Progress* (Hoboken, NJ: Prentice Hall, 2020), 37.

955 Ibid.

956 "Population of Chicago," *Annual Report of the Board of Trade of the City of Chicago* 51 (1909), 140.

957 Bessie Louise Pierce, *A History of Chicago, Vol I: The Beginning of a City 1673–1848* (Chicago: University of Chicago Press, 2008), 122.

958 "Population of Chicago," 140.

959 "Impact of the Chicago Fire of 1874," *Connected Fire Safety Services*, April 19, 2017.

960 George H. Douglas, *Skyscrapers: A Social History of the Very Tall Buildings in America* (Jefferson, NC: McFarland, 2004), 24.

961 Carol Willis, *Form Follows Finance: Skyscrapers and Skylines in New York and Chicago* (Princeton, NJ: Princeton Architectural Press, 1995), 50.

962 Norman Bolotin and Christine Laing, *The World's Columbian Exposition* (Chicago: University of Illinois, 2002), *vii*.

963 *Report on Population of the United States at the Eleventh Census, 1890*, vol. 1, *xi*.

964 David F. Burg, *Chicago's White City of 1893* (Lexington, KY: University Press of Kentucky, 2014), 308.

965 Mary Bellis, "The First Skyscrapers," Thought Co., updated January 10, 2020, https://www.thoughtco.com/how-skyscrapers-became-possible-1991649.

966 Ibid.

967 John Patrick Barrett, *Electricity at the Columbian Exposition* (Chicago, IL: R. R. Donnelley, 1894), 2.

968 Ibid.

969 Alice Gordenker, "Japan's Incompatible Power Grids," *Japan Times*, July 19, 2011, https://www.japantimes.co.jp/news/2011/07/19/reference/japans-incompatible-power-grids/.

Author's Note

970 Abraham Pais, *Niels Borh's Times: In Physics, Philosophy and Polity* (Oxford: Clarendon Press, 1991), 179.

971 Ibid.

9723 Jagadis Chunder Bose, "On a Self-Recovering Coherer and the Study of the Cohering Action of Different Metals," *Proceedings of the Royal Society of London* 65 (January 1900), 166.

CPSIA information can be obtained
at www.ICGtesting.com
Printed in the USA
JSHW051140050622
26709JS00004B/222